Evolutionary Concepts in the Nineteenth Century

Portrait of Patrick Matthew

Natural Selection
and
Patrick Matthew

Evolutionary Concepts
in the Nineteenth Century

W. J. DEMPSTER

The Pentland Press
Edinburgh – Cambridge – Durham – USA

First published in 1996 by
The Pentland Press Ltd
1 Hutton Close,
South Church
Bishop Auckland
Durham

Typeset by Carnegie Publishing, 18 Maynard St, Preston
Printed and bound by Antony Rowe Ltd, Chippenham

To Cherry and our children

Contents

List of Illustrations

Acknowledgement

I have been encouraged to bring out an expanded account of Patrick Matthew's involvement in the controversy about evolutionary ideas in the nineteenth century by the Trustees of the Patrick Matthew Trust – Ian Hardie and Min Hunter. Funds from that Trust covered production costs. I would like to thank the production team of the Pentland Press for all the co-operation I have received. I am grateful to the Pentland Press for the courage demonstrated in taking aboard a subject which, in the past, has not been a money spinner.

Preface to the second edition

Further research has revealed that Patrick Matthew's *Appendix* involved more aspects of the species problem than was at first appreciated. Evidence has been discovered that the Wallace–Darwin essays contained data that were already discussed in the essays of Patrick Matthew and his contemporary Edward Blyth.

The first five chapters of the first edition have been revised in the light of new information. These chapters deal with biographical and social aspects of early nineteenth-century conditions. The early history of artificial selection as used by breeders is shown as fundamental to the later Natural Selection.

The remaining chapters deal in detail with the various aspects of the species problem which had been published in the decade 1826–1836. Charles Darwin returned home at the end of 1836 and had access to all the published work during the previous decade. It is shown that Darwin's autobiography is unreliable and his *Historical Sketch* was economical with the truth. The priority and originality of the so-called Wallace–Darwin theory is disputed. It is also revealed that Darwin scholars down the years have been rather careless with historical accuracy.

Darwin's false statement about Patrick Matthew's *Appendix* have conditioned generations of naturalists to dismiss Matthew as unimportant and deserving only a mere footnote to a book on evolution. Darwin started the crude jibe that he could not be expected to find natural selection in a book on *Naval Timber and Arboriculture*. Why not? Darwin used to boast that he had exhaustively searched the horticultural and agricultural journals. When it came to Matthew's *Arboriculture* Darwin stressed the 'Naval Timber' part of the book's title. The journal Darwin seems to have valued most was *The Cottage Gardener* which was hardly in the same intellectual class as *Naval Timber and Arboriculture*. *The Cottage Gardener*, however, gave him all the news in the world of breeding, shows and selection. But Darwin and his set failed to notice the review of Matthew's book in a journal subscribed to by Darwin himself. Not only that but they failed to pick up Mendel's paper in a well-circulated journal. In the *Historical Sketch* (1872), having stated there was little difference in their views, Darwin then adds with a sneer '. . . he seems to think that the world was nearly depopulated at successive periods, and then restocked.' At that time this concept would be considered scientifically incorrect – a heresy in fact – and Darwin, no doubt, intended this to be the *coup de grâce*.

Matthew had based his analysis on the work of Cuvier and Lamarck. His analysis led him to consider the organic history of the world involved periods of steady states (Lamarckism) interrupted by catastrophes producing massive extinctions (Cuvier) without miraculous creation of the new species. This concept has recently been resurrected as 'punctuated equilibrium'. This has never been a part of Darwinism because uniformitarianism had no use for catastrophes; catastrophes were seldom mentioned in any edition of the *Origin*. Without catastrophes and massive extinctions what was the point of the debate about new species being miraculously created – as Cuvier maintained – or evolved from surviving species of previous epochs as Lamarck demonstrated?

For over a hundred years English academics have taught that evolution (a word Darwin never used in any editions of the *Origin*) is Darwinism and Lamarckism is no more than the inheritance of acquired characteristics. The 'injustice' Lamarck has suffered was initiated by Charles Lyell, was continued for many years by Darwin, savagely reinforced by Thomas Huxley and perpetuated by Alfred Wallace.

No influential scientist has ever come out in support of Patrick Matthew. Publishers feel that any book about him would have too narrow an appeal because he is not well known. He is not well-known because publishers are not interested in publishing. The publication of *The Origin of the Species* was pushed through by Sir Charles Lyell although John Murray, the publisher, demurred at the way Darwin had presented the manuscript. Darwin was quite unashamed about his tactics which he explained to Lyell (30 March 1859): 'I am sorry Murray objecting to the term Abstract, as I look at it as the only possible apology for not giving references and facts in full . . . I am sorry about the term "natural selection" . . . I again most truly and cordially thank you for your really valuable assistance.' That is how it was done. Ten years later Lyell was actively supporting Lamarck!

That Lamarck was the true founder of evolution is nowhere better demonstrated than in Charles Lyell's 12th edition of the *Principles of Geology*. In that edition he recanted his 'injustice' – even Darwin tried to make amends in later years. Yet, in Julian Huxley's *Evolution: the Modern Synthesis* there is no place for Lamarck or Charles Lyell in its bibliography or indices.

Patrick Matthew's importance derives from the fact that he was the first naturalist to set correctly the organic history of the world. To that he added the mechanism of the Natural Process of Selection. And to that he added a piece of inspired speculation: 'Does organized existence, and perhaps all material existence, consist of one protean principle of life capable of gradual circumstance-suited modifications and aggregations, without bound under solvent or motion-giving principle, heat or light?' That principle we now call DNA!

Under the influence of Charles Lyell's Uniformitarianism, Darwin rejected any role for catastrophes in the history of the earth. In the section on extinction (Chapter X, 1859 Edition, and in Chapter XI, 1872 Edition) is this statement: 'The old notion of all inhabitants of the earth having been swept away at successive periods by catastrophes, is very generally given up, even by those geologists . . . whose views would naturally lead them to this conclusion.'

W. J. Dempster
Lockerley, Hampshire, 1995

Preface to the first edition

It is a very English distortion of scientific history which claims that evolution by natural selection was a scientific innovation first promulgated by Charles Darwin. It has been a popular myth in England for so long that the name of the great man has become synonymous with evolution itself.

However, in 1831 a Scots commercial fruit grower and hybridist – Patrick Matthew – published a book entitled *Naval Timber and Arboriculture*. This book was the culmination of twenty years' field work and observation. For the first time the term appeared in print, 'natural process of selection', which Matthew regarded as the fundamental law of evolution. As far as geological evolution was concerned, Matthew completely ignored biblical mythology and rejected Cuvier's Catastrophism – the theory that successive disasters had wiped out whole generations of species and that afterwards entirely new species was created – miraculously! Matthew extended his views to include man and his society. Logically, therefore, he was against hereditary titles, and the Corn Laws which he regarded as an outrage against competition and hence an offence against the fundamental law of evolution by a natural process of selection. What was later on to be called 'Social Darwinism' is already there as 'social Matthewism' with its accent on imperialism, the descendants of the Angles as the super-variety of *Homo sapiens* and the glorification of war. Matthew's book made no impact and a library in Perth banned it.

It was not until 1859 that Darwin's *The Origin of the Species* was published; it was well reviewed in the national press and one of these reviews was read by Patrick Matthew. Outraged, Patrick Matthew confronted Charles Darwin with his 1831 publication and staked his claim for first enunciating the principle of evolution by natural selection. Darwin, honourably enough, made a public acknowledgement of the claim. But the furore nationally was over *The Origin of the Species* and not only all the praise but all the obloquy as well was directed at Darwin.

During all this furore Patrick Matthew's contribution disappeared almost without trace.

That *The Origin of the Species* stimulated interest in evolution and natural selection throughout the world is historical fact. But Darwin claimed that the theory was entirely original and his own and that he owed nothing to his predecessors. This was clearly false, but it was and still is largely believed.

W. J. Dempster
London, 1982

Patrick Matthew, Horticulturist and Writer

As Sir Walter Scott remarked, 'Every Scottishman has a pedigree. It is a national prerogative as inalienable as his pride and poverty.' Patrick Matthew was no exception. He was born in 1790 the second son of parents descended on both sides from long lines of distinguished and prosperous gentlemen-farmers. The Matthews had farmed in the Carse of Gowrie, between Perth and Dundee, since the sixteenth century. His mother was a Duncan and amongst her distinguished kinsmen was Admiral Viscount Duncan – the victor of Camperdown (1797) and, in his day, as famous and distinguished as Nelson and just as unorthodox – who by sending his ships through to leeward of the Dutch navy quickly routed and captured de Winter. Patrick Matthew was educated at Perth Academy but this school holds no records before 1870.

According to the records in the Department of Rare Books and Manuscripts, Edinburgh University Library, the name of Patrick Matthew appears in the Matriculation Index in 1804–05 and again in 1808–09. His name is on the class list of Professor Gregory who held the chair of medicine. The subjects studied were anatomy, surgery, chemistry, medical practice. In 1808 Patrick Matthew attended Professor Hope's classes in chemistry. There is no evidence that Patrick Matthew graduated from Edinburgh and he appears never to have mentioned in his writings that he had attended Edinburgh University, where his studies were interrupted when he was seventeen years old by the death of his father. He took over the management of his mother's estate at Gourdiehill and quickly set about extending the orchards there.

Between the years 1807 and 1831 when he published his first book *Naval Timber and Arboriculture* with its important *Appendix*, he appears to have travelled widely on the continent. Between 1831 and 1839 he became involved with the Chartist Movement. In 1839 his second book

Emigration Fields was published. The aim of this book was the solution of mass unemployment in Britain in the 1830s. No doubt he canvassed as well in favour of free trade, abolition of monopolies, repeal of the Corn Laws, and against hereditary titles and wealth. This book was not simply a traveller's guide to the climate, flora and fauna of the countries suitable for emigrants. It was clearly all derivative from a geographic point of view but introduced natural selection as a justification of colonization. Between 1830 and 1850 he was travelling a great deal in Germany and purchased farms in Schleswig-Holstein. The farms were amalgamated into one estate – Schenefeld – between 1845 and 1850 and his third son, Alexander, was put in charge. Alexander married a German woman and settled and died in Germany without mastering the German language. Schenefeld was sold in about 1874 when Alexander moved to another estate – Mafenfelde – near Ploen in Holstein. About 1885 the estate was sold and Alexander retired to Wandsbek near Hamburg where he died in 1911. It was through the German line that a cousin, Pastor Dr Beneke, passed on some information concerning Patrick Matthew and Darwin to Professor May, who presented a biographical sketch to German scientists celebrating the centenary in 1909 of the birth of Charles Darwin. The name of Matthew has now died out in what was West Germany, but a Matthew family has been found in the former East Germany.

About 1860 Charles and James, the fourth and fifth sons of Patrick Matthew, emigrated to New Zealand. These sons had apparently been trained in the production and care of fruit trees and they set up at Matakana, near Aukland, the first commercial orchards in the Antipodes. The seeds of apple and pear were sent from the orchards at Gourdiehill. Young trees were also sent in barrels by sea. Alas like the orchard at Gourdiehill itself, those at Matakana are no more. A few descendants of these sons still survive in New Zealand but the name of Matthew has died out. A personal communication from one of these descendants records that, in her childhood in the 1920s, there was still an enthusiastic tradition of the annual hybridizing of apples and pears. It is clear that the two sons of Patrick Matthew had acquired the techniques from their father at Gourdiehill, introduced the practice at Matakana and passed on to succeeding generations an enthusiasm for hybridizing.

Between 1860 when he confronted Charles Darwin and 1874 when he died, Patrick Matthew continued to supervise his orchard at

Gourdiehill, to travel to Germany to visit his son Alexander, and pursued various business interests. The Prussian invasion of Schleswig-Holstein gained his full support and prompted him to write his third book *Schleswig-Holstein* in 1864; he sent a copy of this to Darwin but it has disappeared from the Darwin collection in the care of Cambridge University. In 1869 he started a series of long letters to the *Dundee Advertiser* opposing the building of the proposed railway bridge across the River Tay. In 1871 the Franco-Prussian War brought him into the public eye because of a series of letters to the same newspaper pointing out that the aggressors were the French under Napoleon III.

Patrick Matthew carried on in the Carse of Gowrie a tradition of apple and pear growing founded by the Cistercian monks of the nearby Cupar Abbey who early in the twelfth century had drained the area and organized farming. Gourdiehill is a flat and unattractive estate and about the least picturesque area north of the Tay. 'Gourdie' in the Gaelic tongue originally meant 'dregs' but it came to mean any low-lying area. An account of the orchards in the Carse of Gowrie appeared in the *Memoirs of the Caledonian Horticultural Society* (Machray and Gorries 1, 317, 1814) in the early nineteenth century but there is no mention of Gourdiehill. If there was an orchard there at the time of this survey it was clearly of little consequence. Patrick Matthew extended the orchard to over 10,000 trees during his lifetime and Gourdiehill later on in the century became recognized as one of the largest in Scotland (L. Melville, 1935). By the time the extension was complete Patrick Matthew had acquired vast professional experience in arboriculture and hybridizing. The estate was sold by Patrick Matthew's second son Robert in about 1880. The Georgian mansion dominating the Gourdiehill was burned out in the late 1970s and the red sandstone house is now in a sad condition. A few sick fruit trees are all that remain of a once famous orchard. The estate would appear to have run down in the last few years prior to Patrick Matthew's death because his son could no longer make a living from the orchard and sold it.

Patrick Matthew died in 1874 and is said to have been buried in nearby Errol cemetery. A thorough search of the cemetery did not reveal the site of his grave. Only a brief notice of his death appeared in the *Scotsman*. No obituary notice appeared in any newspaper or journal and it is doubtful if Charles Darwin ever heard of his demise. Such is the price a man must pay for pioneering before the time is ripe – especially if no influential writer comes to his defence. Sad to say, none of his eight children gathered together his books, letters and other documents and put them in safe keeping. Indeed the few remaining descendants today were quite unaware of the biographical sketches which appeared in 1910 and 1912. Had the children of Patrick Matthew been as attentive as those of Charles Darwin in safeguarding the memory of their father, a fuller picture of the man might have appeared.

Although accepted by Wallace and Darwin as an anticipator of evolution through natural selection, Patrick Matthew is not mentioned in any biographical dictionaries for the period 1828–1899.

A Perthshire farmer, in about 1890, jotted down a few memories of the old man at Gourdiehill. He was a man who stayed aloof but was a kindly, studious and well-read man who believed in neither God nor the devil! The laird of Gourdiehill, it must be admitted, was outspoken when occasion demanded. Anyone entering the kind of public debate which Matthew engaged in from time to time could easily be accused of being tactless and crotchety. In his opening letter opposing the proposed plans for an iron bridge across the River Tay, he wrote, 'Those who have been accustomed to read some of my thoughts, which I have now and then laid before the public, will smile at the very correct description you give of me – venerable, crotchety old man with a head stuffed with old-world notions, quite unsuited to the present age of progress. But let that pass as a mere figure of speech, given *pour rire*.' (*Dundee Advertiser*, 1869). After his confrontation with Darwin, Matthew sent him some very civil letters which showed a real concern for Darwin's poor health and even suggested that a trip to Scotland might benefit him. In return, Darwin put up something of a smoke-screen of ill-health so that they never met on any occasion when Matthew was in London on business.

Slater's *Directory of Scotland* (1873, pl. 543) lists Patrick Matthew of Gourdiehill as a member of the nobility and gentry for the parish of Errol, Perthshire. Had Charles Darwin known this he might have been more deferential to Matthew. Darwin wrote to Charles Lyell on one occasion (22 January 1865), 'I have the true English instinctive reverence for rank.' There is no evidence that Darwin or indeed any other naturalist of the period made the slightest effort to get to grips with Matthew. After 1859 all the praise as well as the obloquy were directed at Darwin and Matthew's protest in the *Gardeners' Chronicle* made no impact on anyone at the time. Indeed, if Darwin had not acknowledged Patrick

Matthew in the third edition of the *Origin,* he might never have been heard of again.

His efforts to comment on natural selection at the 1867 Dundee meeting of the British Association for the Advancement of Science met with rebuff. He wrote a letter to the *Dundee Advertiser* (1867) complaining about his treatment at the hands of the organizers of the meeting. Matthew applied for permission to present nine communications. The committee of management rejected all but two. His communications ranged from botany to natural selection and political economy! The annual report did not publish a communication he is said to have delivered, before the section on economic science and statistics, on 'Capital and Labour'.

It is clear that not all the discussions that took place during the 1867 meeting were published. However, W. Sharpey, in his presidential address, made no reference to natural selection and there was no published paper on this subject. It may be that Patrick Matthew attempted to discuss the subject after the address but was effectively suppressed. There was a paper on 'Arboriculture as a Science', which should have appealed to Patrick Matthew but there is no evidence that he made any contribution to this subject.

His name cropped up again in 1879, five years after his death, when Samuel Butler discussed his claim to priority in *Evolution, Old and New.* Butler so damned Matthew with faint praise together with absurd and unfair criticism, that the anticipator of Darwin disappeared almost without trace.

For the British Association meeting at Dundee in 1912 Calman, a deputy director of the Natural History Museum, was given the duty of presenting some facts about Patrick Matthew. Calman's contribution is largely a translation from the German essay by May (1911). It is clear from a letter sent, prior to the meeting, to D'Arcy Thomson that Calman had little regard for Matthew who is referred to as 'an old bore'. However, Calman lets slip the remark '. . . it is perhaps not always recognized how complete the anticipation really was.' How complete! So now he had the opportunity to counter Darwin's damning criticism that Matthew had 'merely enunciated' the theory of natural selection. Alas, only a few brief extracts from Matthew were included in an all too short biographical essay.

Although Darwin made no effort to get to know more about Patrick Matthew the parallel with himself is remarkable: a landed gentleman from a wealthy family and large estate, married about the age of 27 to a cousin of considerable means and from a distinguished family, a large family of eight children living in a Georgian mansion, widely travelled, rich and independent of any institution, a synthesizing mind and absorbed in natural history. Matthew died from the effects of valvular disease of the heart and Darwin from coronary thrombosis. He differed from Darwin in having a robust constitution, worked for his living on his orchard and farms, intellectually was an early starter and had a wide interest in naval supremacy, emigration and politics. They both started but later abandoned the study of medicine at Edinburgh University. Matthew because his father died and he was needed to run the family estate; Darwin because he was bored and disgusted with the course.

One thing they did not have in common was smoking. Matthew was a vigorous anti-smoking agitator. He envisaged, for mankind, a health crisis in the future. He thought that the brain would be affected. The nicotine addiction does involve the brain but we now appreciate that the target organs are the heart and lungs. Darwin, on the other hand, was a cigarette smoker. After lunch he would lie on the sofa in his bedroom and smoke cigarettes. This, apparently, continued for forty years (Atkins, 1974). Like any other cigarette smoker he must have smoked at other times of the day. In later life he would pay the price for all those years of cigarette smoking.

In a letter to Hooker, Darwin referred to Edward Blyth as one 'who will never do what he could do, from not sticking to any one subject' (MLD 1, 63). Similar criticism could be directed at Patrick Matthew. Having written on arboriculture he was distracted during his book's printing by events in Europe and because of this he added the *Appendix* to *Naval Timber and Arboriculture* explaining in its closing paragraphs why he did not pursue his interest in rural affairs; with that he turned his back on natural philosophy and seems to have thought no more about it until he read in 1860 Huxley's review in *The Times* of *The Origin of the Species by Natural Selection*.

The revolution in France in 1830 seems to have given Matthew some hope of a peaceful Europe. At the same time, however, the Chartist Movement was getting under way and Matthew joined up with enthusiasm. He was made the representative for his area for the Great Chartist Convention of 1839. The leader of the Chartists – Feargus O'Connor – wanted the Chartists to become more revolutionary. Matthew and his

The sad remnants of a once-famous orchard at Gourdiehill

Photograph of Gourdiehill, the home of Patrick Matthew

constituents disagreed with this policy and so he resigned from the movement. Obviously for some time before 1839 he had become involved in his next project – emigration. There was mass unemployment and Matthew's solution was emigration of the unemployed and to this end he produced *Emigration Fields*. This book revealed the harsh character of the time and in many ways his policy coincided with that in Darwin's *The Descent of Man* which he reviewed for the *Scotsman* in 1871. His various interests are told in his collection of letters.

2

Natural Selection – The Appendix to *Naval Timber and Arboriculture*

The last chapter is a political one; and, indeed, throughout the book proofs abound that our author is not one of those who devote themselves to a subject without caring for its ultimate issues and relations; consequently his habit of mind propels him to those political considerations which the subject, 'our marine', naturally induces: benefiting man universally is the spirit of the author's political faith.

(Loudon's review of *Naval Timber and Arboriculture*)

Shortly after Charles Darwin sailed away on the Beagle, in the autumn of 1831, there was published in Edinburgh and London Patrick Matthew's book *Naval Timber and Arboriculture*. To this orthodox publication was attached, as an afterthought, an appendix about which J. C. Loudon wrote in a review in 1832: 'This may be truly termed, in a double sense, an extraordinary part of the book. One of the subjects discussed in the appendix is the puzzling one, of the origin of species and varieties . . .' The author, Patrick Matthew, sharply reminded Darwin of this appendix a few months after the publication of the *Origin* in 1859. The book had not sold well, so within six days of reading Matthew's letter in the *Gardeners' Chronicle* (7 April 1860), Darwin was able to purchase a copy. To his profound chagrin he found that the basic principles of natural selection were set out in a few brief sentences more succinctly than he had achieved himself. Darwin honourably replied (12 May 1860): 'I freely acknowledge that Mr Matthew has anticipated by many years the explanation which I have offered of the origin of species under the name of natural selection. I can do no more than offer my apologies to Mr Matthew for my entire ignorance of his publication. If another edition of my work is called for, I will insert a notice to the foregoing effects.'

Matthew sent his long letter to the *Gardeners' Chronicle* but it did not reach a wide scientific audience. What eventually did reach a wide audience was Darwin's letter to de Quatrefages a few weeks later: '. . . an obscure writer on forest trees . . . clearly anticipated my views . . . though he put the case so briefly that no single person ever noticed the scattered passages in his book . . .' Such remarks were not only quite untrue but were sufficiently damning to inhibit any further interest in Matthew.

When Matthew's book was published only a few of the leading personalities in the Geological Society had begun to reject the Mosaic account of the origin of the earth; Lamarckian Evolutionism was almost entirely confined to France, Cuvierian Catastrophism was the dominant theory in England; God was still in the heavens. Matthew was clearly well ahead of the intellects of Europe in regarding artificial and natural selection as manifestly analogous. 'The unremitting operation of this law . . . by careful selection of the largest or most valuable as breeders . . . only the hardier, more robust, better suited to circumstances, who are able to struggle forward to maturity . . . this circumstance-adaptive law, operating upon the slight but continued natural disposition to sport in the progeny . . . Man's interference, by preventing this natural process of selection among plants . . . has increased the difference in varieties . . .'

The *Appendix* was added after Matthew had read his main work in proof form and was an outline sketch of material he had intended to expand into a large volume dealing with rural economy and other matters germane and, evidently, not so germane. But then, quite suddenly, the French Revolution of 1830 changed all his ideas about devoting himself to rural economy. It makes one wonder if many of his contemporaries were voicing but not writing such thoughts. When he confronted Darwin thirty years later he made the most extraordinary statement that he did not realize that he had discovered a new law. Matthew nowhere claims his *Appendix* to be original. His whole approach is derived from the French evolutionists and Cuvier. He had visited Paris and Germany many times and so became embroiled in the evolutionary debate in those countries while England remained in chilly silence. He would also be aware of what was going on in Edinburgh where students had returned from Paris full of Lamarckian ideas. Indeed, the anonymous essay of 1826 was a eulogy of Lamarck. If one were irreligious one became a Lamarckian; if one were devout one became a Catastrophist according to the teaching of Cuvier. Considering how influenced he had been in his youth by Lamarck and French science one can understand that by adding natural selection to the scientific tale he could hardly claim to have discovered a new law.

In the last section of the *Appendix*, Matthew explains why he did not pursue his interests in rural affairs.

> Since this volume went to press there has been some changes of scenery of the political European stage, even rivalling what has been accomplished by sylvan metamorphosis on the face of nature by Sir Henry Steuart. The intense interest excited by these efforts towards the regeneration of man, has completely thrown into the shade our humbler subject – the regeneration of trees . . . They, by obliterating national distinctions and diminishing the occasions for going to wars, will, it is hoped, bring the European family close into amity. At any rate, they have completely thrown out the calculations of our politicians regarding the balance of power and international connection as natural allies and foes, and bind the French and the British together by ties on the surest principle of friendly sympathy . . . which no Machiavellian policy of cabinets, nor waywardness of political heads will be able to sunder.
>
> We had intended to bring out *Naval Timber and Arboriculture* as a portion of a work embracing Rural Economy in general, but this is not a time to think of rural affairs . . .

The *Appendix* is divided into six notes and a short sketch.

The first note deals with the crucial importance of sea power to world domination.

The second note outlines the law of nature which has subsequently come to be known as Blyth's localizing principle. 'This law sustains the lion in his strengths the hare in her swiftness and the fox in his wiles.' This is followed by another law which subsequently would be associated with the Malthusian doctrine. 'Nature . . . has a power of increase far beyond what is needed to supply the place of what falls by Time's decay . . . those . . . who possess not the requisite strength . . . fall prematurely without reproducing . . . generally induced by want of nourishment.'

These two laws are used to indicate that the law of entail is an outrage against the laws of nature. Quite suddenly we find ourselves in a political statement which could not be more radical. Leaders must be renovated 'by selection anew' if the stock is to improve. The abolition of inherited wealth and land is the logical conclusion.

The third note deals with the supposed increased vigour resulting from emigration of peoples. There is a great deal of generalization about Caucasians and Celts which does not seem to lead to any clear conclusion.

The fourth note is very brief and deals with the mighty opposites – peace and wars good and evil. There is a hint of lauding imperialism through fire and sword.

The fifth note criticises the method of measuring the register tonnage which adversely affects the principles of ship construction. The injurious effect from vessels being constructed on the principle of avoiding tolls or dues, rather than for sailing, will occur to everyone. This, according to Matthew, derives from the ignorance of parliament '. . . consequent to defective representations.'

The sixth note is a discussion of the geological feature of the Firth of Tay. From some local features he draws the conclusion that Holland at one time extended over to Scotland and that later raising of the level of the sea must have occurred around the coast of Britain. The effect of the motion of sea water in shaping the coast is well understood. There is certainly no recourse to a Noachian Flood as the principal geological agency shaping the coast line. There is no reference to any defunct biblical explanation. Matthew reveals, therefore, that there was sufficient information available just prior to the writing of the *Appendix*, at least, to allow a liberated mind to seek natural explanations for geological features.

In the sketch Matthew introduces the dynamics of geology in order to explain fossil deposition. 'The destructive liquid currents, before which the hardest mountains have been swept and comminuted into gravel, sands and mud, which intervened between and divided these epochs, probably extending over the whole surface of the globe, and destroying nearly all living things, must have reduced existence so much, that an unoccupied field would be formed for new diverging ramifications of life, which, from the connected sexual system of vegetables, and the natural instincts of animals to herd and combine with their own kind, would fall into specific groups, these remnants, in the course of time, moulding and accommodating their being anew to the change of circumstances, and to every possible means of subsistence, and the millions of ages of regularity which appear to have followed between the epochs, probably after this accommodation was completed affording fossil deposit of regular specific characters.

There were few men of science anywhere in Europe in 1831 quite as clear, confident and radical in their assessment of the history of the earth. The Copley medal had been awarded in 1823 to William Buckland for proving the Noachian Flood had taken place. Not until 1830 did Adam Sedgwick announce his rejection of the Flood as the principal geological agency shaping the earth. Soon afterwards Buckland followed and a great deal of calumny was heaped upon him by the clergy, a majority of whom still believed literally in Holy Writ.

The Scottish naturalists were far ahead of Sedgwick's announcement. Hutton's *Theory of the Earth* (1795) was a complete rejection of Holy Writ and by 1826 the Reverend John Fleming had rejected Noah's Flood. It is even more astonishing that Matthew, having entered the front ranks of the liberated intelligentsia and having established himself in his own sector of arboriculture and gained the applause of his peers, should renounce it all for European politics and so fade into obscurity in the process.

There would not appear to be anything in the *Appendix* which was original or, indeed, claimed to be. If the contents were not original they must have been derived from what he had read – and he had obviously read widely in many subjects. In the preface to the main work, Matthew points out that he deliberately went beyond mere arboriculture to include the species problem because of the great interest in this subject. In the *Appendix* he returns to this theme and in a few sentences conveyed most of what Darwin took twenty years to enunciate and even then not quite so succinctly. Matthew had only to look around him to be convinced of the obvious truth of natural selection and clearly his work in the orchard would involve hybridization and the weeding out of the weak saplings. Animal and plant breeders in the eighteenth century were aware of dominance, segregation and hybrid vigour. To the animal and plant breeder of the day the process of artificial selection was obviously analogous to natural selection. Darwin did not start off with any particular breeding problem but was concerned with amassing facts which, when synthesized, would make natural selection the only explanation.

Let us set the *Appendix* in its context in the history of science. From the mid-eighteenth century, after the classification of species by Linnaeus, a continuous wrangle developed, mainly in France. With one eye on the bishops of the Sorbonne, Buffon wrote and rewrote for and against transmutation of species. Buffon did not believe in species – only in individuals. The Encyclopaedists, like Diderot, postulated that the only way to account for the diversity of living plants and animals was change over a vast time scale of millions of years. At the end of the eighteenth century only one Englishman had contributed anything to this wrangle and that was Erasmus Darwin. His contemporaries at this stage in France were Lamarck and Cuvier. In the 1820s a bitter controversy continued in Paris between St Hilaire and Cuvier; the former argued in favour of transmutation while the latter was dogmatically opposed to the concept of the mutability of species. Lamarck argued gently in favour of continuous change. In England at this time the naturalist-parsons of Oxbridge were won over to Cuvier's theory of Catastrophism.

In 1830–1833 an *émigré* Scot, Charles Lyell, published his *Principles of Geology* which dealt the death blow to Cuvierian theory, and introduced the term Evolution; it was, however, a term picked up from Lamarck. The Noachian Flood, as the principal geological agency, was quickly abandoned and the foundation of Genesis undermined. Because of his religious beliefs, the delicate social climate and superb diplomacy, Lyell drew back from championing the evolution of the organic world including man himself though he already had sufficient evidence to do so. Although Lyell brilliantly extended the theory of the evolution of the rocks propounded by the Scot James Hutton in the eighteenth century, another Scottish *émigré* – John Hunter – clearly wrote out the basis of Uniformitarianism in 1792 but the essay was not published until 1859 through the persistent efforts of Richard Owen. This essay has been ignored by historians of geology ever since.

In 1844 another Scot – Robert Chambers – published anonymously *The Vestiges of the Natural History of Creation*. Although severely criticized by T. H. Huxley and others it had a great influence on many members of the educated public; Darwin was influenced too. The theme of the book was that the Creator had, over a period of time, laid out like a carpet the animal and plant kingdoms, involving a process of higher forms evolving from lower forms. What Lyell had shown for the inorganic world Chambers now showed for the organic world including man. But there is no mention of evolution by natural selection in this book.

In 1847 in his *History of the Inductive Sciences* Whewell argued on the same lines as had St Hilaire and Cuvier twenty years before '. . . either we must accept the doctrine of the transmutation of species . . . or else believe in many successive acts of Creation and extinction of species.' Whewell clearly dogmatically adhered to the latter theory for later on he banned the *Origin of Species* from Trinity Library!

But what were these successive acts of Creation? Cuvier had shown that the history of the earth was one of steady state interrupted at intervals by catastrophes which exterminated most of the plants and animals of that epoch as judged again by new fossils. The problem was: were they created miraculously or were they the ones that had survived the Catastrophe and over time had changed?

Matthew had thus come to his conclusions at a time when Cuvier's Special Creationism and Catastrophism were widely accepted, even in scientific circles in England, and at a time, also, when Holy Writ was regarded as fundamental by the Oxbridge scientific establishment; Matthew therefore interpreted the information of his day and age in a truly Lamarckian-Cuvierian manner. Darwin's *Origin* came after the *Vestiges* had cleared the way and had prepared a section of intellectual society which could respond immediately. The *Origin* sold out its 1,200 copies on the first day. Between 1800 and 1830 theological restrictions were severe; by 1859 they were less severe and beginning to disintegrate. Matthew's book and its *Appendix* went unread except by a few reviewers who praised it. A library, now defunct, in Perth banned it. Matthew seems to have accepted that his interpretations were too radical for his age and he turned to other pursuits.

As we have noted, Darwin quite freely admitted that 'in the scattered passages' Matthew had completely pre-empted him and Wallace in enunciating the principle of natural selection. Even so, there is no evidence that anyone else rushed to read Matthew's book. Reference was made to it again rather scathingly in 1879 by Samuel Butler in *Evolution, Old and New*. What Matthew had presented, he argued, was no more than an excellent summary of the views of Buffon, Lamarck and Erasmus Darwin. The whole thesis, in his view, was vitiated by its brevity. If this was all why should Darwin and Wallace agree that Matthew had pre-empted their theory of natural selection? Indeed, Wallace, magnanimous as ever, wrote to Butler after reading his books: 'To my mind your quotations from Mr Patrick Matthew are the most remarkable things in your whole book, because he appears to have completely anticipated the main ideas of *The Origin of the Species* . . .' If the *Appendix* was a mere recapitulation of eighteenth-century ideas why did Darwin himself not produce such a document after his return from the voyage on the Beagle? However, the comments of Samuel Butler were sufficient to curb any interest by the scientific public in what Patrick Matthew had written in 1831.

It is rather difficult to understand Wallace's attitude to Patrick Matthew. Although Charles Darwin wrote to him in 1860 to tell him that Matthew had already enunciated the principle of natural selection in 1831, Wallace appears to have made no comment until 1870. Perhaps the fact that Wallace made no comment from the other side of the world in 1860 is understandable but his changing attitude in subsequent years is quite incomprehensible. In his *Contributions to the Theory of Natural Selection* (1870), Wallace referred to Wells and Matthew in a rather disparaging manner *vis-à-vis* Charles Darwin. In his view '. . . they certainly propounded the fundamental principle of "natural selections" before himself but who made no further use of that principle, and failed to see its wide and immensely important applications.' So far as Patrick Matthew was concerned this was not true. Long before 'social Darwinism' provided a rationale for imperialistic expansion, and before the concept that 'might is right' came to be seen as a logical deduction from the biological observations of Darwinism, Matthew had expressed an imperialistic jingoism which was to become popular thirty years later. As a result of his belief that superior varieties of *Homo sapiens* (that is, the British but particularly those derived from the Angles) should spread their influence and control the world he went on to write *Emigration Fields* in 1839. He encouraged his sons to emigrate to New Zealand. As a result of his admiration for a variety of *Homo sapiens* – the descendants of the Angles in the Schleswig-Holstein region – he came out in support of Bismarck's invasion in 1864. Only in his later years did Matthew mellow and recant on his imperialistic jingoism.

In 1902, when Wallace wrote his essays on Darwinism he had forgotten all about his comments on Patrick Matthew in 1870 and 1879.

Although Darwin, honourably enough, conceded that Patrick

Matthew had anticipated his views on natural selections he also made assertions which were not true. In his letter to the *Gardeners' Chronicle* he went on, 'I think that no one will feel surprised that neither I, nor apparently any other naturalist, had heard of Mr. Matthew's views . . .' Matthew protested about this too but without further comment from Charles Darwin.

By 1832 several journals had reviewed *Naval Timber and Arboriculture*. All the reviews were favourably impressed and acknowledged their respect for Matthew as a practical arboriculturalist of front rank. Contrary to what Darwin, in his ignorance, had claimed, the reviewers did not miss what was written in the *Appendix*. The reviewer for the *Gardeners' Magazine*, December 1832, was J. C. Loudon (1783–1843) – the magazine's editor, the most distinguished authority on arboriculture and editor of several encyclopaedias still in use today.

Loudon was the father of horticultural journalism. He was a lowland Scot who came south to seek fame and fortune achieving both quite soon. He became an expert in the design, construction and glazing of conservatories which ultimately influenced the building of the Crystal Palace. He played an important role in laying out London's public parks and advocated green belts around cities. He was mainly a landscape gardener but was instrumental in founding the Horticultural Society. By 1830 he was editing five journals simultaneously as well as editing an encyclopaedia. Through his friendship with Joseph Banks he came into contact with the scientific world. He was not impressed with the standard of English farming and was a firm advocate of becoming independent of the import of corn. Although his editing of an encyclopaedia involved him in speciation and classification of varieties, there is no evidence in his extensive writings that he thought philosophically about the origin of species (Gloag, 1970). Had he been so interested he would certainly have detected in Matthew's argument something quite new. One can only surmise that his busy life prevented him from reading more carefully what Matthew had concentrated into the *Appendix* to *Naval Timber*. However, he commented, 'This may be truly termed, in a double sense, an extraordinary part of the book. One of the subjects discussed in the *Appendix* is the puzzling one of the origin of species and varieties – and if the author has hereon originated no original views (and of this we are far from certain) he has certainly exhibited his own in an original manner.'

It is difficult to follow Loudon's comment because what Matthew had written on geology and natural selection was quite out of step with both Cuvierian and English attitudes at that time. The utter irreligiosity of Matthew's statement was also something new, unless, of course, animal and plant breeders in the course of their everyday life acted and thought like Matthew had expressed himself. Darwin himself, after 1859, claimed that during the twenty years of preparation for the *Origin* he had never met any one postulating natural selection. Yet, on his own submission, he gained the term from animal and plant breeders. So far as the learned societies and official scientific meetings are concerned Darwin probably was right in claiming that he had met no one discussing prior to 1859 natural selection and searches confirm this. The first edition of the *Gardeners' Magazine* appeared in 1826 with Loudon as the founder editor. Between that date and 1832, when the review of Matthew's book appeared, not one article or review of a topic relating to evolution of the origin of species, let alone natural selection, was published. Loudon was a distinguished member of the Linnean Society but during this period the transactions show that there were no discussions on such topics. In 1829, the first edition of the *Magazine of Natural History* was published (again, Loudon was the editor). The first number carried a long review of Cuvierian zoology and a recognition that geology was essential to a liberal education.

Further on reference will be made to an article published anonymously in 1826 which made a plea for the recognition of geology as a new important scientific discipline. Clearly between 1826 and 1829 the repressive political atmosphere had become more liberal as the Whigs' liberal policy was gaining support so that a review was allowed on the subjects of Cuvier's zoology and geology as an accepted science.

Not until the edition of 1835 is there to be found any article dealing with the problem of varieties and that is the article by the young Edward Blyth on 'An attempt to classify the "Varieties" of animals, etc.' Had Loudon reviewed Matthew's book in the *Magazine of Natural History,* it would have reached a wider audience particularly the Oxbridge establishment. There is no evidence that it was read or banned by Cambridge. And Loudon's final comment was '. . . a book which we would be sorry should be absent from our library.'

Another review in the *United Services Journal* (33, August 1831) ran to twenty pages. Early on, the reviewer made his own position clear: 'In thus testifying our hearty approbation of the author, it is strictly in his capacity of a forest-ranger, where he is original, bold and evidently experienced in all the arcana of the parentage, birth and education of trees. But we disclaim participation in his rumination on the law of nature, or on the outrages committed upon reason and justice by our burthens of hereditary nobility, entailed property, and insane enactments.' It is clear that the *Appendix* was too hot to handle.

No wonder Patrick Matthew failed to influence the English academics and small wonder he had to pay the price of extinction for expressing his political and social ideas amidst his scientific observations. Mixed modes of writing which enlist the reader's feeling as well as his thinking are dangerous and rather repugnant to English readers. Similar criticism was directed against his contemporaries – Blake, Turner and Dickens. Blake was ridiculed for mixing the spiritual and the material; critics disliked the variety and energy displayed in Turner's 'crude theatrical blotches'; Dickens was condemned for mixing the tragic with the comic. Such criticism no longer obtains and Matthew's mixing political economy and biology became social Darwinism. Desmond (1989) remarks that, 'Matthew's *Appendix* was not a chance juxtaposition of radicalism and transformism.' This author goes on to probe 'the link between their democratic politics, free-trade demands and doctrines of self-development . . . the way the radicals' materialist sciences harmonized with calls for a capitalist free market.' Many no doubt recognized the dangerous ideas in the *Appendix* and laid the book aside.

Far from being accused of vomiting his book from the jaws of hell, Matthew occasioned no public outcry in spite of the atheistic tone of his natural philosophy. Unlike the reviewers of the *Vestiges* (1844) and the *Origin* (1859), the reviewers of Matthew's book were extremely tolerant considering that after 1815 there was a strong religious movement in England which for a number of years attracted able men to the Church in greater numbers than at any time since the Reformation. Charles Darwin himself originally intended to be part of this movement but the experiences gained on the Beagle changed his mind. There was, emanating from France, a strong irreligious movement as well and it would seem that Patrick Matthew was allied to this intellectual current which was to grow into a flood by the end of the century.

Darwin's use of 'obscure' and 'briefly' was echoed by other authors

right down to 1959 in an influential book *Darwin's Century* by Loren
Eiseley: 'Matthew's system perished, not only because it had been
published obscurely by an obscure man . . .' But Matthew's book was
published simultaneously in Edinburgh by Adam and Charles Black and
in London by Longman and Co. So what was so obscure about the
publication? Patrick Matthew was not an obscure man. He was the
owner of one of the richest and largest orchards in Scotland. He was
well known locally. Matthew became the representative of his area for
the Chartist Convention of 1839 so he had clearly been in active politics
all through the 1830s. The simple answer to the problem of obscurity
is the fact that the book was not read by a sufficient number of
influential people and, even more important, that Matthew abandoned
the subject.

We cannot agree with Eiseley that Patrick Matthew was, from a
geological point of view, a Catastrophist allied to the Cuvierian doctrine.
Although it was now clear that many species had become extinct and
that several cataclysmic changes had taken place over the surface of the
earth, Matthew did not accept Special Creationism. Far from it. He could
not have logically argued the case for natural selection and the mutability
of species if he had at the same time agreed with Special Creationism
within the general concept of Catastrophism which dominated European
thought in the 1820s and for some decades after. By the same token
Cuvier, Lyell, Richard Owen and indeed Edward Blyth were unable to
argue a case for natural selection and the mutability of species while still
retaining a lingering belief in a Creator. It would seem clear from the
following statement in the *Appendix* that Matthew rejected Special
Creationism: 'There is more beauty and uniformity of design in this
continual balancing of life to circumstance, and greater conformity to
those dispositions of nature which are manifest to us, than in total
destruction and new creations.'

This statement is not one which would appeal to the Special
Creationists. It is more in line with what was to become known as
Uniformitarianism. Yet Eiseley continues on from the 'obscure' basis of
why Matthew's system perished '. . . but because uniformitarian geology
at the hands of Lyell was about to weaken and overthrow the catastrophist
philosophy.' Just because Matthew believed that the geological facts
demonstrated large scale changes on the crust of the earth did not make
him a Catastrophist. In any case there is evidence that uniformitarianism

was being seriously discussed by John Hunter in 1792 and probably by others before Lyell concentrated the evidence in his famous *Principles of Geology.*

Eiseley joins in the old Darwinian complaint of Matthew's brevity. Why Matthew should in a few sentences sketch out and enunciate the principle of natural selection is quite a mystery. To proceed to extend the principle to all social and political thinking is also baffling. Could he have completed the great work he had planned? If anyone looked at nature with a steadfast, uncompromising eye unencumbered by the theological dogma of his day, it was Patrick Matthew. In his book he was not just content with nature as he saw it but proceeded to the political and social consequences of selection for man himself. Neither Darwin nor Wallace pursued such consequences of a theory of natural selection.

Although Matthew wrote out his thoughts on natural selection quickly and without any further modification or correction during his lifetime, he was always truly naturalistic. Darwin had the advantage of Lyell's *Principles of Geology* and twenty years of study but even so he was never more naturalistic in his approach than Matthew. Although the 'chain of being', so strongly believed in by the early-eighteenth-century authors, was a dead concept when Matthew was writing the *Appendix,* his feeling for evolutionism forced a belief in a chain of being. It was Lamarck who dismissed 'the chain of being'! Cuvier also with his four distinct groups in the animal kingdom – Vertebrata, Mollusca, Articulata and Radiata – put an end to what the French Naturalists called the Serie. There was diversity but not unlimited. Cuvier, of course, could offer no proof for such a concept as extended diversity because each level of the geological strata showed different species which seemed unrelated, genetically, to the ones underneath. This palaeontological snag to the evolutionists' argument was still there when Darwin came to write the *Origin.* Like Darwin, Matthew regarded the fault to lie with the geological record and not with the concept of evolutionism. It would not have been possible for Matthew to speculate on how lifeforms of one epoch changed into other forms in other epochs any more than it would be possible today. Matthew's brevity so deplored by a frustrated Darwin was actually a triumph of human thought and concentration. So far as the written record goes, Patrick Matthew seems to be the first of the British evolutionists. Patrick

Matthew was Scottish and so were Darwin's closest supporters Chambers, Lyell and Falconer; maybe these Scots were heir to an education and method of thinking lacking further south.

What these people were heir to was the Scottish Enlightenment of the eighteenth century. At a time when the Industrial Revolution was being forged in England the intellectuals in Scotland, inspired by Newton, launched what is known as the Scottish Enlightenment. A similar Enlightenment spread to every other European country except Spain and Ireland. This movement in Scotland involved a few moral philosophers and historians but soon sparked inventive minds into diverse sciences, art and architecture. However, like the intellectual brilliance of fifth-century Athens, the Scottish Enlightenment did not last long. By the time Patrick Matthew was born in 1790 the repercussions of the French Revolution in England put a sudden brake on liberal ideas in the United Kingdom. The series of Seditious Acts were introduced to counter French atheism. Any criticism of Holy Writ could mean the death penalty or transportation for life. Tom Paine had to flee the country for writing *The Age of Reason*. The Enlightenment in Scotland was confined to the educated classes who, unlike the Oxbridge intellectuals, were free to debate liberal ideas. The 'kirk' mentality with all its religious bigotry remained dominant and continued so into the nineteenth century. In spite of the incredible naïvety of those intellectuals – Francis Hutchinson, Adam Ferguson, David Hume, Adam Smith, Lord Kames and Lord Monboddo – they set up a climate in which the university lecturers and school teachers and not the clerics became the illuminators of society.

It was mentioned above that the influence of Newton was the spur to the Scottish Enlightenment. On the surface Newton was a mathematical genius and so great was his influence that mathematics came to be regarded, by the intellectuals of the period, as the key to the universe. But below the surface Newton was a Freemason as were many of his contemporaries. Back in 1661, after the restoration of the monarchy, the Royal Society was founded by well-known Freemasons. Sir Robert Moray, a Scot with scientific interests, was the guiding spirit along with Elias Ashmole the antiquarian; there were others like Robert Boyle and Christopher Wren. The Royal Society, for many decades, was one conduit for the spread of Freemason values. Newton became President of the Royal Society in 1703 and remained so until his death in 1727. Freemasonry insisted on universal brotherhood and an indifference to organized religion and so it offered an alternative philosophy based on science. It was this aspect of Freemasonry one can detect in their belief in science as a liberating force and also in the appeals of Adam Smith and David Hume and others for better and good relations between employer and employee and condemnation of exploitation of the work-force. It is known that Buffon was much influenced by Newton and even translated some of his works: not only Buffon but also Diderot, so that one can see the simultaneous development of the Scottish Enlight-enment with the French Encyclopaedists both struggling against religion. One can see the struggle of Buffon with the clerics of the Sorbonne up until just prior to the outbreak of the French Revolution. That episode freed the French scientists, like Cuvier and Lamarck, to state what they really believed. The same episode brought to an end the first flush of the Scottish Enlightenment by the Seditious Acts which followed im-mediately upon the outbreak of the French Revolution. It was this alternative philosophy during the preceding decades, the Age of Reason, when myth and religion were condemned as fetters on free thought that culminated in Lamarck classifying man as just a mammal! The stark materialism of this shocked the pious Charles Lyell and led to his denouncing Lamarck.

The sudden flowering of the intellectuals was essentially rooted in a financially comfortable middle class and some aristocrats. They were convinced by Adam Smith that there was a basic harmony between private self-interest and social welfare. The harmony depended on not taking self-interest to extremes. Here was the flaw in this argument when we realize the extreme misery of the labouring classes for the next two centuries. Free trade was the banner under which Adam Smith expressed the needs of a country that already controlled a major proportion of world trade.

David Hume rejected miracles as subverting the principles of under-standing but at the same time he regarded the Creator as an engineer because he looked on nature as a machine. Hume's scepticism persuaded Adam Smith, while believing in a beneficial Creator, to precipitate a revolution by giving pride of place to education over religion; he even demanded that prayers at the University should be abolished. Adam Smith had every confidence in science's supreme ability to benefit mankind. His political economy, which was to stimulate the equally naïve Karl Marx in the next century, was an extension of the moral philosophy advocated by Adam Ferguson. This philosophy involved the law, politics and labour relations. This led to pleading for good neighbourly relations and respect for the common man. Self-interest could be beneficial but it must not be allowed to develop into ruthless exploitation of fellow men. Marx also had the same naïve ideas.

Although the intellectual effort was considerable the Enlightenment was flawed. For all their concern for good human relations there was nowhere a hint that slavery, on which Glasgow as a staging post prospered, was morally wrong and inhuman. Only Robert Burns lamented 'Man's inhumanity to man'.

By the turn of the eighteenth century James Hutton, John Playfair and Robert Jameson supervised the debate on how the earth arose and evolved. At this time in England only Mosaic cosmology was allowed. Robert Burns, Byron and Walter Scot dominated literature. The Munro brothers were supreme in anatomy, the Hunter brothers dominated the medical scene in London, the Adams family were supreme in architecture, and Black's experiments on heat were to lead to momentous discoveries.

The forces of religious bigotry and oppression were still entrenched and shored up with the Seditious Acts after the Napoleonic wars. Even in 1846 Robert Chambers of Edinburgh had to publish anonymously *The Vestiges of the Natural History of Creation* because he feared his family's publishing business would be destroyed. In spite of this the basis for future liberation from the fetters of Holy Writ had been laid. The candle of enlightenment was not out but in the early nineteenth century only those of independent means could afford to keep the spark alive – Robert Grant, Robert Knox, Patrick Matthew, Charles Lyell and later on Charles Darwin who had spent two years in Edinburgh with the Lamarckian enthusiast Robert Grant who later was to set London alight with his Lamarckian teaching. Patrick Matthew's *Appendix* is the first completely irreligious statement about evolution. He made no concessions to a religious society at a time when Edinburgh and Aberdeen were priest ridden. Darwin in the last paragraph of every edition of the *Origin* dragged in the Creator, on the other hand, and only later regretted he had truckled to society.

Although the university at Edinburgh had sunk so low that a government enquiry was set up there were many active minds about in the 1820s (Morrel J.B., 1972). There were many attached to the university who were preparing for the attack on out-worn ideas which was to develop over the next decade. These intellectuals and many more had been to Paris which for a long time had strong links with Edinburgh. There was a great deal of discussion of biological ideas; there were fights in the streets between geologists who were Neptunists and those who were Vulcanists. Darwin was in Edinburgh for two years during this hectic period. In later life he tried to obliterate the influential tracks by claiming that everything and everybody was boring. Out of this intellectual ferment came Robert Grant, Robert Knox, Patrick Matthew, Robert Chambers, Charles Lyell and many others. At this time so far as London and Oxbridge were concerned Holy Writ cosmology was sacrosanct.

For all the flaws in the Enlightenment there were lasting effects. Kant came to the rescue of materialism driven to a standstill by Hume and, with the slogan 'dare to know', established materialism on a strong base. Religion was forced to retreat as science advanced. Among the more leisured section of the country, religion was regarded as divisive and becoming secularized. There was a passion for ideas and Newton's initial inspiration resulted in increasing popularity for mathematics and mathematical tools. There was a drive to absorb elegant English but at the table there was to be the native tongue.

To crown it all in shame it was an English cleric – Sydney Smith – arriving in Edinburgh in 1798 who more than anyone was horrified by the spectacle he saw. For all the moralizing that had gone on there was abject poverty and a miserable state of the labouring classes which the Scots intellectuals had done nothing to change or apparently noticed. In the post-Napoleonic period there was no escape from riots and revolutions all over Europe.

3

Confrontation with Darwin

Great is the power of steady misrepresentation.

(Charles Darwin 1876)

Patrick Matthew read with some astonishment an annotation in the *Gardeners' Chronicle* of 7 April 1860 on *The Origin of the Species*. This editorial was copied almost entirely from a leader in *The Times* (3 March 1860) written by Thomas H. Huxley.

Matthew's protest covered three columns in the *Gardeners' Chronicle*. It acidly commented on the 'recent discovery' being the result of 20 years' investigation on the part of Darwin but which '. . . turns out to be what I published very fully and brought to apply practically to forestry in my work . . . published in 1831,' Matthew then proceeded to quote extensively certain relevant passages from the appendix to *Naval Timber* which can be further condensed here. 'There is a law universal in Nature, tending to render every reproductive being the best possibly suited to its condition . . . this law sustains the lion in its strength and the fox in his wiles' (later to become the 'localizing principle' of Blyth). '. . . As Nature, in all her modifications of life, has a power of increase far beyond what is needed to supply the place of what falls by Time's decay, those individuals who possess not the requisite strength, generally induced by want of nourishment, fall . . . without reproducing,' (the Bejamin Franklin-Townsend-Malthusian doctrine). '. . . geologists . . . discover an almost complete difference to exist between the species . . . of one epoch and that of every other . . . We are therefore led to admit, either of a repeated miraculous creation' (Cuvier's doctrine of Catastrophism) 'or a power of change' (Evolutionism) '. . . that circumstances have been very different in the different epochs, though steady in each, tend strongly to heighten the probability of the latter theory . . . the unremitting operation of this law . . . by careful selection of the largest or most valuable as breeders . . . only the hardier, more robust, better suited to circumstances, who are able to struggle forward to maturity. This circumstance-adaptive law, operating upon the slight but continued natural disposition to sport in the progeny.' 'As far back as history reaches, man had already had considerable influence . . . probably occasioning the destruction of many species, and the production and continuation of a number of varieties or even species,' (Artificial selection) 'which he found more suited to supply his wants, but which, from the infirmity of their condition – not having undergone selection by the law of nature,' (Natural selection) 'of which we have spoken – cannot maintain their ground without its culture and protection.' The terms added in brackets serve to summarize various concepts which were freely available to Patrick Matthew in the 1820s.

We can appreciate here Matthew's logical grasp of the problem of change in recognizing that facts 'tend strongly to heighten the probability of the latter.' Huxley, twenty years later, just prior to the publication of the *Origin* was still perversely confusing the issue by suggesting that separate acts of creation were 'conceivable'. There were only two hypotheses and one had to be relatively more probable, not 'conceivable', than the other. One was testable by scientific method but the other was not; a *vera causa* versus a sterile, vague notion impossible to verify. Up until 1859 Huxley was all things to all men, '. . . defending the tenability of received doctrines when I had to do with the transmutationists and standing up for the possibility of transmutation among the orthodox,' (*Science and Pseudoscience*, 1887).

Although Huxley is better known for his agnostic stance he tried to divorce himself from Christian theology. He was married, however, to a pious High Anglican and so was forced to have his children christened. Other naturalists were also, for the most part, prisoners of their Christian environment – state religion, compulsory school religion, outspoken piety as a necessary prerequisite for climbing the social ladder, memories of Tom Paine who had to flee the country during Pitt's government, the death penalty for any criticism of Holy Writ at that time, and the constant terrorizing of people's minds. There is still no statue of Tom Paine in Britain.

The way intelligent people tried to square scientific findings, particularly Darwinism, with orthodox Christian theology in the latter part of the nineteenth century, is well surveyed by Moore (1978). It never seems to occur to Moore that unless one became a convinced atheist it was virtually impossible, in a Christian environment of that era, to be at ease with evolution, particularly human evolution, and Darwinism. The usual compromise was to assert that evolution and all the rest were ordained by a Creator.

Patrick Matthew was a convinced atheist whose writings made no reference to a Creator or Christian theology. Perhaps the only one, at that time, to accept without reservations *The Origin of the Species* but had the temerity to point out that he had covered most of its message by 1831. Darwin, of course, made a point of ignoring him in spite of the fact that Matthew was the only firm supporter after the *Origin* was published. When Darwin cared to mention the name of Patrick Matthew in later years it was to nail him as a Cuvier– Lamarckian which, at that time, was scientifically incorrect. That did the trick! Although Darwin dragged in the Creator to the last paragraph of every edition of the *Origin* he protested that his Creator had nothing to do with the Pentateuch! This perhaps was forgotten because Karl Pearson in 1923 picked on this paragraph in a lecture to show that Darwin still believed in a first cause!

Herbert Spencer took a positive position akin to that of Matthew: 'The special creation belief had dropped out of my mind many years before; I could not remain in a suspended state; acceptance of the only possible alternative was imperative.' (*Life and letters of Herbert Spencer*, 1908). Darwin dished out the same treatment to Herbert Spencer, a fact which Sir Arthur Keith could never understand (Keith 1955). Why should Darwin cold-shoulder Herbert Spencer when he was one of the few men at that time who had dropped all religious prejudices and was vigorously supporting evolution?

We can now catch a glimpse of how tortuous a character Darwin could be. Darwin purchased a copy, now in the care of Cambridge University Library, of *Naval Timber and Arboriculture* six days after the publication of Matthew's protest. He replied to Matthew's letter (21 April 1860) 'I freely acknowledge that Mr Matthew has anticipated by many years the explanation which I have offered of the origin of species under the name of natural selection. I think that no one will feel surprised that neither I, nor apparently any other naturalist, had heard of Mr Matthew's views, considering how briefly they are given and that they appeared in the appendix to a work on naval timber and arboriculture.'

Dennett (1995), in a very pretentious book, has referred to Darwin's letter with the astonishing remark that Darwin 'graciously conceded'.

Without producing Darwin's letter how was any casual reader to know whether Dennett had given an accurate assessment? Matthew is not mentioned again in Dennett's book. I have pointed out in several parts of my book that Darwin enthusiasts are prone to make inaccurate statements or attribute concepts to Darwin which other people have originated. It has been the object of my book to demonstrate, with documentary evidence, that the three characters in the basic development of evolution are Cuvier, Lamarck and Patrick Matthew. These three introduced three new ideas. *The Origin of the Species* has no new ideas.

Dennett (1995) has not grasped that the really dangerous idea was Lamarck's conclusion that evolution was a fact and that species mutated. That is what inflamed the grandees of the Church and the rest of society. Natural Selection was the concern only of professional biologists. Furthermore, what is one to make of an author who writes about Darwin and yet omits from his bibliography the works of Buffon, Cuvier, Lamarck, St Hilaire, Charles Lyell and Edward Blyth – to mention just a few? The intellectual mugging of Lamarck and Patrick Matthew has lasted too long.

In June 1860, Darwin wrote to de Quatrefages and referred to Matthew as 'an obscure writer on forest trees . . . clearly anticipated my views . . . though he put the case so briefly that no single person ever noticed the scattered passages in his book.'

Darwin had no evidence for this rash and untrue statement; he did not even know the book had been well reviewed. Matthew's book had been well reviewed in the *Gardeners' Magazine* in 1832, pages 702–703. On page 703 the review following that of *Naval Timber and Arboriculture* is that of Professor John Lindley's book *An Outline of the First Principles of Horticulture*. Now John Lindley was and still is a well respected scientist in the history of horticulture: his library, founded in 1866, is well used today. Most naturalists of the period would certainly have read this review and at the same time noticed what Julius Loudon had to say. That John Lindley was very well known to Darwin is confirmed in a letter from Darwin to Hooker (November 1853). Darwin, in his long and exhaustive readings of the journals of his day, must have read that review. Just a few lines above the Lindley review Loudon introduced this: 'One of the subjects discussed in this *Appendix* is a puzzling one, of the origin of species and varieties . . .' Loudon had no views on the subject and neither would most naturalists of the period. Although Darwin denied that he had any hand in the dishonourable episode of 1 July 1858 he did not hesitate to pursue the same tactics in April 1860. Not only that but he kept up the denigratory remarks to 1872 in the *Historical Sketch*. Most historians of natural science have accepted Darwin's criticism without any real effort to check the facts. If one reads what Mayr (1982) has to say about Patrick Matthew, and he is reasonably kind, one will find that he had never read a word of Matthew's book but relied on an essay written by another individual. (Wells 1873). And that goes for many more critics of Matthew's book.

Matthew's letter to the *Gardeners' Chronicle* was civil and polite. The letter indicated the names of the publishers of the book and listed the journals which reviewed the book soon after it was published. Matthew even pointed out that Mr Loudon had reviewed his book. Now Loudon must have been known to Darwin as he was the most distinguished arboriculturalist in England in his day. In spite of this Darwin rashly claimed in his letter, and apparently checked by Joseph Hooker, that no naturalist had ever seen the book. Darwin never withdrew his ill-tempered and false claim and made it clear that Matthew was some obscure individual in the wilds of Scotland. Twelve years later in the sixth edition of the *Origin* Darwin continued with the same disparaging remarks. The unhappy side of this story is that academics over the years have believed everything Darwin had to say and so present-day academics get to know Patrick Matthew via Darwin's remarks.

On 12 May Matthew, in another letter to the *Gardeners' Chronicle* refuted Darwin's assertion that no naturalist had noticed his book. Matthew pointed out that the book had been well reviewed and that a professor of a celebrated University had told him privately that he feared to teach what he believed to be true in *Naval Timber*. Matthew also pointed out that his book had been voted 'unfit' for a Perth library. One might think that Darwin would have been magnanimous enough to withdraw his peevish, unfounded remark. Up to this moment, one's sympathies are with Darwin because the appendix to *Naval Timber and Arboriculture* covered so much ground in such a short space and in such a bewildering manner that the message which was later to shake the world could well be overlooked. Darwin did not let up and although his very frank letter to the *Gardeners' Chronicle* has long been forgotten, the reference to the 'obscure writer' stuck.

Having read Darwin's grudging admission that Matthew had merely enunciated the concept on Natural Selection one can imagine the displeasure this must have occasioned the Scot. But when Darwin went on to add that no naturalist had ever seen the work, that it was brief and published under the title of *Naval Timber and Arboriculture,* Matthew was roused. Off went another letter contradicting Darwin's unwarranted assertions; there had been favourable and indeed high-praising reviews of Matthew's book.

This second letter was a short but concentrated rebuke to Darwin but it has not been recognized as such. The age, he claimed, was not ready to accept his concepts in 1831 which was true. Although the species problem and evolution were doing the rounds in Paris there was a chilly silence in England until Matthew's statement appeared. Nor did Matthew believe 1860 was ready for evolution which was also true. Although those who had been impressed with the *Vestiges* welcomed the *Origin*, and that although there had been several favourable reviews, they were lukewarm about Natural Selection. Even Darwin's collection of friends, including Charles Lyell who helped to get the *Origin* published, were not stressing the importance of Natural Selection. Wallace refused to employ the term and Lyell never accepted the term even when he accepted evolution as a fact later on. Even then he was on the side of Lamarck after confessing to have done him an injustice. To a man the Linnean Society demanded Darwin's resignation.

Matthew continues in his letter with a diatribe against the 'ultrasceptics' with 'a limited power of perception'. Then comes a statement which his detractors have seized upon and offered as proof that Matthew had no concept of the general importance of Natural Selection. Here it is: 'Mr Darwin here seems to have more merit in the discovery than I have had – to me it did not appear a discovery.' Having been actively engaged in hybridization and mixing with breeders all his life the terms artificial and natural selection were Matthew's everyday parlance.

The introduction of natural selection by Matthew thirty years before was just, to a breeder, an incremental but speculative advance – almost a truism to an active breeder. One should remember that Natural Selection and its full implications were not accepted until about 1931. It should also be remembered that Darwin himself lost some faith in the overall importance of Natural Selection at a time when he was becoming more concerned with Pangenesis. One should consult the prefaces to Darwin's

The Descent of Man (1874) and *Variation in Animals and Plants under Domestication* (1868). In *Emigration Fields* (1839) Matthew tried to explain the thickness of the skulls of the Aborigines by the process of Natural Selection induced by a bizarre method of combat. So, Natural Selection was still uppermost in his mind.

But then the deductive Scot ended with a piece of boastful bravado 'He seems to have worked it out by inductive reason, slowly [*sic*] and with due caution to have made his way sympathetically from fact to fact onwards; while with me it was by a general glance at the scheme of Nature that I estimate this select production of species as an a priori fact.' This boastful bravado was aimed at portraying Darwin as a slow plodder compared to himself. Jay Gould (1983) completely misread this second letter.

Well, it did not pay off. It is doubtful if Darwin ever read it. In any case Matthew was not to know that Darwin came to the concept of Natural Selection through his constant contact with breeders and then applied the natural interpretation to the collected data over the years.

Again, for Matthew to declare that the conception 'came intuitively as a self-evident fact, almost without the effort of concentrated thought' was sheer bravado. Anyone who reads the *Appendix* carefully must appreciate that a great deal of concentrated thought went into reducing the basic principles of the natural process of selection to a few concentrated paragraphs. Matthew wrote his *Appendix* without giving any sources for his data but anyone aware of the works of Cuvier and Lamarck can clearly see their influence. For instance – the steady state between upheavals is from Lamarck. Matthew stated that the current animal species were, at least, forty centuries old. Cuvier made this point in presenting the Egyptian mummified animals as the new species following Noah's Flood! The information provided by Cuvier and Lamarck became such a part of him that he failed to see that he had written anything new. Even his rejection of the miraculous birth of new species was probably widespread among the Scottish intellectuals in the 1820s. Noah's Flood was rejected in Scotland – even by the clerics – by 1826. In England the rejection took much longer to be accepted although the Reverend Adam Sedgwick in 1830 had ruled that the Flood was no longer of any geological significance.

The *Appendix* is an extreme deduction which could never please inductive English authors. What the biological critics of the *Appendix* seem to have forgotten is that long periods of induction precede deduction. What the detractors of Matthew do not consider is that he had spent over twenty years actively engaged in breeding fruit trees as well as wide travelling abroad to Germany and especially in the beginning, to France where, obviously, he absorbed the essentials of the scientific debate about species and whether they mutated or not. Only Mayr (1982) seems correctly to realize this: 'The choice of words indicates that he had read Erasmus Darwin, Lamarck, Malthus and Lawrence.' Had Mayr thought about the fact that Matthew was regarded as a Catastrophist it would surely indicate he was acquainted with Cuvier; indeed, in one of Matthew's letters to Darwin, Cuvier is actually mentioned as one who could determine the structure of an animal from one bone.

Patrick Matthew was not the only person to point out to Darwin that concepts claimed as his own had already been published. Huxley had the painful experience of telling Darwin that his Pangenesis theory had already appeared in Buffon's works. Darwin sent a disarming letter to Huxley in 1865 about this affair 'I have read Buffon: whole pages are laughably like mine . . . I am rather ashamed of the whole affair − . . . there is a fundamental difference between Buffon's views and mine.' Had it been anyone other than Darwin who had reproduced Buffon's theory, is there any doubt that the full weight of Huxley's 'needless savagery' would have descended on him? However, Huxley was such a vigorous propagandist for Darwin that all protests were swept aside as usual and were soon forgotten.

To be fair, Darwin himself found his theory of the effects of the glacial period had been attributed to Forbes although, as he wrote to Asa Gray (LLD 2, 135, 1858), 'This is E. Forbes' theory which, however, I may add, I had written out four years before he published.'

In 1862, Darwin replied to a very civil letter from Matthew with a show of forced but cool deference: 'I presume that I have the pleasure of addressing the author of the work on naval architecture and the first enunciator of the theory of Natural Selection.' The rest of Darwin's letter is taken up with obvious signs of panic and the usual references to his ill health and the impossibility of a meeting.

In spite of having received from Matthew another very civil letter with an invitation to Scotland and a photograph, Darwin wrote to Hooker in October 1865 with obvious satisfaction: '. . . So poor old Patrick Matthew is not the first and he cannot, ought not, any longer to put on his title pages "Discoverer of the principle of Natural Selections".' The 'title pages' referred to a political pamphlet by Matthew in 1864 entitled *Schleswig-Holstein* and recently published following the invasion of this small principality by Bismarck. Darwin received a copy of this résumé of the political history of Schleswig-Holstein but there is no evidence that he read it. Indeed, Darwin, in his letter, used the word 'discoverer' whereas the title page of the document actually bears the rather pathetic announcement by Patrick Matthew 'Solver of the species problem'. Eiseley (*Darwin's Century*, 1958) misinterpreted Darwin's letter and thought that Matthew had printed cards announcing his status in the theory of Natural Selection. Even so, Matthew was ill-advised to mix his scientific work with the highly controversial political stance he assumed in 1864 when he defended the German invasion of Schleswig-Holstein. His scholarly review of the historical events leading up to the invasion went against public opinion at that time.

Darwin was well aware that Dr Wells in 1813 had not, like Matthew in 1831, given a concise outline of the principle of Natural Selection. The Dr W. C. Wells (1725–1817), referred to by Darwin in his letter to Hooker, was born of Scottish parents in South Carolina. He was a graduate of the Edinburgh medical school and had read a paper (1813) to the Royal Society in which he argued the relation between artificial and natural selection. He gained fame for an essay on dew.

In spite of Matthew's considerate letters, his concern about Darwin's health, his invitation to the Darwin family to visit Scotland and the recognition that he was advancing natural science, Darwin remained distant, pleaded ill health and rebuffed him. To be fair to Darwin, the years 1860– 66 were difficult years for him; his health was poor and his children were also ill.

Patrick Matthew was not the only individual to be treated by Darwin to this double standard of deference in public statements and denigration in his private letters. Lamarck, as one might perhaps expect, also received this treatment. In the *Origin,* Lamarck is referred to as a 'justly-celebrated naturalist' but in his private letters, as for instance in the letter to Hooker (LLD Vol 2, 23, 1844), we can read about 'Lamarck nonsense' and several misinterpretations. Through the medium of the widely-read *Collected Letters*, succeeding generations were to meet the 'obscure writer on forest trees' and 'Lamarck nonsense' more frequently than Darwin's public statements. In the *Origin,* wherever possible, Darwin would omit names such as Lamarck. In the course of reading the proofs of the *Origin*, Lyell was astonished to read, '. . . the most eminent naturalists have rejected the view of mutability.' He wrote to Darwin, 'You do not mean to ignore G. St Hilaire and Lamarck?' But this was certainly Darwin's intention since the above sentence was altered to '. . . eminent living naturalists'! Even this was wrong because the distinguished Robert Grant and associated radicals had canvassed Lamarckian ideas since 1828. Only the conservative individuals opposed Lamarckism (Desmond 1989).

In the fourth edition (1868) of the *Origin*, Darwin wrote, 'As far as the mere enunciation of the principles of Natural Selection is concerned it is quite immaterial whether or not Prof. Owen preceded me, for both of us, as shown in this historical sketch, were long ago preceded by Dr Wells and Mr Matthew.'

One may note Darwin's continued sneer '. . . mere enunciation . . .' Matthew made no other claim but that he had briefly outlined the principle based on extensive work in arboriculture. There would have been no *Origin* without the basic theory of Natural Selection so that Darwin's peevishness was ill placed. The *raison d'être* of the *Origin* was the enunciation of the principle of Natural Selection. That Darwin had marshalled a great deal of evidence in support of the principle was apparent to all – and none more so than Matthew who wrote a kind note to him in 1864: 'I hope you are now able for your vocation of forwarding natural science.'

Matthew never seems to have wavered in his strong opinions about nature. In April, 1860, replying to Darwin's assertion that no one had read his work, Matthew had this to say: 'It was at least in part this spirit of resistance to scientific doctrine that caused my work to be voted unfit for the public library of the fair city itself,' (that is Perth). 'The age was not ripe for such ideas, nor do I believe is the present one, though Mr Darwin's formidable work is making way. As for the attempts made by many periodicals to throw doubt upon Nature's law of selection having originated species, I consider their unbelief incurable and leave them to it. Belief here requires a certain grasp of mind. No direct proof of phenomena embracing so long a period of time is within the compass of short-lived man. To attempt to satisfy a school of ultra-sceptics, who have a wonderfully limited power of perception of means to ends, of connecting the phenomena of Nature, or who perhaps have not the power of comprehending the subject, would be labour in vain. Were the exact sciences brought out as new discoveries they would deny the axioms upon which the exact sciences are based. They could not be brought to conceive the purpose of a handsaw though they saw its action, if the whole individual building it assisted to construct were not presented complete before their eyes, and even then they would deny that the senses could be trusted. Like the child looking upon the motion of a wheel in an engine they would only perceive and admire, and have their eyes dazzled and fascinated with the rapid and circular motion of the wheel, without noticing its agency in connection with and modifying power towards affecting the purposed end. Out of this class there would arise no Cuvier, able from a small fragmentary bone to determine the character and position in Nature of the extinct animal . . . I think that few will not see intuitively, unless they wish not to see, all that has been brought forward in regard to the origin of the species.' (*Gardeners' Chronicle.*)

In Matthew's letter, the nub of the problem is stated as clearly as Darwin would have wished: 'Belief here requires a certain grasp of mind. No direct proof . . . is within the compass of short-lived man.' A belief in speciation and evolution over millions of years is not so much a problem of the intellect as of the imagination. The mind boggles. It is interesting that Darwin too came to the same conclusion in his Recapitulation (*The Origin of the Species*, p 433): 'The mind cannot possibly grasp the full meaning of the term of a hundred million years; it cannot add up and perceive the full effects of many slight variations, accumulated during an almost infinite number of generations.'

One would have thought that Darwin would have warmed to this support since there were so few with him in 1860. On the contrary, Patrick Matthew had anticipated him and Darwin proceeded to belittle the only other person in Britain whose support for Evolutionism was unquestioned.

This vast deductive sweep of imagination presented by Matthew cut no ice with the inductive English academics. It was in strict contrast to the painstaking fitting of facts into the jigsaw puzzle of Nature which was Darwin's approach. Darwin was in no frame of mind to extol Patrick Matthew or even to acknowledge his letters. It would seem that Darwin made no effort to discover what Matthew did for a living or that he owned one of the largest orchards in Scotland.

Darwin was less than fair to write off Patrick Matthew as 'an obscure writer on forest trees'. If one compares the relevant passages in the *Appendix* with similar passages in the Recapitulation of the *Origin,* there is no question that the *Appendix* expresses a philosophy of Nature far more clearly and succinctly than does the Recapitulation. Whereas the *Origin* is virtually unreadable today, the content of the Appendix could not be more modern since nowhere does Matthew seek refuge in a Creator instilling life into 'a primordial form', as Darwin incredibly inserted in the Recapitulation. Nor does Matthew refer to the power, wisdom and goodness of the Creator which was fashionable among the establishment scientists in the 1830s and, as a concept, was the foundation stone of the Bridgewater Treatises. As such, all the new facts in science had to be squared, as well as possible, with theological doctrine if authors wished to live quietly in peace with the establishment at Cambridge.

Patrick Matthew was 70 years of age when he confronted Darwin. In his introduction to *Naval Timber* written during the late 1820s, he made the point that he introduced the problem of species because it was of great moment at that time. Of course it was and had been ever since Linnaeus had concluded that species were immutable. The debate whether species were fixed or had evolved from more primitive forms continued all through the second half of the eighteenth century, and during the time that Patrick Matthew was engaged in writing *Naval Timber* a long and bitter debate on the mutability of species continued in Paris between Cuvier and St Hilaire. On the basis of the palaeontological record Cuvier could not support the concept of the mutability of species. On the basis of common sense, artificially produced varieties and a complete rejection of Biblical mythology, St Hilaire supported the ideas put forward by Diderot and others in France several decades before. The scientific establishment in England totally supported Cuvier. The Noachian Flood was still regarded as the principal geological agency shaping the earth as it was known in the 1820s. For Matthew to write in 1860 that he came out in support of evolutionism in the 1820s ' . . . without an effort of concentrated thought . . .' surely points to the fact that there was sufficient evidence in the hands of intelligent plant and animal breeders at that time to make Evolutionism self-evident.

Patrick Matthew read and travelled widely in addition to supervising his large orchard on the north bank of the River Tay. He was heir to the glittering intellectual debates which made Edinburgh famous in the second half of the eighteenth century. He was not obliged to show

deference to any man or institution and certainly religious dogma was
set aside. As a practical hybridist he was searching for principles and the
proof of the principles of evolution he found in his every day work. In
the *Appendix* he found that the principle of Natural Selection '. . . is in
constant action, it regulates the colour, the figure, the capacities, and
instincts; those individuals of each species, whose colour and covering
are best suited to concealment or protection from enemies, or defence
from vicissitude and inclemencies of climate, whose figure is accommodated to health, strength, defences and support; whose capacities and
instincts can best regulate the physical energies to self-advantage according
to cirumstances in such immense waste of primary and youthful life,
those only come forward to maturity from the strict ordeal by which
Nature tests their adaptation to her standard of perfection and fitness to
continue their kind by reproduction . . .' And Patrick Matthew, as a
working hybridist, was well aware that, 'As far back as history reaches,
man had already considerable influence, and had made encroachments
upon his fellow denizens, probably occasioning the destruction of a
number of varieties or even species, which he found more suited to
supply his wants, but which, from the infirmity of their condition – not
having undergone selection by the law of nature, of which we have
spoken – cannot maintain their ground without his culture and protection.'

If Patrick Matthew could write this statement in 1830: '. . .without
an effort of concentrated thought . . .' it was clearly because every
hybridist was aware of the process but perhaps never consciously framed
so irreligious a concept. It is quite obvious that Matthew is boasting
about how easy it was for him to write the *Appendix*. A great deal of
concentrated thought and research had gone into every sentence of the
essay. One only comes to realize this on reading Blyth's essays, the *Origin*
and a host of criticisms introduced by various authors out to decry
Matthew. Mathew could not have covered all the scientific data which
were available in the 1830s without a wide-ranging search. Most of his
dogmatic statements turn out to coincide with 'Darwinian' approaches
to the species problem. Varieties themselves presented a problem to
thinking orthodox naturalists of that period.

Varieties, especially wild ones, were very inconvenient from a special
creation point of view! Matthew, 'without an effort of concentrated
thought', saw Nature and Man as shapers, by selection of plant and animal

life – and said so. And the term 'selection' continued to be used by plant
and animal breeders but apparently not by other sections of society.
Darwin's publisher of the *Origin* was quite unfamiliar with the term and
rather jibbed at its inclusion as part of the title to the *Origin*. When
confronted with opposition such as this Darwin always turned for help
to his Celtic fringe supporters – Lyell, Hooker and Falconer. In a letter
to Lyell he betrayed the plant-breeder origin of the term 'natural selection': 'Why I like the term is that it is constantly used in all works on
breeding, and I am surprised that it is not familiar to Murray . . .' But
the term used by breeders was 'selection' or 'artificial selection' and not
'natural selection'. Darwin always boasted of his careful searches through
the literature dealing with horticultural and agricultural matters so it
seems odd that such a careful search did not find the review by Loudon
in 1832 *(Gardeners' Magazine)* – the only review of a book dealing with
species and varieties to appear in the literature of the 1830s. Darwin
wrote exonerating himself '. . . one may be excused in not having
discovered the fact in a work on Naval Timber,' (*Life and Letters*, Vol 2,
301). But the work was on *Naval Timber and Arboriculture* and reviewed
by the most outstanding arboriculturalist of the period in a widely
circulating journal subscribed to by Darwin himself.

To breed is to select and to select is to promote one variety or varieties
over the others. The use of the principle of selection is fundamental to
man's whole social and cultural history. Such terms as 'natural process
of selection' or 'selection by the law of nature' reflected Matthew's
thoughts as a practical hybridist. It was a formal expression of rational
experience. Breeders were aware that selection was central to the process
of variation. Hybridization techniques were responsible for all the new
varieties of domestic animals and plants in the late eighteenth century
(Trow-Smith, 1959). To the techniques of hybridization Darwin added
nothing nor did he seem to grasp, as did Matthew, their central role in
elucidating the factors controlling variation. Naudin's work on hybrids
(1852), for example (brought to Darwin's notice by Hooker), made no
impression since no mention had been made of struggle for existence.

Matthew was just as much aware of 'sports' as was Darwin and just
as ignorant of their cause. But Matthew, unlike Darwin, was fully
confident that experimentation rather than continued pondering was the
way to unravel the mystery, as indeed, it proved to be: 'This circumstance-adaptive law, operating upon the slight but continued disposition

to sport in the progeny (seedling variety), does not preclude the supposed influence which volition or sensation may have over the configuration of the body. To examine into the disposition to sport in the progeny . . . is open to examination and experiment. In the first place, we ought to investigate its dependency upon the preceding links of the particular chain of life, variety being often merely types or approximations of former parentage; thence the variation of the family, as well as of the individual, must be embraced by our experiments.' Darwin, on the contrary, slid into speculation with Pangenesis – a theory Buffon had advanced a century before!

Darwin never conceded, what the reviewers of *Naval Timber and Arboriculture* had conceded back in 1832, that Patrick Matthew had exhibited a detailed personal knowledge of arboriculture and related subjects. As a result of this experience, Matthew recognized selection by the law of nature as fundamental to all living things including human society. The appendix to his book revealed a mind that had ranged over a wide area of human knowledge and had reached momentous conclusions about certain laws of nature. To brush off Patrick Matthew as 'an obscure writer on forest trees', was peevish, unwarranted and a disservice to the cause of Natural Selection.

Darwin made much play of his complaint that Matthew had only briefly enunciated the theory of natural selection. Others have protested that ideas are not enough and to have any claim on priority would involve conducting studies upon a wide basis of fact. Matthew was rebuffed although he had experimented and observed for twenty years before drawing the same conclusions as Darwin. It is one of the injustices of the history of science that Matthew, the pioneer of the natural process of selection, should be brushed aside. The pity is that there was no audience in 1831 ready to accept the stark realism contained in the *Appendix*. By 1859 there was a sufficient climate of opinion ready to receive the *Origin,* for how can one otherwise explain that the first print of 1,200 copies sold out on the first day of publication?

Had Darwin read *Naval Timber* more carefully than he appears to have done, he would have realized that much of what is contained in the chapter on Natural Selection in the *Origin* had formed the basis of Patrick Matthew's main cause for concern: the low state of the forests due to man's perverse selection methods.

In the chapter on Natural Selection, Darwin remarked, 'Man selects only for his own good; Nature only for that of the being which she tends . . . As man can produce and certainly has produced a great result by his methodical and unconscious means of selection, what may not Nature effect?. . . How fleeting are the wishes and efforts of man! how short his time! and consequently how poor will his products be, compared with those accumulated by Nature during whole geological periods. Can we wonder, then, that Nature's productions should be far 'truer' in character than man's productions; that they should be infinitely better adapted to the most complex conditions of life, and should plainly bear the stamp of far higher workmanship.'

So far as agriculture, horticulture and domestic animal breeding are concerned, Matthew concedes that man has pursued beneficial ends but as regards timber trees the opposite course has been pursued:

'The large growing varieties being so long of coming to produce seed, that many plantations are cut down before they reach their maturity, the small-growing and weakly varieties, known by early and extreme seeding, have been continually selected as reproductive stock, from the ease and conveniency with which their seed could be procured; and the husks of several kinds of these invariably kiln-dried, in order that the seeds might be the more easily extracted. May we, then, wonder that our plantations are occupied by a sickly short-lived puny race, incapable of supporting existence in situations where their own kind had formerly flourished – particularly evinced in the genus *Pinus,* more particularly in the species Scots Fir; so much inferior to those of Nature's own rearing, where only the stronger, more hardy, soil suited varieties can struggle forward to maturity and reproduction?'

Patrick Matthew had no need of Malthusian spectacles to perceive a struggle for existence in Nature. It was, in any case, an old concept propounded by the philosopher Hobbes. Matthew did not view the struggle in such a one-sided way as Darwin did, nor did he link it with a Malthusian theory of Population. Nor did Matthew fall into Darwin's error of mixing and confusing selection under pressure of population and selection involving greater adaptive plasticity in new circumstances.

On the struggle for existence Darwin concluded '. . . as more individuals are produced than can possibly survive, there must in every case be a struggle for existence . . . It is the doctrine of Malthus applied with manifold force to the whole animal and vegetable kingdom.' This was nonsense and in any case such a concept shed no light on how living things change.

Matthew spread his thoughts across a much wider canvas and so strove to ascend from propositions of lesser to those of greater generality. Nowhere in the *Origin* are conclusions set out as concisely and succinctly as this:

> The self-regulating adaptive disposition of organized life may, in part, be traced to the extreme fecundity of Nature, who, as before stated, has, in all the varieties of her offspring, a prolific power much beyond (in many cases a thousandfold) what is necessary to fill up the vacancies caused by senile decay. As the field of existence is limited and pre-occupied, it is only the hardier, more robust, better suited to circumstance individuals, who are able to struggle forward to maturity, these inhabiting only the situations to which they have superior adaptation and greater power of occupancy than any other kind; the weaker, less circumstance-suited, being permanently destroyed. This principle is in constant action, it regulates the colour, the figure, the capacities and instincts; those individuals of each species, whose colour and covering are best suited to concealment or protection from enemies, or defence from vicissitude and inclemencies of climate, whose figure is best accommodated to health, strength, defences and support; whose capacities and instincts can best regulate the physical energies to self-advantage according to circumstances – in such immense waste of primary and youthful life, those only come forward to maturity from the strict ordeal by which Nature tests adaptation to her standard of perfection and fitness to continue their kind by reproduction.

If Darwin ever read this statement he never betrayed any hint of being impressed. So far as he cared to acknowledge Matthew, it was merely to complain about Matthew's brevity and his enunciation only of the theory of Natural Selection. A great deal of the material marshalled in the *Origin* was neither original nor indeed relevant to the actual origin of species by Natural Selection. This did not escape the scrutiny of the reviewer (probably Richard Owen) of the *Origin* in the *Edinburgh Review* (April, 1860). Darwin's extensive account of his work on pigeons drew the following comment: 'These are the most important original observations recorded in the volume of 1859; they are, in our estimation, its real gems, few indeed and far apart, and leaving the determination of the . . . origin of species very nearly where the author found it . . .'

For the most part the statements of Patrick Matthew are crystal clear in spite of his not having a loyal and intellectual friend to help him. In the course of reading the proofs of the *Origin,* Joseph Hooker had to inform Darwin that he found many passages obscure. This word obscure was going to crop up for the next one hundred and fifty years. Darwin replied, 'Thank you for telling me about obscurity of style. But on my life no nigger with lash over him could have worked harder at clearness than I have done,' (Darwin, ii, 156, 1888). Darwin paid little attention to Hooker's criticism. The reviewer referred to above was quick to notice Darwin's obscurities and had this to say about the very first sentence: 'What is there − what can there possibly be − in the inhabitants . . . of South America, or in their distribution on that continent, to have suggested to any mind that man might be a transmuted ape . . . But what the "certain facts" were, and what may be the nature of the light which they threw upon the mysterious beginning of species, is not mentioned or further alluded to in the present work.'

Even so, it is tragic that Richard Owen could not bring himself to realize that the solid mass of observations assembled by Darwin could not be explained by the doctrine of Creation but all could be explained by a theory of evolution.

Matthew stressed the 'plastic quality' of living things and that it required 'a certain grasp of mind' to imagine a species transformed into another over a time scale almost beyond comprehension. A deductive mind would more easily imagine transmutation. Cuvier and his pupil Richard Owen were inductivists and never drew conclusions without evidence. So far as these two scientists were concerned the fossil evidence for transmutation in the reptilian and mammalian sections was little if any in their day. They both demonstrated that life had existed in past ages but the evidence as far as they could see was a series of miraculous new creations. But scientists are influenced by more than just scientific facts. Cuvier was a Swiss Huguenot and although he kept his faith steadfast he did not mix his scientific assessments with reference to Holy Writ as Owen and Charles Lyell did. The latter came round to accepting evolution in Lamarckian terms but jibbed at accepting man descended from an ape.

The lack of 'a certain grasp of mind' was to continue for many decades into the future.

It is a sad reflection on Darwin's personality that he could not be magnanimous in acknowledging the claim of Patrick Matthew but rest content in having assembled, as Huxley said, '. . . one of the greatest encyclopaedias of biological doctrine that any man ever brought forth.'

Patrick Matthew and Charles Darwin both gathered evidence in favour of the concept of natural selection before committing themselves to print. As if the facts themselves were not sufficient both felt it necessary to appeal finally to their readers with an aesthetic judgement:

'There is more beauty and unity of design in this continual balancing of life to circumstance, and greater conformity to those dispositions of nature which are manifest to us, than in total destruction and new creation . . .' (*Naval Timber and Arboriculture*, 1831).

'There is grandeur in this view of life, with its several powers, having been originally breathed by the Creator into few forms or into one; and that, whilst this planet has gone cycling on according to the fixed law of gravity, from so simple a beginning endless forms most beautiful and most wonderful have been, and are being, formed.' (*The Origin of the Species*, 1859.)

Later on Darwin deeply regretted involving the Creator in the origins of life and, indeed, he threw away his whole natural case in so doing. He himself had said, 'I would give nothing for the theory of Natural Selection if it requires miraculous additions at any one stage of descent.' However, had Darwin been sincere in regretting the 'Creator' reference he could have deleted the phrase in the second edition. He did not. Although Darwin regretted his truckling to society with his 'Creator' and maintained he meant by the 'Creator' some unknown cause. All his regrets were lost on many of his admirers. Incredibly, Karl Pearson some 63 years later in a eulogistic lecture on Darwin stated, 'Some of you will remember the wonderful paragraph with which the *Origin of Species* closes. I cannot refrain from citing it again here. It indicates that in 1859 Darwin still looked to a First Cause having an intelligent mind in some degree analogous to that of man.'

Darwin was, like Patrick Matthew, financially independent and hence not obliged to bow to the Oxbridge clerics who controlled academic thinking. After all there was the precedent of his old teacher, the Reverend Adam Sedgwick, who unwittingly caused the collapse of belief in

Holy Writ by his statements in his presidential address to the Geological Society in 1830: 'We ought, indeed, to have paused before we first adopted the diluvian theory, and referred all our gravel to the action of the Mosaic Flood. For of man, and the works of his hands, we have not yet found a single trace among the remnants of a former world entombed in these deposits.' Thirty years later Darwin could have been more daring than he was, especially since the religious test for entrance to Oxbridge had been abolished in 1856. As always, Darwin's mistakes were quickly forgiven and forgotten. But the reader can judge which author was the more consistent in expressing the concept of evolution by Natural Selection.

Patrick Matthew has frequently been criticized for the brevity of the *Appendix*. Matthew covered the important concepts of the origin of species which is very prolix. Matthew retained the catastrophes as an important factor in the history of the Earth; Darwin did not. Matthew made no room for a Creator; Darwin introduced the Creator into the last paragraph of every edition of the *Origin*. Some critics have argued that Matthew had no idea how to develop Natural Selection, but did Darwin? If Pangenesis is anything to go by clearly not. Darwin's contradictory statements have provided Matthew's detractors not only with scoring points: '. . . the first enunciation of the theory of Natural Selection . . .' but points that are never mentioned: 'saw clearly the full force of Natural Selection.'

The next incremental advance was already in the press with Mendel's paper of 1865. How was it that expert mathematicians like Lord Avebury and Karl Pearson failed to notice that paper? How was it that with two chapters devoted to varieties in the *Origin* no biologist in the 1860s noticed a paper dealing with the statistics of variation? Had Mendel's paper been recognized by biologists at that time there is no doubt that Natural Selection would have suffered the same fate as it did after 1900. It would certainly not have been in Darwin's interests to pay any attention to Mendel's paper.

4

The confrontation between scientific observation and biblical orthodoxy

Historical searches covering the late eighteenth and early nineteenth centuries indicate that the debate concerning the fixity or mutability of species was a subject of great interest to many sections of society in Europe. When Patrick Matthew completed *Naval Timber* he was forty years of age and had lived through a tumultuous time – politically as well as scientifically. By 1830 geology and palaeontology had been set on a modern scientific course and all well-educated people were familiar with the broad outlines of these subjects. The Geological Survey of the United Kingdom was started in 1836. Although the belief that the Noachian Flood was the principal geological agency shaping the crust of the earth had been discarded only by 1830 and then only by a few, religious dogma restricted and would continue to restrict men's views about man's place in nature, about evolution of species and the significance of extinct species of plants and animals. When Matthew was engaged on his book, Cuvier's Special Creationism was widely accepted in scientific circles in England but the 'great chain of being' so confidently believed in by Pope in the early eighteenth century was now, due to Cuvier's palaeontological evidence, discarded. But even Special Creationism and Catastrophism pulled at the heart-strings of religious men for they implied that the Creator had changed his mind on several occasions in the past and had wiped out whole species from the face of the earth. It was still widely believed that man had been specially created in 4004 BC. This belief was sacrosanct for some decades and many who publicly repudiated it, like the historian Froude, would pay the price of public repudiation and dismissal from Oxford as late as 1849. The diplomacy of beliefs among the Oxbridge set would continue to ensure that most men did not speak or write their real thoughts. The will to understand is always dominated by fear and insecurity.

Matthew grew up during the struggle against Napoleon. By 1830 he was a fervent imperialist and convinced that the navy was the most important basis of maintaining and even extending imperialist power. To build a navy required naval timber and Matthew was keenly aware that all was not right in the royal forests and elsewhere. In the course of extending and supervising his own orchards at Gourdiehill, Matthew obviously had taken great trouble to acquaint himself with arboriculture with respect to forest trees as well and particularly their relation to the supply of timber for naval purposes. It was thus his socio-political ideas which provided the incentive to study naval timber and those ideas were derived from his deep belief in certain biological laws. The struggle for survival amongst animals and plants was to him the same kind of struggle facing an imperialist nation. The selection by man of varieties of plants and animals which were vigorous and commercially profitable was the same kind of selective process employed by nature. Only someone divorced from the front line of struggle could doubt the analogy. Only someone divorced from all religious restrictions could accept it without further thought.

Matthew emerged in the early 1830s as a confident evolutionist in every aspect of his thoughts. God is not mentioned in the *Appendix* one way or the other. The Bible is not referred to either. His evolutionary principles were entirely naturalistic. Charles Darwin emerged from the 1830s with his views beginning to take shape but resolved to believe only privately in the mutability of species. The fossil evidence, domestic hybridization, John Hunter's comparative anatomy and its museum with fossil bones lying alongside extant counterparts, the exhaustive writings of Erasmus Darwin and the French eighteenth-century biologists, the notorious debate on the mutability of species in Paris between Cuvier and St Hilaire and Lyell's *Principles of Geology* – all these were available to Patrick Matthew and to Charles Darwin. It is nonsense to suggest that the theory of evolution by Natural Selection was Darwin's own theory. How many facts have to be marshalled before a law can be deduced? It would seem that the Scottish leanings towards deduction enabled Patrick Matthew to see all the available facts and reduce them to a universal law and then publish without fear of financial or other reprisals.

Virtually all the points discussed by Darwin in his *Ornithological Notes*, his 1837 *Notebook on the Transmutation of species* and the *Journal of Researches* were observations many other naturalists had made and pondered. One did not have to travel around the world to get this information. Much of what Darwin wrote about in his early work had already been reported by other travel naturalists. An example of the fund of information floating back to England from explorers in the 18th century can be found in a geological essay of John Hunter written in 1792. Hunter was concerned with the significance of sea shells on the surface of islands: 'The upraising of the bottom of the sea above the surface of the water, will also raise up along with it all shell-fish that lay on the surface at the bottom, as also dead shells, and in the substance of the earth all the deeper-seated substances, embedded or enclosed in stone, chalk, clay etc; which I have said constitutes the true fossil. This appears to be the state of the case on and in the island of Ascension; the whole surface of this island is covered with shells, and some so perfect as to have their ligaments still adhering: and the very name implies its rise.'

John Hunter had never journeyed further south than Portugal but Darwin during his voyage on the Beagle called in at Ascension. In the 1845 edition of his *Journal of Researches* he describes what he saw on the island. There is not one word about shells on the island. During his stay in Edinburgh, Darwin had attended Professor Jameson's course in geology. Jameson was a confirmed Neptunist and must have taught the significance of shells on the surface of islands. But it is quite possible that Darwin missed this point in the lectures because, on his own admission, he found the lectures of Jameson as boring as the anatomy lectures of Monro.

De Beer (1961 – 62) writes as if no other naturalist had ever written a word on transmutability of species before Darwin in the 1830s. Facts would remain mere facts without special significance until the all-embracing law was propounded: and, so far as the written record goes, Patrick Matthew was the first to do this and had the confidence to do so on the basis of an active life as a fruit hybridizer. The deductive Scot Charles Lyell could not proceed to the stark naturalism of Matthew. It would be too unsettling, and soul destroying even, to the man who could think only in evolutionist terms when surveying the inorganic world. But for Lyell's religious scruples, he would have pre-empted Darwin for he, like Matthew, had sufficient evidence to do so. Religious dogma and intellectual obtuseness prevented men taking a naturalistic view in the 1830s.

It is difficult to understand why Matthew added, as an afterthought, the appendix to his book. What readers was it intended to reach? He explained in his 1860 letter to the *Gardeners' Chronicle* how he came to formulate the principle of Natural Selection: 'To me the conception of this law came intuitively as a self-evident fact, almost without the effort of concentrated thought . . .'

But Matthew realized that his age was not ready for such views and having delivered himself of them, involved himself in politics and the Chartist movement.

Matthew could draw on the views of Lord Monboddo about population pressures, the simian origins of man, struggle for existence as a stimulus to improvements, emigration and the like. Matthew seems to have written down in a very cryptic fashion what many people had not dared to voice before much in the same way as Marx denounced religion as the opium of the people.

Matthew is to be taken seriously not only for what he said but also for what he did not say. The fact that biblical references are absent all the way through his statement has already been noted. There is also no reference to 'a chain of being' or a striving upward in linear fashion of the lower to higher forms of life. Progressionism was a weak point in the argument of most of the other early evolutionists and it was one which the Cuvierian palaeontologists, like Richard Owen, vigorously denied and with good reason. Before Matthew had started to write his *Appendix*, Cuvier had broken down the concept of a 'chain of being' which in any case had few adherents by the end of the eighteenth century. With Cuvier's palaeontological demonstrations it was no longer possible to think in terms of all animals evolving in linear fashion since it was now clear that development had occurred concurrently in at least four distinct branches of animal life. It would seem that Matthew took from Cuvier's teaching those aspects, catastrophes and multi-lineal development, which are acceptable today, but rejected special creationism. No one else in Britain at that time was quite as prescient.

In the preface to *Naval Timber and Arboriculture*, Patrick Matthew explains that his intention was to go beyond mere arboriculture. 'The very great interest of the question regarding species, variety, habit has perhaps led a little too wide.' He was also interested in arboriculture because timber was vital to the construction of a navy. In the 1830s Patrick Matthew was a jingoistic imperialist: '. . . the periodical return of war is indispensable to the heroic chivalrous character and love of freedom which we have so long maintained . . . It is by the jar and struggle of the conflict that the baser alloy and rust of our manners and institutions must be removed and rubbed away.' All this was to change in later life but his imperialism of that moment was derivative from the struggle for survival of the living things he saw around him. Matthew put his faith in race – in the Angles to be precise – whereas the scientific establishment praised Providence for the wisdom in arranging the deposition of rich mineral wealth in England. A later generation was greedy for more in beseeching, 'God who made us mighty, make us mightier yet.'

It appears clear from what he wrote that the law of natural selection was the one great universal law and as such the basis of action for the British. Under a section heading, 'Causes which benefit Britain for being the first naval power, and the emporium of the world', Matthew argues in favour of the logic of universal struggle in nature. This logic demanded the 'absolute necessity of abolishing every monopoly and restriction on trade in Britain', hereditary titles, the encouragement of the superior varieties (that is, the Anglo-Saxons) of man by emigration and wars.

His policies, more or less logically derived from the universal law, can be briefly stated:

Navigation is of first importance to the improvement and perfecting of the species in spreading, emigration, the superior varieties of man, and diffusing the arts and sciences over the world . . .

'The law of entail', necessary to hereditary nobility, is an outrage on this law of nature which she will not pass unavenged – a law which has the most debasing influence upon the energies of a people, and will sooner or later lead to general subversion, more especially when the executive of a country remains for a considerable time efficient, and no effort is needed on the part of the nobility to protect their own, or no war to draw forth or preserve their powers by exertion.

The outcome of these policies was *Emigration Fields* published in 1839 as a kind of travel brochure for intending emigrants – Anglo-Saxons, of course. His policies had not a word of comment on slavery or any pity for the wretched condition of the toiling masses.

From these statements of 1831 one can realize that long before social

Darwinism and 'nature red in tooth and claw' there was Patrick Matthew giving voice to thoughts which must have been passing through the minds of many men following the Napoleonic wars. The intellects of Edinburgh in the 1820s had been actively engaged in discussion of such subjects.

Eiseley (1958) draws attention to an article published anonymously in the *Edinburgh New Philosophical Journal* in 1826 which argued the case for evolutionism. It was Lamarckian from a biological point of view but such views were anathema to English intellectual society at that period. As will be shown later the author was only too aware of Lamarck. Patrick Matthew never mentions Lamarck or the Bible. He does not mention Cuvier either although in his letter to the *Gardeners' Chronicle* in 1860 he introduces Cuvier with great respect. The anonymous author of the journal article rejected Catastrophism and so did Matthew. Clearly there were people who were thinking along the lines of uniformitarianism before Lyell published his *Principles of Geology*. The concept of evolutionism had been bitterly attacked since the mid-eighteenth century. The prescience of Patrick Matthew to group evolutionism, uniformitarianism and Natural Selection together as fundamental to all natural processes has been undervalued – and, ironically enough, by Darwin most of all: '. . . an obscure writer on forest trees . . .'!

Eiseley, (1958) is not quite fair in assessing Matthew's statements about the laws of nature as 'obscure flashes in the dark . . . It was time for something weightier to appear . . .' The hour came in 1844 with the publication of *The Vestiges of the Natural History of Creation*. The assessment is not fair because *Vestiges* (Robert Chambers, 1844) did not contain one word about Natural Selection! Chambers, another Scot with Edinburgh connections, quite rightly argued that what Lyell had shown for the inorganic world was true for the organic world as well. Besides many scientific mistakes it still retained the concept of a deity rolling out, step by step over the millenia, the natural record. Although it was savagely attacked, most vehemently of all by T. H. Huxley within four years of the publication of the *Origin*, it created a climate favourable to evolutionists and ran to ten editions. *Vestiges* contains more facts than the *Appendix* but it was less naturalistic and devoid of 'the natural process of selection'. However briefly Matthew presented his case it was essentially a complete anticipation of the *Origin*. What Matthew presented in 1831 could have been presented by any other synthesizing mind heir to the Scottish deductive philosophical attitude and intellectual ferment of the eighteenth and early nineteenth century. And Darwin was in Edinburgh during the years 1825–1827 when he certainly was introduced to Geology, Lamarckism and Progressionism (Ashworth, 1935).

Some people have expressed surprise that Darwin was an evolutionist before he was a evolutionist by Natural Selection. There is nothing odd about this since Adaptation, Progressionism, Transmutationism and Evolutionism (introduced by Lyell) were concepts widely discussed for a hundred years prior to the publication of the *Origin*. Only Darwin's failure to present the historical perspective has led to the erroneous idea that the whole concept of evolution and Natural Selection sprang entirely from the mind of Charles Darwin.

Since there is evidence that Charles Darwin was thinking about varieties and species before he claims to have read Malthus, Eiseley (1959) has argued that the work which really sparked off Darwin's interest in speciation were Edward Blyth's essays of 1835–37 and published in the *Magazine of Natural History* – a journal founded and edited by J. C. Loudon. Most of the apparently incriminating evidence marshalled by Eiseley, however, does not stand up to scrutiny (Schwartz: 1974). But, apart from his jottings in the diary of his voyage on the *Beagle*, it is clear that Darwin was an avid reader of the *Magazine of Natural History*. It is unlikely that he could overlook Blyth's essays because copies of this journal were forwarded to him at various ports round the world. *The Magazine of Natural History* started publication in 1829 and during its first decade the only articles on the species problem were those by Blyth published in 1835–37. How could Darwin fail to read them? Although during the voyage on the *Beagle* Darwin was mainly concerned with geology, Gruber (*Darwin on Man*, 1974), on the basis of recently published material, suggests that the first faint hints of Darwin's interest in species classification came in his ornithological notes of 1836 written while still on the *Beagle* and homeward bound.

Darwin, however, in his short biographical sketch informs us that when he read Malthus in 1838 he at last had a theory on which to work. Francis, his son, found it '. . . surprising that Malthus should have been needed to give him the clue, when in the notebook of 1837 there should occur – however obscurely expressed – the following forecast of the importance of the survival of the fittest . . .' (*Foundations of the Origin of the Species*, a sketch written in 1842). Schwartz (1974) has made the comment, 'As Darwin's notebooks show, before he read Malthus Darwin knew that selection was the principle.' If Malthus had exerted such a profound effect on Darwin how are we to explain a letter from his friend Hooker in 1863: 'Did you ever read that painful book *Malthus on Population?*' These two had corresponded regularly since the 1840s and Hooker had not only read the *Origin* when it was published but had come to Darwin's rescue in piecing his notes together after the arrival of Wallace's paper in 1858. Certainly Hooker had not got the impression that Malthus had been of any importance to Darwin especially since Malthus is not even indexed in the *Origin*, and he is only mentioned briefly in the sections dealing with the struggle for existence and natural selection.

In his 1857 letter to Asa Gray there is no mention of Malthus. If this individual had been of such fundamental influence he would surely have brought Malthus into his confession. I say confession because Darwin was very much afraid that the devout Asa Gray would be offended with his new theory. Darwin's fears were ill founded because Asa Gray was able to reconcile a naturalistic interpretation of the animal and plant world with a firm belief that all was directed by a Creator. There are individuals around today with similar beliefs. Why would Darwin in his letter to Asa Gray urge him not to divulge to any one if Malthus was its inspiration? Darwin made it clear that he feared the author of *The Vestiges* might get to hear about it but the anonymous author had no use for Malthus!

If Malthus was such an inspiration why did Darwin not subscribe to the main argument which was the necessity of limiting the size of the family? In writing about 'survival of the fittest' Darwin meant reproduction ability; the fittest in his book were the most reproductive. Malthus considered continence was the only answer to limiting family size but, of course, he was mainly concerned with the poorest sections of society. Darwin could excuse himself from such strictures because he was a member of the richer section. Charles Darwin had ten children, his father Robert had six children and the grandfather had fourteen children by two wives and some out of wedlock. The three Darwins produced about thirty children; Malthus would have been horrified. In spite of his long debility, his daily throwing up and his frequent nervous interludes Darwin's sexual ability did not decline. Allowing for the frequent miscarriages so common in those days he kept poor Emma almost permanently pregnant from 1839 to 1856.

Frederick Engels writing in 1872 had this to say: 'However great the blunder made by Darwin in accepting so naïvely and without reflection the Malthusian theory, nevertheless anyone can see at first glance that no Malthusian spectacles are required in order to perceive the struggle for existence in Nature.' Engels had no reason to doubt Darwin's confession to Wallace that Malthus had such a great influence in the writing of the *Origin*.

The terms 'Natural Selection' and 'the survival of the fittest' occasioned a good deal of confusion for many decades. Frederick Engels writing notes on evolution about 1872, seems to have had a clearer idea of the muddle than most people at that time. This is what he had to say: 'Darwin's mistake lies precisely in lumping together in "Natural Selection" and the "survival of the fittest" two absolutely different things.'

Engels went on to say: 'The struggle for Existence above all this must be strictly limited to the struggles resulting from plant and animal over-population, which do in fact occur at definite stages of plant and lower animal life. But one must keep sharply distinct from it the conditions in which species alter, old ones die out and newly evolved ones take their place, *without* this over-population: e.g. on the migration of animals and plants into new regions where new conditions of climate, soil, etc., are responsible for the alteration. If there the individuals which become adapted survive and develop into new species by continually increasing adaptation, while the other more stable individuals die away and finally die out, and with them the imperfect intermediate stages, then this can and does proceed *without* any Malthusianism, and if the latter should occur at all it makes no change to the process, at most it can accelerate it.'

It is clear from the testimony of Hooker (LLD, 2, 20) that he was acquainted with Darwin's ideas for many years before the publication of the *Origin*. 'It has been a permanent source of happiness to me that I knew so much of Mr Darwin's scientific work for so many years before that intimacy began which ripened into feelings as near to those of reverence for his life, works, and character as is reasonable and proper.' And then Darwin's son Francis informs us, 'The history of my father's life is told more completely in his correspondence with Sir J. D. Hooker than in any other series of letters; and this is especially true of the history of the growth of *The Origin of the Species.*'

The influence which Malthus is supposed to have had all started after he had been in contact with Wallace who, after a bout of malaria, thought about Malthus. So in 1859 Darwin wrote to Wallace: 'You are right, that I came to the conclusion that selection was the principle of change from the study of domestic products (i.e. he got it all from the breeders) and then, reading Malthus, saw at once how to apply this principle.'

What was there, what could be there in the essays of Malthus that could throw any light on how species change over millions of years or even hint that species mutate? But let us continue to produce more evidence that Malthus was seldom in Darwin's mind up until 1859.

Malthusian ideas were already well incorporated in the writings of Paley and Lyell whose views Darwin was steeped in before and during the voyage on the *Beagle*. 'I do not think I hardly ever admired a book more than Paley's Natural Theology. I could almost formerly have said it by heart.' (Darwin to Lubbock, 1859.) But Malthusian ideas were current earlier on in the eighteenth century. Amongst John Hunter's essays is a statement which may or may not be original for its time, but has a Malthusian slant: 'Carnivorous animals are only to be considered the correctors of quantity. There is an equilibrium kept up among the animals by themselves.' (Essays, 1, R. Owen [ed].) In any case, Malthus had been pre-empted by an essay on the Poor Laws written by the Reverend Joseph Townsend in 1785 and before that by an essay written in 1755 by Benjamin Franklin. These essays influenced not only Malthus but Archdeacon Paley as well. It is clear also that Patrick Matthew had absorbed Malthusian ideas. The only reference Matthew makes to Malthus is in *Emigration Fields*. A few pages in this book are devoted to the dangers of smoking. He refers to some reduction in the north European population caused by smoking. This reduction, Matthew dryly remarks, should be considered by the Malthus philosophers!

There is no mention of the mathematics that Malthus introduced into his essay; the mathematics which are a nonsense in any case especially in relation to human society. This nonsense was quickly spotted by Marx: 'What amuses me in Darwin is his assertion that he applied the theory of Malthus to plants and animals alike, whereas the whole joke in Malthus was that he applied the theory to men alone, with the geometrical progression, in opposition to plants and animals.' (18 June 1862, Marx to Engels, in Briefwechsel correspondence, p77.)

In Blyth's 1835 essay is expounded the view that speciation preserves the species because, '. . . the slightest deviation from the natural line must generally prove fatal to the animal.' In this he had stated no more than the others, including Matthew, before him. Blyth, who at the time was only twenty-five years old, and not yet, or ever to be, extricated from contemporary English theological restrictions, exposes his philosophical weakness: 'The same law, therefore, which was intended by Providence to keep up typical qualities of a species, can be easily converted by man into a means of raising different varieties; but it is also clear that if a man did not keep up these breeds by regulating the sexual intercourse, they would all naturally revert to the original type.' Matthew had already covered this point but in a more truly naturalistic vein: 'Man's interference, by preventing this natural process of selection among plants, independent of the wider range of circumstances to which he introduces them, has increased the difference in varieties particularly in the more domesticated kinds.' By the way, note the magical words written in 1831: '. . . natural process of selection . . .'

Did Blyth himself read the work of Patrick Matthew? The review of his book in the *Gardeners' Magazine* by its editor would surely have caught his attention. The subject of speciation does not appear in that journal in its first ten years of publication except for that one review by Loudon in 1832. Blyth read everything he could lay his hands on and the magazine was readily available.

It would be strange also if Blyth's essays of 1835–37 did not meet the eye of an obscure trainee naturalist rapidly gaining experience aboard the *Beagle* and who considered it worth his while to spend the next twenty years marshalling evidence against Blyth's conservation thesis and substituting for it the theory that any deviation from the norm will be preserved by Natural Selection if it is advantageous, a theory which Matthew had already deduced from his general studies on arboriculture. Deduced is perhaps conveying too conscious a conclusion so far as Matthew is concerned: '. . .with me,' he wrote thirty years later, 'it was by a general glance at the scheme of nature that I estimated this select production of species as an a priori recognizable fact – an axiom, requiring only to be pointed out to be admitted by unprejudiced minds of sufficient grasp.'

By concentrating more on the stabilizing force than on the factors which produce the emergence of something new, Blyth could not sustain further thought on the species problem. He was essentially a collector of facts about species and varieties rather than a synthesizer of collected facts as Darwin was. Patrick Matthew could not sustain further thought on the species problem because for him the natural process of selection was too blatantly obvious to require further debate. He, like Mendel, had practical problems to solve in the daily management of his large commercial orchard. Weeding out of weak specimens and the selection of vigorous stock for future preservation was his daily routine. The mathematically minded hybridist Mendel moved on to the quantitative assessment of hybridization. Darwin had no immediate horticultural problem to solve but by dint of careful study of collected facts he was able to sustain and concentrate his interest in the species problem like no one before him.

In the 1830s Blyth saw speciation as a means of preserving the norm. He was impressed with the disadvantages to the individual born with any deviation from the norm. The so-called 'localizing principle' is attributed to Blyth but it is presented clearly in Matthew's appendix to *Naval Timber* and was widely recognized in the eighteenth century. It is an aspect of the evolutionary process and is recognized as such today.

Blyth's essays of 1835–37 in the *Magazine of Natural History* are concerned with detailed observations, the posing of unanswerable questions, but contains little about selection. Blyth was a Providentialist believing in special creation and hence could never present the clear, unequivocal laws of nature as Matthew could. He writes in tones reminiscent of Paley: '. . . the unity of design pervading which, all is demonstrable to be the workmanship of One omnipotent and all-foreseeing Providence, under the beneficent dispensation of whom nought that ever exists or occurs stand isolated and alone . . .' All of this trend of thought was well known to Darwin who had learnt Paleyism off by heart. Blyth, like Darwin, did not have an immediate practical problem to solve and was not a breeder but was caught up in a profound wonder of natural things. With all their detailed observations these essays could have given much impetus to Charles Darwin still, supposedly, searching for a theory.

It is true that in these essays Blyth discussed the vexed problem of adaptation and intermediate species prior to full adaptation. But adaptation was fully recognized and discussed in the eighteenth century by Buffon and his school; and particularly by John Hunter for whom the demonstration of the principle of adaptation was the *raison d'être* of his famous museum. If, by adaptation, Blyth was arguing for evolutionism he was merely following Lamarckism but even this was dangerously avant-garde for the time. Blyth softened the cold, heartless materialism of the eighteenth-century French naturalists by introducing a kind and benevolent Providence. Blyth ended the first part of his 1835 essay with typical humility: 'The above is confessedly a hasty and imperfect sketch, a mere approximation towards an apt classification of "varieties", but if it chance to meet the eye and be fortunate enough to engage the attention of any experienced naturalist who shall think it worth his while to follow the subject and produce a better arrangement of these diversities, my object in inditing the present article will be amply recompensed.' Truth to tell this was as far as Blyth could carry the story and he raced on compulsively to the next subject which interested him.

And so Blyth, as curator of the Bengal Museum, continued all his life compulsively collecting facts most of which got back to Darwin who then neatly fitted them into his own argument. Darwin refers later on to Blyth as '. . . a very clever, odd, wild fellow who will never do what he could do from not sticking to any one subject.' All the same, Darwin never threw away any of Blyth's observations. Some of them appeared in the *Origin* as part of the massive factual evidence but mainly in *The Descent of Man*. Arguing about the origin of domestic poultry Darwin cited Blyth '. . . whose opinion, from his large and varied stores of knowledge, I should value more than that of almost any one, thinks that all breeds of poultry have proceeded from the common wild Indian fowl.'

Blyth's opinion is again valued by Darwin in the *Origin*: 'From facts communicated to me by Mr Blyth, on the habits, voice, constitution, and structure of the humped Indian cattle, it is almost certain that they are descended from a different aboriginal stock from our European cattle.' Both these communications were field reports from Calcutta. They were in letters, unpublished, in the care of the Central Library, at Cambridge.

Blyth died in London in 1873 poor and broken in health. He held no position of any significance nor was he ever awarded any distinction in this country, though he was widely recognized as one of the leading zoologists of his day; the acknowledged founder of Indian zoology and the localizing principle. It was not in Darwin's nature to promote anyone who might approach his own theory. Gentle-mannered as he was, Darwin saw competition rather than co-operation as a natural law and so never canvassed Blyth's election to the Royal Society. That Darwin was involved in adjudicating for the Royal Society may be seen in a letter from Lyell in 1855: 'I have seen a good deal of French geologists and palaeontologists lately, and there are many whom I should like to put on the RS Foreign List . . . But the man who has made the greatest sacrifices and produced the greatest results . . . is Barrande . . . Should you succeed in making Barrande FRS, send me word.' Despite his great indebtedness to Lyell, Darwin merely passed on this message to T. H. Huxley with the usual moan about ill health. He planned, health permitting, to go to the Crystal Palace on the very day of the RS adjudication! Barrande was not elected that year or any other, and neither, to Darwin's eternal shame, was Edward Blyth.

Because of ill health, the jobless and financially insolvent Blyth was advised to go to Bengal. This is quite a surprising piece of medical advice because anyone who has spent any time in Bengal would know how deleterious to the European its climate is. Blyth worked wonderfully well for over twenty years as curator of the Bengal Museum but by 1862 was so ill that he was invalided home from his curious exile in the East. This was achieved through the persistent efforts of Sir P. Catley and Dr Hugh Falconer who were his close associates in India. Through their efforts Blyth was granted a pension of £250 a year; this was the sum of money that Darwin expended annually on charities (Atkins, 1974). These two associates of Blyth were also friends of Darwin and, indeed, it was Falconer who arranged the award of the Copley Medal of the Royal Society to Darwin in 1864. Darwin, who gained more than anyone from the field studies of Blyth, did nothing nor did he offer to help. Darwin by this time was a very rich man and would get even richer through shrewd working of the Stock Exchange. There was never to be a parallel to the Engels–Marx financial relationship between Darwin and Blyth. In a letter to Lyell in 1860, Darwin referred to Blyth as 'Poor Blyth of Calcutta . . .' The obituary notice in *The Leader* (3 January 1874) brought no response from Darwin: 'The numerous references to Mr Blyth's writings which appear in *The Descent of Man* testify to the high esteem with which his opinions were regarded by Mr Darwin.' There are about forty references to the work of Blyth in the *Descent of Man*.

Although many contemporaries pointed out how dependent Darwin had been on Blyth for field information, he did not pen one word to an obituary when poor Blyth died in December 1873. Patrick Matthew followed him six months later. Darwin appears never to have mentioned the name of Blyth or Matthew again and certainly betrayed no clues about whether he was aware of their demise or not.

Whatever the reasons, the vomiting which had afflicted Darwin most of his life ceased about this time and new symptoms of coronary thrombosis started. This sudden change of symptoms rules out Chaga's disease as the cause of Darwin's persistent vomiting and debilitude. In his *Darwin Revalued* Sir Arthur Keith who was aware of the details of Darwin's life remarks: '. . . his health during the last ten years of his life was better than it had been in the previous thirty years . . . as Darwin passed into his sixties a change seems to come over what we may call his constitution. We hear no more of crippling illnesses which laid him aside for days on end; he came to really enjoy his holidays instead of suffering them.' Karl Pearson, on a visit to Darwin in 1870s, recognized how well Darwin appeared to be. In the end, however, Darwin died a smoker's death. Mendel was a heavy cigar smoker but apparently died from other causes.

I have said that Darwin died a smoker's death because the diagnosis of Sir Andrew Clark, the Queen's Physician, was angina pectoris caused by coronary thrombosis. That fits in with the chest pain that Darwin had suffered for the last ten years. The pain became more severe in April 1882. Over a period from April 15 to April 19th Darwin suffered severe attacks of chest pain. Three authors have described these four days and they give different accounts of these last days. Desmond and Moore (1990) describe severe vomiting and blood streaming down his beard. Henrietta, Darwin's daughter, witnessed what took place during these days but there is no mention of the gory details of these other authors. Irving Stone (1981) makes no mention of it. He attributes 'I am not afraid to die' to moments before Darwin died. Other authors disagree and stipulate 16 April. Atkins (1974) based his account on that of Henrietta. The Queen's physician, Andrew Clark, hurried down from London but could only spare half an hour, diagnosed the condition in a matter of minutes and then sat down to his dinner. That dispensed with he left rapidly for London. The family who witnessed all this were shocked. At least the three authors agree that Darwin died at 4 p.m., 19 April 1882.

Although Darwin arranged a pension for Alfred Wallace he made no effort to secure one for Blyth, his greatest supplier of scientific facts and observations! Why?

As an active hybridist, Matthew would be familiar with the term 'selection'. Amongst breeders the term was in current use for over a hundred years. Artificial selection was selection by the hand of the breeder and so breeders knew how domestic varieties came into existence and how some disappeared. So far as the written record goes it would appear that the first person to coin the term 'natural process of selection' and enunciate it as a fundamental law of nature was Patrick Matthew in the *Appendix*. We are drawn to the conclusion that selection was a term commonly used in his society. Darwin assures us that he spent most of the years from 1838 to 1858 reading horticultural and agricultural journals. It would not be hard to find the word 'selection' in print in these journals and it is likely that Darwin picked up the term in conversation with breeders. By 1859 it was not a word in wide usage as can be judged by the reaction of Darwin's publisher to the subtitle to the *Origin*. Murray, Darwin's publisher, demurred over the introduction of, to him, the strange words 'Natural Selection'. In a letter to Lyell about this time Darwin expressed his frustration towards his publisher and claimed that 'selection' was a term constantly used in breeding circles in England. It is strange that Darwin missed reading the law relating to Natural Selection as set out for the first and only time in print in Matthew's *Appendix* of 1831. If Patrick Matthew's laws of nature are inspired deduction but are derivative from his practice as a fruit-hybridist from his reading of the European literature up to 1830, from his Scottish education, from his travels abroad in France and Germany, from the intellectual ferment in Edinburgh and Paris, then he was the greatest synthesizer of his age. During the 1830s, it is clear, there was sufficient evidence available to Charles Darwin to enable him to formulate a theory of evolution by Natural Selection. Malthus had nothing to offer in this respect and one can discount the importance of Malthusian theory to Darwinism. In any case, the political and social opposition to Malthus from Hazlitt in 1807 to Shelley and Byron would filter into the Oxbridge of Darwin's day. Malthus was even more alive in the minds of men of the 1820s than at the end of the 1830s.

As Darwin himself admitted, he picked up the term 'selection' from the breeders and it is to the breeders we should extend our thanks for their contribution to the theory of evolution and eventually, via Mendel, to the genetic explanation of how change, at a pace still unknown, can come about.

It appears to be quite a red herring for Darwin to confess to Wallace that on reading Malthus he immediately saw how to apply the principle. Even Marx, a mere journalist with no scientific training, saw how ridiculous an analogy Darwin was drawing. Marx, in the 1860s, reacted to the inhuman Malthusian interpretations by Darwin in much the same way as others had reacted to Malthus's original essay fifty years before.

Although Darwin complained that the enunciation of the principle of Natural Selection was to be found only in scattered passages of Matthew's book, the principle comes at the end of a long and detailed critique of methods of planting and culturing forest trees. Darwin also complained that '. . . he attributes much influence to the direct action of the conditions of life.' Although Matthew does not mention Lamarck by name, he is acutely aware of the principles involved and 'circumstance-suited' or 'circumstance-adapted' are frequently used. 'The use of the infinite seedling varieties in the families of plants, even in those in a state of nature, differing in luxuriance of growth and local adaptation, seems to be to give one individual (the strongest, best circumstance-suited) superiority over others of its kind around, that it may, by over topping and smothering them, procure room for full extension, and thus affording, at the same time, a continual selection of the strongest, best circumstance-suited, for reproduction. Man's interferences by preventing this natural process of selection among plants, independent of the wider range of circumstance to which he introduces them, has increased the difference in varieties, particularly in the more domesticated kinds . . .' And to show that the selection of the varieties of *Homo sapiens* was always in his mind, he continues, '. . . and even in man himself, the greater uniformity, and more general vigour among savage tribes, is referable to nearly similar selecting law – the weaker individual sinking under the ill treatment of the stronger, or under the common hardships.

If Matthew marshalled all this argument from his eighteenth-century predecessors it is legitimate synthesis. No one decries Charles Lyell for marshalling the facts and arguments of other authors and creating a synthesis in *The Principles of Geology*. Both Matthew and Lyell borrowed from the observations and not the speculations of others. In so doing,

Lyell was able in the second volume to deal with the mutability of species in a respectable manner which removed the strait-jacket of Cuvierian Catastrophism and some of the speculations of Lamarck. What is weak in Matthew's principles is the evolution of species from one catastrophe to another. He avoids, quite properly, getting embroiled in speculation and relies on the sheet-anchor of 'a power of change'.

Indeed, 'a power of change' is as near to it as we can get even today. At the end of the Cretaceous period, 70 million years ago, there was a catastrophe of immense proportions which wiped out the dinosaurs, pterosaurs, the ammonites and chalk-forming planktons. The annihilation is considered to have been completed over a short period of five million years. By 'a power of change' and 'without new creation' the fish, amphibians, reptiles, birds and mammals survived in small or reduced numbers. The cause of the catastrophe is still hotly debated today: lethal radiation from exploding stars, excessive cold or poisonous alkaloids from the newly emerging flowering plants; the most recent theory involves the collision with an asteroid. The ability of the survivors to survive and evolve is still unresolved today but it certainly was by 'a power of change'.

By the time Matthew was writing, Cuvier had already presented the evidence for the catastrophe or a series of catastrophes. It was his belief that a new special creation of animals and plants emerged after each catastrophe. This theory was widely accepted in England at that time. There were those who found this theory unsettling because it implied that the Divine Creator had frequently changed his policy and might do so again with man as the victim. There was but one man who disputed the geological aspect of Cuvier's theory and that was Charles Lyell with his *Principles of Geology*. It is clear that Patrick Matthew did not accept Cuvier's conclusions regarding special creations after each catastrophe. It is clear that Matthew had discarded Holy Writ as indeed had Cuvier in strictly separating biblical beliefs from his scientific observations. The whole argument about the immutability or not of species was purely scholastic since it was based on a biblical account of Creation. Reject the biblical account and there was no alternative to evolutionism of the organic and inorganic worlds unless religious scruples, as portrayed in Lyell, intervened. To accept evolutionism required, as Matthew declared in support of Darwin in 1860, 'a certain grasp of mind'.

Matthew and Lyell, together with the classificatory essays of Edward

Blyth, then, could have provided any rational man with a theory of the origin of species if he was looking for one in the late 1830s. Darwin relates that he found a theory in 1838 after reading Malthus. Indeed, by the time Darwin set off on the *Beagle* in 1831 there was already a body of knowledge available to any young man interested in varieties, species and evolution.

Shortly after, Darwin claims to have at last found a theory to guide him a journalist with no scientific training set out secretly to synthesize the work of other scientists. By 1844 the work was complete and was published anonymously as *The Vestiges of the Natural History of Creation*. Not until after his death, some thirty years later, was it made known that Robert Chambers was the author. The theme of the book was that Providence had progressively evolved the organic and inorganic worlds over an immense time range. Not being a practical breeder, he does not mention the term natural selection as the means whereby the change occurred. The book contained many small errors of fact which infuriated people like T. H. Huxley and the Oxbridge establishment. The educated public responded well and over the next ten years thousands of copies were sold. The climate for open discussion of evolution was now created. Darwin and Wallace were sympathetic to the ideas in the book but refrained from public statements.

Robert Chambers in his *Vestiges* writes with the same sweeping generalizations in support of Progressive Development, which was God-inspired, and natural law. 'Two principles are thus seen at work in the production of the organic tenants of the earth — first, a gestative development pressing on through the grades of organization, and bringing out particular organs necessary for new fields of existence; secondly, a variative power connected with will and dispositions in animals, re-acted upon by external conditions, and working to minor effects, though these may sometimes be hardly distinguishable from the other.'

In a rather poetic generalization, reminiscent of Robert Chambers fourteen years later, Patrick Matthew states his view of evolution through time and catastrophes: 'There is more beauty and uniformity of design in this continual balancing of life to circumstance, and greater conformity to those dispositions of nature which are manifest to us, than in total destruction and new creation.' With a statement, such as this, it is incomprehensible that Eiseley (1958) should claim that Patrick Matthew was an English Catastrophist.

In passing one can compare this naturalistic statement with one far less naturalistic and with which Darwin closed the *Origin*: 'There is grandeur in this view of life, with its several powers, having been originally breathed by a Creator into a few forms or into one; and that, whilst this planet has gone cycling on according to the fixed laws of gravity, from so simple a beginning endless forms most beautiful and most wonderful have been, and are being evolved.'

However, Darwin explained to Hooker (1863, LL3, 18) what he meant by the Creator: 'I have long regretted that I truckled to public opinion and used the pentateuchal term of creation, by which I really meant "appeared" by some wholly unknown process.' This may be so but Darwin failed to stop his 'truckling' in the later editions of the *Origin*.

It is true that Darwin's belief in a First Cause grew weaker as he grew older, but this statement indicates his philosophical limitations in 1859. Patrick Matthew, on the other hand, writing in the late 1820s always conducted his argument in truly naturalistic terms and is clearly more allied to the notions of Diderot and Lamarck than of Cuvier. There would not appear to be anyone in England at that time with such a confident, naturalistic attitude to the organic and inorganic world. And this naturalistic attitude was carried on to his old age as can be seen in Matthew's second letter to the *Gardeners' Chronicle* (1860): 'As for the attempts made by many periodicals to throw doubt upon Nature's law of selection having originated species, I consider their unbelief incurable and leave them to it. Belief here requires a certain grasp of mind . . . I think that few will not see intuitively, unless they wish not to see, all that has been brought forward to the origin of species . . .'

And Thomas H. Huxley who had steered an equivocal course all his life and had savagely attacked the *Vestiges* as late as 1855, suddenly acquired 'a certain grasp of mind' when he read the *Origin* four years later. Having made himself master of the central of idea of the *Origin* Huxley reflected, 'How extremely stupid not to have thought of that!' Huxley from then on was bent on making others look extremely stupid who did not immediately espouse the evolutionist cause. And it was by a curious twist of history that it fell to Robert Chambers, still unknown to Huxley as the author of the *Vestiges,* to persuade Huxley to defend the evolutionist cause at the Oxford meeting of the British Association in 1860.

Now here was another chance to boost himself. Huxley had leaped to fame with his review of *The Origin of the Species*. All his previous magnificent scientific work got him nowhere, in spite of the Royal Medal from the Royal Society, but the *Origin* landing on his desk with an invitation to review it in *The Times* was an opportunity not to be missed. That review established him as a leading Darwinist although evolution had meant nothing to him before. It was that review which enraged conservative society virtually worldwide, *The Origin* could not otherwise have gained such a wide and emotional publicity. It was that review which startled Patrick Matthew from his long isolation since 1831. Not really understanding what *The Origin* was all about, Huxley wrote to Darwin for advice about how he could learn more about the subject. Darwin replied curtly that he did not know. Huxley never really penetrated the wealthy trinity of Darwin, Lyell and Hooker although no one more than he had aroused the furore that was to shake the foundation of Christian doctrine in Victorian England. Darwin referred to him as 'the best and worst of men': Huxley was never forgiven for pointing out to Darwin that his beloved Pangenesis was in Buffon's writings of almost a hundred years before. But the Oxford meeting consolidated Huxley as a great hero of the irreligious section of society. All that on a chance meeting in Oxford with Robert Chambers! Luck, at last, had entered Huxley's life. He could now hob-nob with the élite. He became distinguished enough to ask Lord Avebury to be Godfather to one of his children: his wife, a High Anglican, demanded a christening and poor Huxley had to conform.

The forthright Huxley said in private what he said in public. Although he recanted on his savage attack on Chambers later on in his life, he never let up on his scurrilous attacks on Lamarck. Huxley unfortunately started off with the misconception that Lamarck had plagiarized Erasmus Darwin and compounded this by incorporating in his general attitude the mistranslations of Lyell. Huxley as a propagandist saw no contradiction in his intellectual stance in 1854 against the *Vestiges* and his ready acceptance in 1859 of the *Origin* although the latter had not solved the problems he had previously posed. So in his relationship to Lamarck he saw no inconsistency in rejecting Lamarckism because Lamarck had not proved his ideas experimentally and his continued allegiance to Darwinism although it had not been possible experimentally to produce two forms from one particular stock. In his *Lectures to Working Men* (1863), Huxley not only passed on the mistranslations of Lyell but added his own gross mistranslation of Lamarck's argument about wading birds and their long legs. Lamarck did not receive a fair hearing in Victorian England and Huxley ensured his scientific demise by writing him off as a trumpeter of Erasmus Darwin's music.

Not only Huxley but most of the Oxbridge naturalists were opposed to the evolutionary basis of the *Vestiges*. Here, for example, is what Sedgwick, the Cambridge Professor of Geology, had to say: 'The work finds much favour in London, and is now in a 4th edition! Why? Because of the shallowness of the fashionable reading world and because of its intense dogmatic form of the work itself. I believe the author is a woman.' (Sedgwick to Napier 1845, Selections from the correspondence of the late Macrey Napier, London 1879.)

It is surely not just coincidence that Robert Chambers was a citizen of Edinburgh – a highly educated one at that and so heir to the tradition of radical thought. Within the space of the fourteen years 1830–1844 three Scotsmen laid out the guidelines for organic as well as inorganic evolution – Charles Lyell, Patrick Matthew and Robert Chambers. In the wings, another person with a Scottish academic background – J. D. Hooker – was with great circumspection at Kew Gardens leaning towards the mutability of plant species. Later on, in the next decade, only Herbert Spencer was entirely free from any northern influence. It is also no coincidence that all these promoters of evolutionism were independent financially from an institution and to a varying extent unfettered by religious bigotry. To the three deductive Scots above mentioned we must add a fourth – James Hutton. In addition to founding the school of Vulcanism he wrote, but did not publish, on the principle of Natural Selection. Significantly, he was also a farmer and animal breeder. It is also no accident that he, too, was inspired by his mentors in Edinburgh and hence heir to the radical thought of the time. Hutton made what for his time and until recent times was a profound observation: 'No vestige of a beginning no prospect of an end.' We now think the 'ripples of the universe' are signs of the beginning and in the end the sun will be a cold, black globe. To this distinguished list one must add perhaps the greatest of them all, John Hunter – who by his extensive demonstrations of comparative anatomy, embryology, physiology, fossils and geology did much to provide the tools for evolutionary research.

It would be very odd if Patrick Matthew did not read the *Vestiges* but there is no record of any comments he may have made. He could have claimed that the *Vestiges* was not as naturalistic as his *Appendix* and had omitted the natural process of selection. It is probably not just coincidence that Darwin's second trial essay was written in 1844. It took another fifteen years before the *Origin* appeared. During these fifteen years Darwin was patiently collecting observable facts and collating the observations of others. A great deal of what Darwin gathered together was established or recorded in the 1830s or before as, indeed, Robert Chambers had shown. Edward Blyth continued all his life to supply Darwin with observation and fact concerning species and varieties but Darwin gave nothing in return. It will perhaps be profitable now to continue past the 1830s in order to set the scene for the publication of the *Origin* which shook Patrick Matthew from his farming and political activities.

The *Vestiges* inflicted the first traumatic experience of the new science on the English-speaking world but it came 100 years after the French biologists Buffon and Diderot had argued that 'transformisms' over thousands of years was a necessary postulate in order to explain nature. It came 54 years after the death of John Hunter whose museum of comparative anatomy, to which Darwin himself contributed, set out to demonstrate that organs arising from simple structures become more complex through adaptation and monstrosities were natural departures from the norm of adaptation: a demonstration which only makes sense in terms of what was then a European debate, largely dominated by French biologists, concerning the origin and mutability of species. The debate followed the dogma of Linnaeus that species were fixed and immutable.

In later years adaptation became synonymous with evolution but to John Hunter in the eighteenth century adaptation was evolution. Darwin always talked of facts first and speculation later, which was precisely what Hunter was talking about in amassing his specimens into a great museum of natural history. Darwin was certainly in no position to write off that museum, as he did the works of his grandfather Erasmus, as 'part of the error of history'.

Patrick Matthew and Robert Chambers carried out their great tasks single-handed. Without the help on the one hand of his great wealth and on the other of Hooker, Lyell, Lubbock, Blyth, Wallace and many others, it is doubtful whether Darwin, single-handed, could have avoided making a botch of his theory or even whether he could have had the *Origin* published. Even so, in spite of all the outside help, he retreated more and more towards Lamarckism. His scholarship and integrity were at fault in not providing all his references in the *Origin* he had, after 1859, another twenty years in which to do so. What one can say is that his denigration of Patrick Matthew was unwarrantable and inexcusable. Darwin faithfully cited everything Blyth conveyed to him except the essays of 1835–37. Whether or not one can read anything into this is sheer speculation. Blyth obviously did not provide Darwin with the actual theory of natural selection but he presented him with plenty of ammunition before and after 1838.

The correspondence between Blyth and Darwin has only been recently published. All Darwin's correspondence was in the care of Cambridge University Library but is now published. There were at Cambridge University Library about 50 letters from Blyth to Darwin but none from Darwin to Blyth. There are, however, abstracts of Blyth's letters consisting of 25 small quarto sheets entirely in Darwin's hand. Through the courtesy of Cambridge University Library (Mr P. J. Gautrey), the present author has been permitted to read this collection. These letters, more in the nature of scientific despatches, are the most extraordinary letters Darwin ever received. Always deferentially introducing his letters with 'My dear Sir', Blyth immediately strikes the attitude of master to pupil. There is no small talk but line after line of observed facts on the origins of animals, attention drawn to countless relevant observations, constant posing of questions and 'Notes for Mr Darwin'. It is a battle of ideas on an immense front. He draws Darwin's attention to a paper on the cultivated rose and the fact that the earliest historical reference to the subject is 600 BC. And did Mr Darwin know that there was no Sanskrit word for rose? In pursuit of another idea, Darwin is advised to 'try to learn also what humped back cattle there are in China, Madagascar, Africa.' All the points from these letters found their way into Darwin's thoughts and publications. Blyth really was an ill man but never mentions his health in any of his letters. What a refreshing contrast to Darwin's correspondence!

In 1875 Arthur Grote (J Asiat Soc Bengal, 43, 15) composed an obituary of Edward Blyth which included, 'All that he knew was at the service of everybody. No one asking him for information asked in vain.' In a letter to Asa Gray in 1857 Darwin made it clear that however much he enjoyed discussing all manner of problems, he was not so generous as Blyth with information on his central theme when he explained, 'You will perhaps think it paltry of me, when I ask you not to mention my doctrine; the reason is, if any one, like the author of the *Vestiges*, were to hear of them, he might easily work them in, and then I should have to quote from a work perhaps despised by naturalists, and this would greatly injure any chance of my views being received by those alone whose opinions I value.' All this in spite of Darwin's sympathy for the *Vestiges* which, ignoring its many scientific blunders, was clearly arguing that since geologists, like Charles Lyell, had removed the hand of God from geological history, why retain it to explain natural history in terms of separate special creations? In observing these two – Darwin and Blyth – one can understand which one was 'fitter' to survive the 'bleak age' of nineteenth-century England.

In his biography, Wallace referred to the *Vestiges* as '. . . a book which, in my opinion, has always been undervalued, and which, when it first appeared, was almost as much abused, and for the same reasons, as was Darwin's *Origin of Species* fifteen years later.' In his essays on Darwinism (1901), Wallace reviewed the early nineteenth-century attitudes to speciation and claimed Lamarck as the one investigator who tried to prove that all animals are descended from other species of animals. Besides Lamarck, he noted, 'The only other important work dealing with the question was the celebrated *Vestiges of Creation.*'

In a letter to T. H. Huxley in 1860, Darwin in utter frustration asked 'Have you seen the slashing article of December 26th in the *Daily News*, against my stealing from my "master", the author of the *Vestiges*?' Clearly, the argument in support of Chambers' Principle of Progressive Development in the *Vestiges* and the one later in the *Origin* appeared, to some thinking people, quite similar. There was, however, a profound difference between what Chambers had argued and the principles of Natural Selection stated by Matthew and Darwin.

It has been argued that three Scotsmen laid the guide lines for Darwin's *Origin* – and Darwin himself spent almost two years in Edinburgh during a period of intense argument over species mutability. It is often claimed that Darwin came through a process of induction to the principle of Natural Selection. While it is true that the discipline of inductive philosophy forced Darwin to collect fact upon fact before he considered he had a strong case for evolution through Natural Selection, he used deduction as well. Darwin took two facts – all organisms tend to increase in a geometric ratio, but in spite of this tendency the actual numbers of any species remain constant. From this he deduced the struggle for existence – a term introduced by Lamarck. A third fact involved variation and this together with the first deduction led to the deduction of Natural Selection. If we glance back we shall find that Patrick Matthew made the same observations and the same deductions. So why accuse him of brevity? The mass of facts available to Patrick Matthew and Charles Lyell permitted these two deductive Scots to come to their conclusions quickly and, so far as the former is concerned, 'without an effort of concentrated thought'. Deductive philosophy, so admired by the Scots since the days of David Hume and Adam Smith, has not appealed to the practical, pragmatic English since the days of Francis Bacon. It is possible that some of the deductive approach brushed off on Darwin during his stay in Edinburgh between 1825 and 1827.

It is quite interesting to ponder the various reactions to the *Origin* within the context of induction and deduction:

1. The review by the pious Adam Sedgwick (*Cambridge Chronicle*, 19 May 1860): 'Darwin's theory is not inductive – it is not based on a series of acknowledged facts, leading to a general conclusion – he has not undermined any grand truth in the constancy of natural laws, and the continuity of true species.'

2. Charles Lyell (October 1859): 'It is a splendid case of close reasoning and long sustained argument . . .'

3. Patrick Matthew's assessment (*Gardeners' Chronicle*, 2 May 1860): 'To me the conception of this law of Nature came intuitively as a self-evident fact, almost without an effort of concentrated thought.'

4. The refusal of the French Academy of Sciences to elect Charles Darwin to its zoological section; an eminent member wrote to *Les Mondes*: 'What has closed the doors of the Academy to Mr Darwin is that the science of those of his books which have made his chief title to fame – *The Origin of the Species* and *The Descent of Man* – is not science, but a mass of assertions and absolutely gratuitous hypotheses, often evidently fallacious. This kind of publication and these theories are a bad example, which a body that respects itself cannot encourage.'

5. Virchow, the founder of histopathology, advised Bismarck's Government not to teach Darwinism in the schools because it was not factual and only a theory.

6. Karl Pearson (in a lecture delivered in London in 1923): 'Darwin was twenty-five years collecting and digesting material for those

books; no books written before or since have placed before their readers such a mass of well-correlated facts and observations.'

7. Julian Huxley (*Evolution, the modern synthesis*, 1938): 'By Darwinism I imply that blend of induction and deduction which Darwin was the first to apply to the study of evolution . . . on the one hand he amassed enormous quantities of facts from which inductions conceding the evolutionary process could be drawn; and on the other, starting from a few general principles, he deduced the further principle of Natural Selection. It is as well to remember the strong deductive element in Darwinism. Darwin based his theory of Natural Selection on three observable facts of nature and two deductions from them.'

No matter how many facts are assembled there comes a stage when someone must synthesize them into an all-pervading law and after twenty years of arboriculture and fruit hybridizing Patrick Matthew did just that when he propounded the law of the process of Natural Selection. All deduction is preceded by a long period of induction, and Patrick Matthew protested to Darwin that his conclusions were based on twenty years of hybridizing and arboriculture. Patrick Matthew's deduction can also be taken as a fact which can be examined experimentally and supported by observation. Although Matthew concentrated on plants he combined within the universal law animals including man himself. Haldane (1938) has claimed that Darwin was forced to take all his evidence from animals because the repeal of the Corn Laws led to a complete lack of interest in plant breeding. This assessment cannot withstand even superficial scrutiny.

The experiments of Knight between 1787 and 1823 had established the techniques of hybridizing which later were employed by Mendel himself, and, indeed, by Darwin. Since the eighteenth century there had been widespread interest in hybridization and Darwin's contemporaries included famous hybridists in Laxton, Goss and Herbert. In any case, after the repeal of the Corn Laws in 1846 even more wheat was grown by English and Scottish farmers, and more farm machinery and techniques were invented than ever before. At the Royal Agricultural Show of 1853, 2,000 new implements were exhibited. Landowners in Parliament advanced themselves money for improvements on the land. In 1845 a technique was invented for the manufacture of large pipes which led to more land being drained and rendered arable. Darwin's own experiments with antirrhinums produced results quite similar to those of Mendel with sweet peas but he failed to make the deductions from the facts. Furthermore, Darwin had written his second trial essay in 1844 – two years before the repeal of the Corn Laws.

Gruber (1974) commented, 'Why Darwin was not able to do what Mendel did, I cannot say. In one sense he did not try hard enough.' This may be so but the real point is Darwin had a horror of mathematics and relied on John Lubbock for help. But more important Darwin did not have a problem to pursue, although he picked up the term 'selection' from breeders there was no precedent to involving statistical methods into biological studies at that time. Joseph Hooker, John Lubbock and Darwin and it would appear everybody else did not pick up Mendel's paper when it was published in 1865. Breeders over the previous century had found what Sebright had experienced. Even Darwin reported in the first chapter of the *Origin*, 'The offspring from the first cross between two breeds is tolerably and sometimes (as I have found with pigeons) quite uniform in character, and everything seems simple enough; but when these mongrels are crossed one with another for several generations, hardly two of them are alike, and then the difficulty of the task becomes manifest.' This was the problem Mendel faced. He had studied mathematics and physics as well as theology as a student. Mendel also came from peasant stock. These factors ensured that by patient work he would find the ratios. When he did no one was interested or impressed – not even his teacher Nägeli.

Towards the end of the eighteenth century there was great interest in breeding different varieties of wheat by Shirreff and others but there was also intense interest in the selective breeding of domestic animals. It was about this time that our well-known breeds of cattle and sheep were established with confidence. It was on this background that Darwin reviewed the evidence of inherited variation and he continued the tradition with his own work on domestic pigeons. If Darwin concentrated on variation in animals rather than in plants the reason lay in the fact that he had no particular horticultural problem to solve.

If Darwin's autobiography can be relied on, and often it is not, he recalls in it that his interest in cross-fertilization of flowers started in 1838. Darwin picked up from the work of others that somatic variations could be induced in cuttings and this fact helped in shaping his attitude to variation and natural selection by the time he wrote the *Origin*. Darwin knew from the plant breeding experiments of others of such phenomena as sports, pure lines, segregations and confirmed this with his own work on antirrhinums, and he was aware of what would now be called F1 uniformity and F2 variability.

Patrick Matthew had opposed the Corn Laws since their introduction in 1815 because, like hereditary titles, he considered them an outrage against the universal law of competition and the survival of the fittest. His support for the free trade movement was a logical attitude derived from the universal law. And Matthew proved to be right about the biological need to repeal the Corn Laws. The improvement in farming techniques and the increased yield were due to increased demand coming at a time of fear of foreign competition .

The kind of facts and observations which were available to Patrick Matthew were available, but even more so, to Charles Darwin. Nothing fundamentally new had emerged by 1836 when he returned from the voyage and the subject of heredity was still obscure. They both elaborated more facts in support of notions about evolution widely circulated by French biologists in the eighteenth century. It is not too surprising, therefore, that both fell into the same pitfalls because evolution through Natural Selection explained nothing in their day. Patrick Matthew boldly outlined the logical extension of the struggle for existence in much the same way as others extended the Darwinian survival of the fittest to bolster up imperialism and justify man's inhumanity to man as a fact of nature. Even the gentle Lamarck saw, with some justification, the animal kingdom as a vast slaughterhouse. Both Matthew and Darwin confused fitness with betterment and adaptation with physical prowess and the fact of survival was confused with biological development; Malthusian nonsense was made even more nonsensical by the latter.

Both Matthew and Darwin stressed the struggle for external adaptation rather than for internal adaptation – a struggle between individuals rather than between an individual and his environment – an attitude which justified unrestricted competition in human societies. Such an attitude was rejected at first more on sociological grounds than on scientific because it offended against the more lofty historical code of ethics which preached that to give was more noble than to take. However, in mid nineteenth-century Europe only the more sensitive minds cared about ethics. The current successful economic expansion of well-armed nations over weakly armed nations was reflected in the biological thought of the day. Herbert Spencer, who more correctly than Darwin regarded evolution as an adjustment of internal rather than external relationships, came almost inevitably to the same conclusion about the survival of the fittest. In 1866, Wallace, in a letter to Darwin, pleaded for the term 'natural selection' to be substituted by Spencer's 'survival of the fittest'. 'This term is the plain expression of the fact; Natural Selection is a metaphorical expression of it . . . when you say Natural Selection acts so as to choose those that are fittest, it is misunderstood, and apparently always will be.' And Darwin conceded the point. However, by 1889 in *Darwinism*, first edition, Wallace is now quite happy with Natural Selection: 'Further more, I am convinced that Natural Selection has been the most important, but not exclusive, means of modification . . . although I maintain, and even enforce, my differences from some of Darwin's views, my whole work tends forcibly to illustrate the overwhelming importance of Natural Selection over all other agencies in the production of new species. I thus take up Darwin's earlier position, from which he somewhat receded in the later editions of his works, on account of criticisms and objections which I endeavoured to show unsound.' Matthew, it will be recalled, used both 'natural process of selection' and its effect – the survival of the 'best circumstance-suited'. If ever a group of naturalists reflected in their biological thought the dominant economic philosophy of their time it was these early evolutionists.

In his introduction to *Naval Timber* Patrick Matthew thundered out his biological creed in political terms: 'Navigation is of the first importance to the improvement of the species, in spreading, by emigrations the superior varieties of man, and diffusing the arts and sciences over the world . . . thus, perhaps, equally in danger of deteriorating and sinking into caste, both classes yielding to the natural law of restricted adaptation to conditions: when we reflect upon this, the conclusion is irresistibly forced upon us, that the periodical return of war is indispensable to the heroic chivalrous character and love of freedom . . . Patrick Matthew was a far more thorough-going evolutionist through Natural Selection than ever Darwin was. If both these naturalists read back into nature the current means of achieving economic success, it was unconsciously so far as Darwin was concerned but was frighteningly conscious on the part of Patrick Matthew. It is a relief to know that Scotland's honour was rescued from such diabolical interpretations of nature and its post-Darwinian counterpart by another Scot, Patrick Geddes – who restored humanity to biology.

Darwin and his writings have been placed on such a high pedestal to the virtual exclusion of previous writers that Darwinism is frequently applied to their writings. In *Darwin's Century*, Eiseley sets an example. Referring to Matthew's *Naval Timber*, he writes, 'He notes in his book several types of ecological adaptation and he went on to observe that when changed circumstances occur the struggle for existence may be enhanced. Under such conditions individuals of superior adaptive power and "greater power of occupancy" eliminate the less well adapted. All of this is very Darwinian: it is, in fact, pure Darwinism.' On the contrary it is pure Matthewism!

By the end of the third decade of the nineteenth century, Patrick Matthew had logically followed the drift of his thoughts on the superior varieties of *Homo sapiens*. The Angles were, for him, amongst the superior varieties and so he urged them to emigrate – adaptively radiate – into the lonely places of the world as of right. His second book *Emigration Fields* appeared in 1839. It was the right book for the time, for the colonization of New Zealand had started in 1837 and by 1840 some 70,000 individuals of a superior variety of *Homo sapiens* were leaving these shores annually. To complete the logic of his philosophy, in about 1864 two sons of Patrick Matthew landed in New Zealand and set up – with their father's help with seeds, saplings and hybridizing techniques – the first commercial orchards in the Antipodes.

It is ironical that the only book containing clear naturalistic axioms which would have provided the young Darwin with a springboard in the late 1830s was missed by him. That Darwin should choose to ignore and denigrate Patrick Matthew in 1860 when confronted with this book, as 'an obscure writer on forest trees', is one of the more puzzling aspects of Darwin's personal relationships. At a time when Darwin's only support, and pretty lukewarm support at that, came from Hooker and Lyell with the devious T. H. Huxley about to jump upon the bandwagon, it is strange that Darwin should reject the only other naturalist in Europe who supported him whole-heartedly.

Even if we admit that Patrick Matthew was merely synthesizing current thoughts about the mutability of species, we can also admit that no naturalist in Europe at the end of the 1820s, when *Naval Timber* and its appendix were written, wrote in such clear terms as the following:

'Is the inference then unphilosophic, that living things which are proved to have a circumstance-suiting power – a very slight change of circumstance by culture inducing a corresponding change of character – may have gradually accommodated themselves to the variations of the elements containing them, and, without new creation, have presented the diverging changeable phenomena of past and present organized existence.'

The denigratory use of 'obscure' by Darwin has, perhaps unconsciously, been copied by most other writers about Matthew ever since. De Beer, for example, following closely the remarks of Eiseley, referred both to William Charles Wells and to Patrick Matthew's *Naval Timber*. De Beer writes, '. . . predecessors who had actually published the principle of natural selection in obscure places remained completely unnoticed . . .' Wells delivered a lecture to the Royal Society and was widely acclaimed for his essay on dew. Matthew's publishers were Adam and Charles Black in Edinburgh and Longmans in London. Hardly 'obscure places'! De Beer's conclusion is predictable: 'These works show that neither Wells nor Matthew had any appreciation of the magnitude on which they stumbled, or any competence to work it out.' Both Wells and Matthew had a firm grasp of artificial selection but Matthew had clearly a much wider grasp of the whole evolutionary process and certainly did not 'stumble' on the theory. One can only conclude that de Beer never read the *Appendix*.

If Wells and Matthew saw clearly the analogy between artificial and natural selection and J. C. Loudon was not upset by Matthew's views when he reviewed *Naval Timber* in 1832, one should conclude that a number of people were aware of these processes. Still, after the publication of the *Origin* Darwin stuck to his opinion that evolution through Natural Selection was his own theory. 'The only novelty in my work is the attempt to explain *how* species became modified, and to a certain extent how the theory of descent explains certain large classes of facts; in this respect I received no assistance from my predecessors.'

What Patrick Matthew and Charles Darwin had in common was confidence amounting to arrogance. Indeed, this confidence and arrogance can be traced back to Buffon and his followers. In the nineteenth century Matthew, Robert Chambers in the *Vestiges,* Herbert Spencer and Darwin knew full well that evolutionism must prevail. The controversy on the mutability of species was highly artificial. There would be no controversy if those believing in the fixity of species had not based their argument on Holy Writ. One can recognize the arrogance in the *Appendix*. Law after law is presented as a demonstration of how nature works. The absurdly pious Adam Sedgwick wrote to Darwin after reading through the *Origin* and, more in sorrow than in anger, criticised the '. . . tone of triumphant confidence . . . (in a tone I condemned in the author of the *Vestiges*) . . .' This was harsh criticism from the man who, in his youthful exuberance of 1830, had confidently abolished the Noachian Flood from geology and triumphed!

Matthew's arrogant confidence was still there in 1860 when he confronted Darwin: '. . . it was by a general glance at the scheme of Nature that I estimated this select production of species as an a priori recognizable fact — an axiom, requiring only to be pointed out to be admitted by unprejudiced minds of sufficient grasp.' And in 1852, Herbert Spencer was equally arrogant: 'Let them tell us how a new species is constructed and how it makes its appearance. Is it thrown down from the clouds? Or must we hold to the notion that it struggles out of the ground? Do its limbs or viscera rush together from all points of the compass? Or must we receive the old Hebrew idea that God takes clay and moulds a new creature?'

During the late 1820s alert minds were having doubts about the Noachian Flood as a primary geological agency. In Scotland still there was greater freedom of thought than in England. In 1826 in England, Professor Buckland was claiming to have proved that the Flood had taken place. In Scotland at the same date even the clerics were sceptical about the reality of the Flood. The Reverend John Fleming gave a long dissertation to the Edinburgh Philosophical Society and introduced his communication as follows: 'The science of geology was first introduced to public notice, in this country, by philosophers who, while they cherished a reverential regard for the authority of the Scriptures, overlooked those methods of investigation which lead to a discovery of the laws of nature.' He then proceeded to dispense with the Mosaic cosmological beliefs of Cuvier and Buckland.

Although the Reverend Sedgwick got the credit for abolishing Noah's Flood from geology in 1830, his announcement came four years after the Reverend Fleming in Scotland had arrived at the same conclusion.

The Scottish divine had not paid a visit to the Massif Central as Sedgwick had done but based his rejection on the facts. The biblical account of gentle rain falling for forty days and nights could not account for the geological reality.

But even in the 1790s Scottish naturalists had given up the Flood. James Hutton in his *Theory of the Earth* and John Hunter in his essay of 1792. This essay was not published in Hunter's lifetime and probably just as well because the Seditious Acts would have incriminated him. The essay was eventually published in 1859.

'History gives us no determined account of this change of the waters; but as the Sacred History mentions the whole surface of the earth having been deluged with water, the natural historians have laid hold of this, and have conceived that it would account for the whole. Forty days overflowing the dry land could not have brought such quantities of sea-productions on the surface; nor can we suppose, then, taking all possibilities into consideration, that it remained long on the whole surface of he earth; therefore there was no time for their being fossilized.' Perhaps Hunter was influenced by Buffon who claimed he could discover no evidence of the Flood.

It is a sad reflection on Charles Darwin that in spite of the burden of theological truculence and scientific timidity shored up against the theory of Natural Selection and the calumny directed at himself, he chose to smear and belittle the name of Patrick Matthew.

5

The Use of Selection by Nineteenth-century Breeders

'. . . by selecting individuals to breed from, he can effect the most surprising changes in form and qualities, as the example of the pig, sheep, horse, cow, and dog will abundantly evince . . . A superior breed of human beings could only be produced by selections and exclusions similar to those so successfully employed in rearing our more valuable animals . . .'

(W. Lawrence: *Lectures on physiology, zoology and the natural history of man*, 1819)

'Man's interference, by preventing this natural process of selection among plants . . . has increased the difference in varieties . . . but which, from the infirmity of their conditions – not having undergone selection by the law of nature cannot maintain their ground without his culture and protection.'

(P. Matthew: *Naval Timber and Arboriculture*, 1831)

'If we wish to extract from any animal or plant species a variety which will meet our requirements, we select from amongst the great number of individuals of this species as the foundation of a new stock those which differ from the type in the direction we want . . .'

(Charles Naudin: 1852)

'Why I like the term is that it is constantly used in all works on breeding, and I am surprised that it is not familiar to Murray.'

(Darwin to Lyell: LLD 1859, 2, 152)

Murray, the publisher of the *Origin,* was quite unfamiliar with the term 'Natural Selection' which formed part of the title of the *Origin.* Lyell, at this time, was using his influence with Murray to accept for publication Darwin's work on the origin of species and hence Darwin's letter to him.

All collected evidence in the *Origin* of 1859 was directed to the support of the concept of the origin of species by Natural Selection. Darwin spoke and wrote of the concept as 'my theory'. In collecting the vast array of facts for the *Origin* Darwin informs us that he spent a great deal of the twenty years of preparation reading agricultural and horticultural journals and documents. If one reads through a number of such journals published in the first half of the nineteenth century, one comes across the term 'selection' very frequently. In particular, the term is constantly used, as Darwin noted, in all reports on the breeding of new varieties of plants and animals. There is no doubt that breeders used this term by which was meant artificial selection. Upon the judicious selection of animals and plants for certain qualities depended the ultimate success of establishing new varieties. DeVries (1904) was of the opinion that Darwin did not understand what the breeders were really doing. This is odd because in all the breeder reports it was stressed that the right variety must be chosen as the foundation stock in order to have rapid success.

Breeders were using 'selection', as Darwin explained, early on in the nineteenth century and no doubt the term was common currency in the eighteenth century.

This may be deduced from documents such as the Sebright letter to Sir Joseph Banks in 1809: 'Were I to define what is called the art of breeding, I should say, that it consisted in the selection of males and females, intended to breed together, in reference to each other's merits and defects.' Sebright considered breeding an art, highly skilled work and not a simple country pursuit for gentlemen: '. . . the best breeds, after having been obtained by them at a great expense, too frequently degenerate in their hands, from mismanagement. They conceive, that, if they have procured good males and good females, they have done all that is necessary to establish and to continue a good breed, but this is by no means the case.' Here are the words of an eighteenth-century gentleman and skilled breeder spelling out the secrets of breeding by constant and careful selection.

The Memoirs of the Caledonian Horticultural Society for the period 1814–1825 carry many breeders' reports, always involving the term 'selection' whoever the breeder.

'The perfectly double or full varieties of the stock-gilliflower

(*Cherianthus incanus* and *annuus*), have long been supposed capable of impregnating the single varieties of stocks, and have been carefully, regularly, and formally selected for that purpose, by planting single stocks close by them.' (Nicol G., *Remarks on raising new varieties of Pink*, 3, 270).

'I select a few young plants of sorts proper for the purpose: that is, such as have a well-formed small eye or pip, as that prevents the petals from turning backwards, which in an auricula is a great defect . . .' (Henderson W., *On the culture of the Auricula and Polyanthus*, 3, 229).

'Among the numerous varieties now growing in my garden, there are at least twenty that do not give perfect seed, though they all of them furnish culm and spike. From those which give perfect seed, the same variety is thereby produced, provided the plants are selected and separated from other kinds. If they be allowed to stand close by others in the time of flowering, new hybrid varieties will result.' (Whitworth G., *On the varieties of Lolium perenne*, 3, 377).

'Many hundreds of seedlings have I raised with this view, and after bestowing much pains, and submitting to great labour and trouble in selecting, keeping separate and distinct, and making trial of the different kinds . . .' (Dow A., *On the cultivation of the potato, with an account of the Kilspindie Bloom*, 3, 439).

One can see the basic need in all these time-consuming and large population experiments for mathematical treatment; a need which was only satisfied towards the end of the second half of the nineteenth century.

Breeders, if not the academic parsons, were in no doubt as to how artificial or domestic varieties came about. At the show new varieties of poultry, sheep, and other farm animals were regularly exhibited and fanciers found that they were forced to work with great discipline. At one poultry show, reported in the *Cottage Gardener* of 1856, a judge made this comment: 'We feel it is our duty to warn exhibitors in this class for black and white top-knots that they must be more particular in selecting birds with straight backs.' The *Cottage Gardener* gave monthly reports of all the shows in England and it is perhaps significant that Darwin wrote to Hooker in 1861 (*More letters of Charles Darwin*, Vol i, 186) to say he found the *Gardeners' Chronicle* 'intolerably dull' and that he found the *Cottage Gardener* nearer to his needs. Although Darwin had subscribed to the *Gardeners' Chronicle* for years and had even published articles in it, he now found this journal 'intolerably dull'. It is possible that Patrick Matthew's letter of 1860 to the *Gardeners' Chronicle* did not help to endear that journal to Darwin, though as late as 1860 Darwin published his important article on the fertilization of orchids there.

William Lawrence was a distinguished London surgeon who, as part of his duties as lecturer, during the period 1813–1818, at the Royal College of Surgeons gave a series of dissertations on comparative anatomy and physiology. He was clearly a disciple of Cuvier and Blumenbach so far as comparative anatomy was concerned and also in his attitude to religion which had no place in his scientific life: 'I shall not insult your understandings by formally proving that this physiological doctrine never has afforded, and never can afford, any support to religion or morals; and that the great truths, so important to mankind, rest on a perfectly different and far more solid foundation.' He saw man as part of nature and an object to be critically analysed by comparative anatomy. Selective breeding could be applied to man as to any other animal. As was to be expected his lectures met with a great deal of opposition from his colleagues like John Abernethy, as well as from the Church bishops. He vigorously defied his critics in his reply to Abernethy when he published his lectures in 1819. The book was refused copyright by the Lord Chancellor on the grounds that it contradicted the Scriptures; the bishops knew how to bring a radical to his knees. Like persecuted scientists before him Lawrence withdrew his book publicly but several unexpurgated editions appeared up until 1848. So, Lawrence saved his career and later even became President of the College and surgeon to the Queen. Some forty years later the prudent and silent Lawrence warned the young and brash Huxley not to become embroiled in the natural history of man. To Huxley's great credit he turned down this advice.

The lectures reveal Lawrence as anti-religionist in his views; no deference to a Creator or Providence is to be found; no truckling to a clerically-dominated society for which he was made to pay the price. He found support among the radicals and young naturalists like Edward Blyth but took no further part in the debate about the origin of species and man during the rest of his life. It is some measure of how swiftly social thought had progressed by 1863 if we mention Huxley's remark about Lawrence: '. . . one of the ablest men I have known was well-nigh ostracized for his book on Man which now might be read in a Sunday School without surprising anybody.' (*Man's Place in Nature*). It has been suggested by Darlington (*Darwin's Place in History*, 1959) that Patrick Matthew read and was converted by Lawrence's book when it appeared in 1819. It is quite likely because Matthew travelled a good deal via London to the Continent, but Lawrence did not relate natural selection to the origin of species. However, Matthew, like Darwin, did not mention the names of his mentors in any of his books but it is clear that he reflects, to some extent, the views of Erasmus Darwin, Malthus, Cuvier, Lamarck and Stevenson. The latter was a civil engineer with a special interest in the effect of tidal waters on coastal erosion. However, Matthew shows great independence of thought for he went further than Lawrence and did not accept more than nature's superfecundity from Malthus, rejected the special creationism of Cuvier and certainly never accepted Lamarck's inheritance of acquired characters. Furthermore, Patrick Matthew never recanted his thoughts of 1831 about the historical fact of evolution and how it had happened.

Edward Blyth was not a breeder which perhaps explains why in his 1835–37 essays he never mentions the word 'selection'. Indeed, when it comes to the observed results of the mixed offspring of two varieties, Blyth hurriedly refers the reader to the books written by two doctors – Pritchard and Lawrence. Although Lawrence's book was publicly withdrawn in 1820, we find Blyth in 1835 referring to it enthusiastically. For sound remarks on varieties Blyth advises the reader to add Volume 2 of Lyell's *Principles of Geology* to the above two books.

In the second decade of the nineteenth century three distinguished doctors led the field in the study of the natural history of man – Lawrence, Pritchard and Wells. The books written by Lawrence and Pritchard were well known and widely read over the following thirty years. Wells gave but one lecture to the Royal Society before he died in 1818, on the theme of the varieties of man, although he writes with some knowledge of the professional breeder, the word selection is never mentioned. This lecture made no impact on the public or the medical profession. Although none of these three can claim to have described Natural Selection as the mode of origin of species they did prepare the minds of some men to the fact that varieties of animals and plants can emerge through natural causes. The capitulation of Lawrence, when he wrote his publisher in 1820 ('. . . I thought it expedient to withdraw this work from circulation . . .') came as a red warning to other doctors who might have been of like persuasion not to dare express heretical thoughts in public. The warning was well heeded for no doctor entered the controversy during the remainder of the century with the kind of views expressed by

Lawrence. Gideon Mantell, the surgeon who discovered the Iguanodon, followed Lyell so far as geology went but Richard Owen, who identified Darwin's fossils found in South America, bitterly opposed the concept of the evolution of species and of man. Mantell and Owen had a bitter personal feud when Owen was curator at the College of Surgeons which contributed, to some extent, to the unhappy circumstances surrounding the curator's departure in 1856. Owen's supremacy in palaeontology and comparative anatomy was so great that no doctor emerged to challenge his anti-evolutionist doctrine. Although Dr Hugh Falconer proposed that the Copley Medal should be presented to Darwin in recognition of the *Origin* and other works, he died soon afterwards. In any case he had transferred many years previously to palaeontology. The respectability gained by the medical profession during the nineteenth century provided a damper on any doctor with advanced ideas. In the early nineteenth century, based strictly on the considerable evidence available at the time, there was a group of doctors thinking and writing very rationally about the natural history of man – Erasmus Darwin, Lawrence, Wells and Pritchard – but at the end of that century not one medical name comes to mind.

Patrick Matthew after twenty years experience as a fruit breeder wrote out the term 'natural process of selection' in his *Naval Timber* 'without an effort of concentrated thought'. As a professional breeder the term 'selection' would be part of his everyday existence. It would appear, however, that this was the first occasion the term was formally committed to print in a philosophical sense. To the hybridist Matthew the analogy between artificial and natural selection was a fact too obvious to merit further debate on the basis of hypothesis. What he stated, later on to be designated a theory, was a formal expression of rational experience. On the other hand, Darwin who was primarily interested in the origin of species and varieties had little experience as a hybridizer before he published the *Origin* of 1859. Even then, he added nothing to the science of hybridization which is odd considering his prolonged theoretical interest in the subject. Although Darwin realised that the breeders were gradually working out the laws of heredity and that hybridizing techniques had been well established by Laxton, Knight and Naudin he never seriously set about experiments aimed at elucidating the facts of heredity. Already by 1830 the Dutch Academy of Haarlem had posed the problem for which they offered a prize: 'What does experience teach us regarding

the production of new species and varieties through the artificial fertilization of flowers of the one with the pollen of the other, and what
economic and ornamental plant can be produced and multiplied in this
way?' The eight years Darwin spent on classifying barnacles would have
been spent better on hybridizing experiments. However, Darwin knew
where to search for the kind of information he needed for his great
synthesis.

The same cannot be said for Thomas H. Huxley. On his own admission
(*On the reception of the Origin of the Species*) he admits he was slow to take
an interest in the species problem: 'I think I must have read *Vestiges*
before I left England in 1846; but, if I did, the book made very little
impression upon me, and I was not brought into serious contact with
the 'species' question until after 1850s. By the time the *Origin* was
published Huxley was still quite ignorant about breeding and wrote to
Darwin asking for advice. In a letter to Huxley after the publication of
the 1859 *Origin,* Darwin wrote, 'I really do not know how to advise
about getting up facts on breeding and improving breeds. Go to shows
is one way . . . I have found it very important associating with fanciers
and breeders.' (LLD 3, 280, 1889.) Darwin might have told Huxley that
he had actually joined two London pigeon-fancier clubs! And I dare say
Huxley said to himself as he remarked after reading the *Origin,* 'Stupid
not to have thought of that before.' Huxley had at last tumbled to the
fact that the secrets of variation lay in the hands of the breeders. Later
in the nineteenth century Bateson came to the conclusion after spending
some years on embryology that central to the evolutionary problem was
hybridization. Dissatisfied with embryology he went on to study variation
directly by working on hybrids and within two years produced evidence
against blending inheritance. Still unaware of Mendel's mathematical
treatment of variation in his publication of 1865, Bateson came to realize
that any work on variation required statistical treatment. Because he had
come to this conclusion Bateson was among the first to recognize the
importance of Mendel's work when it was rediscovered soon after.

The art and science of breeding new varieties of plants and livestock
slowly developed through the seventeenth and eighteenth centuries. By
the end of the eighteenth century breeders had become confident about
the methods to be employed although empiricism still prevailed. By the
time Darwin was searching through the journals for information on
breeding he would come upon statements like these in the *Gardeners'*

Magazine (1840, 16, 48): 'Mr Roughead, seedsman, Haddingtons informs us that he has paid great attention to the selection of his variety of Swedish turnip for the last ten years, and been always successful in preserving the variety pure till lately.'

Advertisements in journals, such as *Mark Lane Express* (started about 1832), carried the word 'selection' in particular reference to the origin and improvement of varieties of seeds and bulbs. Charles Sharp and Co., Seed Farmers announced, '. . . pleasure in submitting the following list of their most select varieties of turnips and mangels . . . Having for some years devoted considerable attention to the selection and improvement of this variety . . . It was originally selected from Skirving's, and retains the robust and large size of that variety . . . selected to grow with very little top and a small tap-root. (*Mark Lane Express*, 18 April 1870.)

The odd point about Darwin's 'Questions about the breeding of animals', according to Freeman and Gautrey (1969) sent out in 1839, is that quantitative answers were required if any real sense was to be made of the questions. The answers, such as are known, were not quantitative but rather vague recalling of past experiences. Had Darwin set about finding answers to these questions by his own experiments he surely would have pre-empted Mendel. In fact, one set of answers from a Richard Ford enunciates very well one of Mendel's laws: 'In crossing varieties of sheep and cattle, I have observed generally, that although the first cross has usually produced a satisfactory result – such in fact as might have been expected – a remarkable inconstancy has often attended subsequent crossings between this progeny and either of the parent stocks, as well as the breeding from the produce of the cross exclusively.' (Freeman and Gautrey, 1969.) It is clear that long before Darwin sat down seriously to ponder the questions of heredity a great deal was known and sufficient principles of selection were appreciated and practised which led to the improvement of breeds.

Reports of breeding at meetings of farmers' clubs nearly always involved the term 'selection'. 'First and foremost is the selection of your ewe . . . Having judiciously selected the ewe and tup, I am in favour of putting the tups with the ewes in the third week of August – for that purpose have selected some of the best bred ewes and tups I could find.' (A breeder's address to a farmers' club – *Mark Lane Express*, 7 February 1870.)

Like so many other aspects of science in England, the science of breeding developed outside the environment of the universities. It came as a response to the towns demanding meat and vegetables in ever increasing amounts. The breeding techniques were probably passed on verbally at first and only later in print as journals and magazines increased in numbers and circulation in the early nineteenth century in this way the term 'selection' came within the ken of Charles Darwin but by 1859 a well educated person, like the publisher Murray, was quite unfamiliar with its meaning. On the other hand someone, like Patrick Matthew, born into the farming world and specialising in fruit hybridizing, the term was in everyday use – both linguistically and practically – in the early nineteenth century. For someone with a philosophic turn of mind the analogy between artificial selection for domestic purposes and what obtained in nature was essentially exact. The only people competent to formulate the laws of heredity and variation were the breeders and it was no accident that the hybridizer Mendel succeeded in doing this. The irony is that those who had argued so much for and against evolution were not mentally ready for the laws of heredity when they first appeared. And Darwin was among those European naturalists who did not notice or perhaps understand Mendel's paper when it first appeared in 1865. It is not likely that Darwin would have warmed to the results of Mendel any more than he did to the similar results reported by the French hybridist Naudin which were communicated to him in 1859 by Hooker. His lack of experience or understanding with first and second generation crosses made him miss the whole significance of particulate heredity. In a letter to Hooker (LLD 2, 246, 1959) he shrugs off Naudin '. . . But I cannot find one word like the struggle for existence and natural selection . . .' Naudin had published his results in 1852 (Revd Hort ser 4: 1, 102, 1852) but made no impact. Naudin's work is mentioned in the *Historical Sketch* but Darwin has obviously forgotten or chose to forget what he had written in his letter to Hooker in 1852. Had Darwin got to grips with Naudin and particulate heredity, his later retreat to Lamarckism could never have taken place. For all his careful and patient collecting of facts for the purpose of formulating an hypothesis, Darwin made no advance beyond the work of Buffon in actually explaining the origin of species.

From his notebooks it is clear that Darwin was paying attention to breeders from at least 1839 so that his cautious and grudging advice to

Huxley in 1860 was less than frank and helpful. In assessing Darwin's notebook K. Gruber *(Darwin on Man,* 1974) points to the fact that Darwin read or re-read Malthus on 28 September 1838 and that the association of the quasi-mathematical presentation and the superfecundity principle crystalized in Darwin's mind the concept of Natural Selection. This may be so but it should be recalled that Darwin had no mathematical mind. He was dependent on his neighbour John Lubbock for mathematical advice from time to time. In 1839 he did not have John Lubbock as a neighbour and there is no evidence that Darwin noted the mathematics of Malthus or sought advice about their true significance. But Gruber also points out that on 14 September Darwin had numerous conversations about animal breeding with breeders and it had forcibly been impressed on him that man by means of artificial selection – or selection – can breed monsters. Monsters – to John Hunter – were natural deviations from the normal and, as such, deserved attention. Examples of natural monsters were prominent in Hunter's museum to which Darwin had frequent access at that time.

It must surely be obvious that the term selection would crop up repeatedly in those conversations with animal breeders whereas it never appears in Malthus. Animal and plant breeders had an object in mind – a practical problem to solve to which selection was always central. It is not just by accident that Mendel applied mathematics to his experiments because in one way or another the breeders always were committed to numeracy of one kind or another. At the Dorchester Poultry Show (as reported in the *Cottage Gardener* 1856) it was claimed by one breeder that, '. . . by carefully selecting the breed, the same quantity of food may be made to produce at least a third more than it will if given to inferior animals.' In other breeding experiments the aim would be to increase the rate at which flesh was put on, the degree of hardiness or size of litter capacity or the quantity and quality of wool. There was always a numerical end-point prior to its realization into pounds, shillings and pence. A notice such as the above would not be missed by Darwin so that it is extraordinary that when Huxley asked for advice on how to gain more data on breeding that Darwin did not tell him to engage in breeding experiments. It would seem that the breeding of livestock and plant varieties was not sufficiently intellectual to engage the interest of naturalists like Huxley. Only when Mendel's papers were recognized as relevant to the origin of species did this knowledge reach top status among men of science.

It has been argued by Limoges (*La sélection naturelle. Étude sur la première constitution d'un concept* (1837–1859); Paris: Presses Universitaires de France, 1970) that the role of artificial selection played no part in Darwin's first formulation of the evolutionary process. Artificial selection leads to new varieties and even monsters and would be a false guide to natural selection involving the accumulation of slight variations in a population. This rejection of the analogy between artificial and natural selection by Limoges is purely theoretical and is not borne out by other evidence. Patrick Matthew realized fully the analogy. So did Edward Blyth in his 1835 essay. While it is time that artificial selection can breed monsters, the usual result is very slight variation and Darwin would have learned all this from his pigeon-fancier friends and the breeders he chose to consort with.

Darwin showed great prescience in realizing early on the importance of associating with breeders. They were practical men not given to philosophical dissertations and seldom in close contact with academics. When such men had something to say about the techniques of breeding they addressed their remarks to men of their own ilk in farmers' clubs. If their remarks were reported they would appear in journals like *Mark Lane Express* and *Cottage Gardener* and these were journals eagerly read by Darwin but not by people such as Lyell, Huxley or Whewell. In such reports selection was the operative word but still confined to a confraternity until the *Origin* gave it banner headlines. Darwin, then, picked up the term 'selection' in a second-hand manner whereas Patrick Matthew knew the term at first hand and hence enunciated the law of Natural Selection, 'without an effort of concentrated thought'. Or so he said in boast!

The members on the other hand, of academic societies, like the Linnean, frequently described new species and varieties but until 1858 when the joint papers of Darwin and Wallace were presented, no general debate on the mutability of species or techniques of breeding had been held. At least there is no record in the proceedings of that society. The same is true for most other learned societies and so it was not likely that the joint papers would occasion much debate. Hooker reported afterwards that there was no semblance of a debate. Darwin had written some years earlier to Wallace, '. . . very few naturalists care for anything beyond the mere description of species . . .' In any case only the enormous prestige of Hooker and Lyell allowed the joint papers of Darwin and Wallace to be presented and then published by this society in the first place. Later on, after the publication in 1859 of the *Origin* when public furore was at its height, members of this society threatened to resign membership if Darwin, also a member, did not resign.

From 1826, when the anonymous article (attributed to Robert Grant) supporting Lamarckian concepts of evolution was published in the *Edinburgh New Philosophical Journal*, until 1859 with the publication of the *Origin,* the academic debate about Lamarckian evolutionism was kept alive mainly by Lyell in numerous editions of his *Principles of Geology* and by the frank statements of Herbert Spencer − a disciple of Lamarck. Robert Grant from his position at University College continued to publicise his views on Lamarckism. The concept of Natural Selection, however, was never mentioned in these debates.

Robert Grant was a comparative anatomist and zoologist but not a breeder which could explain why he never introduced the term selection into his expositions. The French evolutionists were not breeders either and this may explain why the terms used by breeders does not appear in their writings. Unless scientists are involved in breeding the use of the term selection would not be of any relevance to their studies.

From 1844 Robert Chambers with ten editions in as many years of *The Vestiges of the Natural History of Creation* stimulated many perceptive people, including Wallace, to think in evolutionary terms even though such thinking allowed the retention of the Great Creator. Whewell in *The History of the Inductive Sciences* (2nd edition, 1847) summed up the alternatives in what seemed to many a fruitless debate: 'Either we must accept the doctrine of the transmutation of species and must suppose that the organized species of one geological epoch were transmuted into those of another by some long continued agency of natural causes; or else, we must believe in many successive acts of creation and extinction of species, out of the common course of nature; acts which therefore, we may properly call miraculous.' Like all the leading academics of the time Whewell supported the miraculous origin of species to the exclusion of any other alternative so it was logical for him to decide to ban the *Origin* from Trinity Library. The Oxbridge academics so conducted the muted debate that it was only the foolhardy or the anonymous who dared to support Lamarckian concepts in public.

Only Robert Grant and his radicals kept the memory of Lamarck alive in London (Desmond 1984); Darwin had nothing to say. The history of science shows that scientists like Galileo and Buffon declined to be martyrs for what they believed in – unlike religious men. Even the outspoken Huxley was all things to all men during this period. From his own testimony, recorded in *On the reception of the Origin of Species*, he was totally lacking in any positive approach to evolutionism prior to 1859. He was quite uninfluenced by the *Vestiges*, unlike Wallace and Darwin, he had not got to grips with basic Lamarckian ideas, and there is no evidence that between 1854 – when he wrote his savage critique of the *Vestiges* – and 1859 that he had thrown off his sitting-on-the-fence attitude he called agnosticism. It would appear that he did not even attend the 1858 Linnean Society meeting at which the joint Darwin–Wallace papers were read or, indeed, read the reports when they were subsequently published. Why he was suddenly converted to Darwinism in 1859 is quite a mystery because the *Origin* of 1859 did nothing to resolve the very problems unanswered by Lamarck and Robert Chambers and which previously had driven him to an agnostic stance. And Darwin's steady retreat from Natural Selection to speculation and Pangenesis did not seem to weaken his enthusiastic support for Darwinism which to some extents obliterated from future generations the great zoological contributions which he himself had made.

The deliberate prudence manifested by Lyell and later Darwin in pulling their punches and truckling to the religious feelings of society at that time is an indication of the kind of tightrope the innovator had to tread in order to get a fair hearing without offending too much the feelings of influential people.

Whewell's excellent summary of what was implied in the species debate, as it was blandly discussed in the community of parson-academics, offered no explanation of the origin of varieties and species and 'some long-continued agency of natural cause' gave no hint of Natural Selection although by itself the phrase is beautifully descriptive. Lyell's prudence won his *Principles* many adherents but his exposition of Lamarck's ideas involved mistranslations and a quite disproportionate accent on the inheritance of acquired characters. To some extent the misinterpretations are still with us, thanks to Huxley's uncritical acceptance of Lyell's translations. The terms evolution, transmutations, origin of species and common ancestry are not part of Lamarck's philosophy. He was concerned with the origin of natural living bodies and his observations forced on him that change was manifest everywhere – the climates, the coastlines, the fossil deposits far from the present ocean basins, extinction. Any analysis of organic diversity must admit their mutability in altered conditions. Lyell passed on this philosophy in moderate terms which apparently offended no one, 'the successive creation of species may constitute a regular part of the economy of nature . . .', but made it manifestly clear that man was not included in this natural selection. English opposition to Lamarck was mainly based on the rumour that his zoological ideas formed part of French atheism which was anathema to the Oxbridge dons.

The alternatives were special creation based on Mosaic accounts of the origin of the earth and man, or evolution of species by gradual changes through space and time by causes unknown. Lamarck certainly offered no explanation of how the changes took place but the inheritance of acquired characters is not central to his zoological concept of change. Herbert Spencer and Robert Chambers offered no explanation either except '. . . an impulse imparted to the forms of life, advancing them . . .' (*Vestiges*). Huxley in his reminiscences complained that there was not sufficient explanation of how evolution could occur prior to the *Origin* to make him alter his agnostic attitude. During all the long years of the first half of the nineteenth century only Patrick Matthew offered an explanation which was no more than an extension of his own daily work on hybridization and arboriculture:

> Is the inference then unphilosophic, that living things which are proved to have a circumstance-suiting power – a very slight change of circumstance by culture inducing a corresponding change of character – may have gradually accommodated themselves to the variations of the elements containing them, and, without new creations have presented the diverging changeable phenomena of past and present organized existence . . .
>
> There are only two probable ways of change – the above, and the still wider deviation from present occurrence – of indestructible or molecular life . . . gradually uniting and developing itself into new circumstance-suiting living aggregates, without the presence

of any mould or germ of former aggregates, but this scarcely differs from new creation, only it forms a portion of a continued scheme or system . . .

Patrick Matthew saw no reason to change these views during the rest of his life. His theory was a formal expression of rational experience. Darwin, on the other hand, chopped and changed his ideas between 1859 and 1872 so much it is now rather difficult to decide what is Darwinism and what is Lamarckism. In *The Descent of Man* (1871), Darwin asserts, 'I now admit . . . that in the earlier editions of my *Origin of Species* I perhaps attributed too much to the action of Natural Selection or survival of the fittest.'

This retreat from the early position was due to a variety of reasons but mainly Kelvin's ridiculous estimate of the age of the earth as no more than 30 million years and the criticism of Fleeming Jenkin with regard to the perpetuation of single variations. Furthermore, the shared moral and scientific attitudes of the 1820s had broken down among the parson-academics themselves. The Victorian crisis of faith had arrived. The Reverend Baden-Powell, professor of geometry at Oxford, discarded Hugh Miller's critique of the *Vestiges* as '. . . defunct Biblical geology . . .'(*Christianity without Judaism*, 1857). The Old Testament, he argued, was mere poetic imagery and dramatic allegory best suited to a nomadic Jewish society. This period has been brilliantly reviewed in a scholarly essay (*Genesis and Geology*, C. G. Gillispie, 1951).

It has been pointed out that Darwin's forerunners and contemporary supporters up to 1859 were almost exclusively Scottish. After the publication of the *Origin* the main support came from English and Continental scientists and the most devastating criticism came from Scottish scientists – Kelvin and Jenkin. From the city of Edinburgh which was so liberal and intellectually daring during its golden age when even its dogmatic doyen scientist Jameson could permit the publication of Lamarckian views in the *Edinburgh New Philosophical Journal,* there was forcibly expelled, later in the nineteenth century, a young gardener attached to the botanic garden for expressing sympathy for Darwinism. All praise to Darwin for paying the passage of this Scots exile to Calcutta, which seemed to be the only place of refuge for scientific misfits in the nineteenth century. The golden age of Edinburgh had faded by the time that Patrick Matthew had published his book, which was banned by at least one library in

Scotland and ignored by a generation of academics who were now as bigoted as any in history. It was inevitable that the icy Calvinism which had set in firm by the time the *Origin* was published would damn outright this heresy: the clerics of Oxbridge were at one with a cleric-ridden Scotland of which Buckle (*History of Civilization in England*) wrote: '. . . in no civilized country is toleration so little understood . . .'

A dominating Scots clergy, who wrote to the Home Secretary Palmerston in 1853 pleading for a day of fasting and humiliation as a counter to an outbreak of cholera, were in no mood for the kind of bombshell which exploded in 1859.

Darwin had claimed the theory of Natural Selection as his own but this gradually became transformed into a theory of evolution which seemed little more than Lamarckian evolution. It became more and more difficult to detect any subtle difference because Darwin persisted in ridiculing Erasmus Darwin and Lamarck and disclaiming any influence of these writers on his own work. This was all the more complicated by the fact that Natural Selection had nothing to do with the origin of all living things – which is what Lamarck was interested in. The word evolution is today connected more with the name of Darwin although it was introduced by Lyell and Herbert Spencer; the word is actually to be found in Lamarck's *Philosophy of Zoology* (1801). Selection is not a word which is to be found in Lamarckian writings any more than are such terms as transmutation, Natural Selection, origin of species. What Lamarck observed and wrote about was change in all things and that those changing conditions slowly alter the characters of successive generations. Lamarck assigned to his fourth law the inheritance of acquired characteristics and, unfortunately, his whole case has been judged on this one issue. (Cannon, 1955–56.)

The great debate about evolution as a fact, through the eighteenth century up until its end, was between Linnaeus and Buffon and then between Lamarck and Cuvier. Lamarck carried on Buffon's disbelief in species: 'Meanwhile we should remember that nothing of all this exists in nature; that she knows neither classes, order, genera, nor species . . . there are, in reality, only individuals . . .' But Lamarck also carried on Buffon's faint glimpse of development through time and made out a stronger case for progressive development. Cuvier stood by his belief in Special Creation and denied evolution of species. None of these four was a hybridist and yet they dominated the debate on whether evolution had occurred or not. Selection was a term which never entered this debate although by the time Patrick Matthew came to express his views hybridists had observed the failure of plants to breed true from seeds, dominance, reversion, identity of reciprocal crosses, the uniformity of the first hybrid generation and the variability of the second. It was left to Mendel to discover the ratios which then made sense of natural selection in evolutionary terms and ousted for all time the inheritance of acquired characters and blending inheritance to which Darwin retreated step by step. Instead of concentrating on breeding experiments Darwin became more and more a speculator and crowned his borrowings from other people's ideas by resurrecting Buffon's speculation about how heredity worked and called it Pangenesis. The master wriggler was prepared to wriggle almost on demand but the wrigglings involved speculations rather than hard evidence. All the same Chambers, Lyell, Darwin and Huxley converted an outraged society to an evolutionism which, however ragged and confused, changed the course of biological thought throughout the world. But today one may well ask − what is Darwinism? Even Charles Lyell found difficulty for many years in distinguishing between the Lamarckian and Darwinian view of evolution.

To the society which applauded the *Vestiges*, Darwin's half-baked theory was better than none at all since there was now no arguable alternative. Special creationism '. . . has not a single fact in nature in proof of it . . .' wrote Herbert Spencer (*The Leader*, 20 March, 1852). Stranger still, the *Vestiges*, riddled with scientific errors and vehemently rejected by every academic in the land, prepared the non-academic intelligent section of society for the reception of the *Origin* without even a hint of Natural Selection. But the clear, uncompromising enunciation of the process of Natural Selection by Patrick Matthew in 1831, based as it was on the same kind of observed facts as those in the *Origin*, passed unnoticed and even when it was briefly presented again on the scientific stage in 1860, no one more than Darwin helped to push it off into obscurity. Even so, the historical fact is, as Frederick Engels declared, '. . . the man who gave the impetus to science to investigate how exactly these variations and differences arise is no other than Darwin.' (*Anti-Duhring*, 1878.)

At least some of the reasons for the success story can be seen in retrospect: the winning over of some of the public to the notion of evolution in biology by Chambers in addition to the geological evolution of Lyell. The withering arguments against the special creationists by Herbert Spencer: '. . . let them tell us how a new species is constructed, and how it makes its appearance. Is it thrown down from the clouds? Or must we hold to the notion that it up out of the ground? Do its limbs and viscera rush from all the points of the compass? Or must we receive the old Hebrew ideas that God takes clay and moulds a new creature?' (*The Leader*, 20 March 1852.) The liberations in 1856, of the universities from control by the bishops, broke the manacles which kept the mind in chains. The state of the economy of the United Kingdom gave some credence to the survival of the fittest. Darwin's prudence in truckling to the sensitive spots in the society of his time avoided giving offence to that section of society not yet quite ready to discard a Creator. The long-winded debate with its mass of scientific observations couched in moderate terms gave to the concept of evolution a respectability it lacked before. This all goes to show that, at a stroke, society can not bear too much reality. Certainly not that stark reality, brief though adequate, which Patrick Matthew set out by the time the *Beagle* pitched around in Tor Bay before setting sail for a voyage round the world.

6

The State of the Species
Debate in 1836

Does organized existence, and perhaps all material existence, consist of one Proteus principle of life capable of gradual circumstance-suited modifications and aggregations, without bound under the solvent or motion-giving principle, heat or light?

(*Appendix* to *Naval Timber and Arboriculture,* Patrick Matthew, 1831)

The apparent universality of DNA as the hereditary material and the universality of the genetic code from bacteria to man indicate a common origin of all living things.

(H. H. Smith, 1974)

Attempts have been made to portray the bewildering scientific activity which went on in France from the 1790s and throughout the following decades (Appel, 1987: Corsi, 1988). It was a period of intense research in all the sciences which produced a multitude of theories and counter-theories. Most scientists engaged in political manoeuvrings to gain funds or positions in the scientific institutions or prevented competitors gaining favours. Public quarrels among the leading characters was the norm and many stooped to slander and misrepresentation of scientific ideas. Even so, a sound approach to the study of earth history was established. Not only were the scientific ideas in many cases exotic but the scientists themselves had exotic names, for example this: Jean-Baptist-Julien d'Omalius d'Halloy! All this hectic activity ensued without any religious intervention because the Revolution of 1789 had abolished religion. Most scientists were not under any religious constraints. There was, however, one great disagreement – Lamarck the atheist and Cuvier the religious hypocrite. In spite of this these two scientists laid the basis of evolution and so it will be these two characters who will be mainly

involved in this study. In England, during all this time, this Seditious
Acts ensured that Holy Writ would be rigidly adhered to and that all
scientific conclusions would be required to square with Holy Writ. Such
was the position obtaining at Oxbridge Universities where all the lecturers
were communicants of the Church of England. In Scotland there were
the old links to France and intellectual attitudes were more liberal. For
this reason French scientific ideas took root earlier in Edinburgh than
in England.

During the decade 1826–1836 it is clear that Lamarckism was invading
England and influencing English naturalists. From Patrick Matthew's
Appendix (1831) and Charles Lyell's volume 2 of the *Principles of Geology*
(1832) to Edward Blyth's essays (1835–37) was quite a short time but it
was ten years since the anonymous essay of 1826 which has been attributed
to Robert Grant. This essay appeared in the *Edinburgh New Philosophical
Journal* whose editor was Professor Jameson. The editor was not a
mutationist yet this essay lauds the teaching of Lamarck; this must be the
first introduction of Lamarckism to an English audience, We may use
these authors as representatives of two diametrically opposed philosophical
attitudes to evolution and to the species debate by 1836 when Darwin
returned from the voyage.

Noah's Flood had been rejected in 1826 by the Scottish divine John
Fleming and in 1830 by the Reverend Adam Sedgwick. Holy Writ was
being undermined by the clerics themselves. In London in the 1830s
there were fierce debates between the radicals under the leadership of
Robert Grant and the conservatives who opposed mutation of species as
well as any attempt to alleviate the human situation. French science had
now invaded England; the previous three decades in England were
characterized by a chilly silence caused by fear of the Seditious Acts. The
Reform Bill had helped to liberalize the political situation but more rights
were being demanded by sections of the rising middle class in the course
of which Lamarckism became linked to democracy (Desmond, 1989).
The debate which had gone on in Paris between Lamarck and Cuvier
now spread to England; Lamarck stood for change and mutation of species
Cuvier stood for the opposite.

Cuvier usually only drew conclusions on the evidence. He found that
none of the fossil mammals he studied had living analogues. He concluded
that in each epoch new species were created miraculously. But Cuvier
was also constrained by his religious dogma. So much so that he was

prepared to offer as evidence that species did not mutate the 4,000-year-old mummified animals St Hilaire brought back to Paris from the tombs of Egypt; these mummified animals were identical to their present-day descendants. This was ridiculous because 4,000 years was nothing in geological terms.

Lamarck, on the other hand, had been put in charge of the Mollusc Collection in the Paris Museum which housed both modern and fossil molluscs. After careful examination he found that many of the living mussels and other marine molluscs had analogues among fossil species. The only conclusion was that throughout time species had undergone change perhaps slow and gradual.

English naturalists, dominated by clerics, accepted Cuvier's catastrophism which involved a series of massive destruction of plants and animals caused by upheavals of the earth's crust. After each catastrophe new animals appeared which were believed to have been created miraculously. There was no doubting that catastrophes had occurred but the debate now centred on whether those animals and plants which had survived the catastrophe slowly mutated over the millions of years between the great upheavals. There was a further problem: if species mutate how do they mutate?

The Seditious Acts were still in force in the 1820s but gradually being faded out. These Acts were more concerned with controlling mass meetings rather than individuals; for this reason any meeting with more than three people was obliged to apply for a government licence. Furthermore, any scientific meeting was obliged not to include any reference to religious or political ideas. Unwittingly, this stricture had a beneficial effect in excluding from scientific communications any irrelevant ideas. (Weindling, 1980).

Patrick Matthew, who also visited Paris on several occasions, went straight to the point: 'We are led therefore to admit, either of a repeated miraculous creation, or a power of change . . . The derangement and changes in organized existence . . . tend strongly to heighten the probability of the latter theory.' (*Appendix.*)

Blyth, on the other hand, bluntly stated that he was not concerned about the evidence supporting a view such as Matthew expressed. His attitude to the problem involved a predetermined religious bias which could never countenance mutation of species: 'May not, then, a large proportion of what was considered species have descended from a common ancestor? I would briefly despatch this interrogatory as able writers have often taken the subject in hand. It is, moreover, foreign to the professed object of this paper.' (1837.) That is a firm goodbye to mutation.

Who were these able writers who had 'taken the subject in hand' prior to 1835? The most important and influential of these writers was Sir Charles Lyell to whose second volume of the *Principles of Geology* Blyth refers his readers. Lyell had unwittingly introduced to English readers the ideas Lamarck had been teaching since 1801. Lyell was a traveller to France many times and certainly met Cuvier and St Hilaire and had read Lamarck's textbook and mistranslated several passages which after 30 years he realized was an injustice. Lyell, like Blyth, was not concerned with the evidence assembled by Lamarck because he considered the whole theory contradicted Christian theology. This was the dominant attitude among the parson-naturalists at Oxbridge. Holy Writ had been protected from all adverse criticism by the Seditious Acts and no academic dared to oppose them. Could it be that the devout Blyth was as much horror-struck by Lamarckian ideas as Lyell was when he read them in *Principles of Geology*? Lamarckian ideas were part of French science which was dubbed atheistic and was never accepted by Blyth.

Blyth, however, was prepared to accept his own evidence that, 'There are many phenomena which tend . . . to favour the supposition . . . [that] I have termed the localizing principle, which must occasion . . . what is called "breeding in and in" . . .' To further establish his opinion that species do not mutate he writes, 'It is a general law of nature for all creatures to propagate the like of themselves; and this extends even to the most trivial minutiae.' Matthew, of course, had to have a 'law' for this: 'a circumstance-adaptive law'. 'From the unremitting operation of this law acting in concert with the tendency which the progeny have to take the more particular qualities of the parents, together with the connected sexual system in vegetables, and instinctive limitation to its kind in animals, a considerable uniformity of figure, colour and character, is induced, constituting species; the breed gradually acquiring the very best possible adaptation of these to its condition which it is susceptible of, and then alteration of circumstance occur, thus changing in character to suit these as far as its nature is susceptible of change.' A bit concentrated but there is the localizing factor and its counterpart the ability to change and hence the mutation of species.

Although Blyth introduced the term 'localizing principle' it was certainly not a new observation but it became the main plank of his opposition to the mutation of species. Blyth was a scientist in the making and it was his aim to support his intellectual opposition to mutationism rather than just defer to Holy Writ. Into this essay, entitled a classification of varieties, he noted down all the observations he had made of many aspects of nature which, to his satisfaction, proved that species do not mutate but on the contrary species make every effort to remain as perfect specimens on the basis that the struggle for existence pushed the weakest to the wall. But about all those fossils that Cuvier and others had dug up from ancient geological deposits Blyth had nothing to say.

So far as the 'localizing principle' is concerned Patrick Matthew makes it the first point in Note B of the *Appendix*. For Matthew it was not just a principle but a 'law universal in nature'. The intellectuals of the Scottish Enlightenment always used the term 'law' for any continuous process in nature. Matthew continues, 'This law sustains the lion in his strength, the hare in its swiftness, and the fox in its wiles.' These observations were as old as the hills, so why should Blyth introduce his 'localizing principle' to his essay and stress its overriding importance? This was direct evidence against mutation of species. Matthew on the other hand considered that there are periods when species appear stable and he pointed out that the present day species had existed for 40 centuries. This was clearly a reference to Cuvier who pronounced that the mummies of animals in the Egyptian tombs were identical to those living at the present time. But that was only one aspect of the species problem. Matthew goes on to say that geologists have dug up species but they are quite different from those animals alive today. So how can that be explained? There were but these alternatives – either miraculous creation or a power of change. All the evidence Matthew argues supports 'the probability of the latter'. The same alternatives came up in 1847 when Whewell in his *History of the Inductive Sciences* stated '. . . either the transmutation of species or else believe in many successive acts of creation.' The Oxbridge naturalists were solidly in favour of 'acts of creation'.

If the Creator made the species who made the varieties in the wild? Blyth never faced up to this problem. He was a keen observer but not a breeder but he had associated enough with breeders to understand that the essential for success was to select very carefully.

Only the bare word 'selection' appears in his essay in relation to breeding and this is obviously artificial selection. Although he was aware that breeders were selecting to improve or alter domestic breeds he was not prepared to deduce that in the wild there was a slower but similar process, Natural Selection, at work. Patrick Matthew on the other hand, a hybridist but unfettered by Holy Writ, was supremely confident that the natural process of selection was the means whereby species and varieties evolved in the wild over immense ages in the history of the planet.

By 1836 and indeed for another two decades the debate about mutation got stuck in the mould of science against religion. For the returning Darwin nothing had changed since those days ten years before when Grant introduced him to Lamarckism. Among the academic participants most agreed with Lyell and later Blyth; the few other naturalists kept their peace. A change in the interpretation of geology had taken place but Darwin had read Lyell's *Principles* during the voyage. The new world of Uniformitarianism would not disconcert Darwin. The unified background of the academic naturalists included religious and moral elements as well as scientific. It was possible to accept all the latest scientific information and still remain a devout Christian; Asa Gray, a few decades later, could accept Natural Selection and still remain devout. But cracks had already appeared in this strong academic edifice. In 1823 William Buckland received the Copley Medal from the Royal Society for proving that the Flood had occurred but within seven years Sedgwick, as President of the Geological Society, dismissed Noah's Flood and it never came back! Sedgwick had been induced to visit the Massif Central in France and asked to explain how gentle rain falling for 40 days and nights could have produced that landscape of extinct volcanoes, valleys and streams.

Even the Scottish divine John Fleming ruled out the Noachian Flood as the primary geological agency His rejection of the Flood as the primary geological agency was based on his observations that the biblical account of gentle rain falling for 40 days and nights could not possibly account for the rushing torrents, valleys and mountains of the real world. Later on it became harder to share the common ground because more evidence about geology and fossils came pouring in from all over the world. Students who had been to Paris came flooding back with Lamarckian ideas. Robert Grant had been installed in University College London, and he and the radicals kept the debate running for the next decades. There was still no involvement of Natural Selection in the great London debate. Matthew's 'natural process of selection' went unnoticed perhaps because none of the leading naturalists were breeders. Only the breeders were aware of selection because the nature of breeding required the proper selection of plants or animals for the success of the artificially selected hybrid. Although artificial selection had been used for centuries, by the eighteenth century selection gained centre place in breeding circles. So those radicals who were convinced evolutionists and Lamarckians had no idea how new species evolved. Natural Selection came into the debate in 1859 with the publication of *The Origin of the Species*. Curiously the introducer had dabbled in breeding but cannot be considered as a professional breeder. Charles Darwin was prescient enough to seek out the work of the breeders and kept in close contact from 1838 to the end of his days.

So when Edward Blyth came on the scene he does not seem to have come in contact with the radicals. If he did he chose to ignore them and stuck to his religious beliefs and Lyell's condemnation of Lamarckism. It is possible, of course, that those 'able writers' to which Blyth refers were the opponents of Grant and his radical supporters. To be a radical in London in the 1830s was about as dangerous as advocating communism in the 1930s; both periods of high unemployment and distressing condition of the labouring classes. For a detailed study of the 1830s when Lamarckism and reformism were used by Grant and the radical intellectuals and the artisan classes for political purposes one should consult the essays of Desmond (1984, 1987, 1989).

However, Blyth had read widely and observed nature in great detail and was concerned with varieties rather than species. It was for this reason he came to publish his essays on varieties in a newly started journal, *Magazine of Natural History* in 1835–37. It is to these essays that Eiseley (1959) has drawn attention because he considered that they had a great influence on Darwin on his return to England.

Before we proceed to discuss what is in these essays we should consider some misconceptions about the educated state Darwin was in prior to his voyage. Historians sometimes make out that Charles Darwin was an innocent abroad before embarking on the voyage. Those historians of science forget that Darwin had two years in Edinburgh under the care of a well travelled and experienced naturalist in Robert Grant of Edinburgh University. It was Grant who introduced the young Darwin to study the fauna of the Firth of Forth and encouraged him to give short communications to the Pliny Society. (Desmond, 1984.) Furthermore, he would have had a good grounding in Lamarckism because Grant had returned from Paris full of what was being debated there. Darwin had observed cilia on the larvae of a species of *Flustra* and, to check whether the French had observed this, Grant pushed young Darwin to study Lamarck's system of invertebrate animals. (Desmond and Moore, 1991.) If Darwin carried out this instruction it surely would not have been such a bore as Darwin tells us everything was at Edinburgh. He would find the information that would be required in Lamarck's *Animaux sans Vertèbres*. He later demonstrated his discovery to the Plinian Society. If he had also read through Chapter 8 'Natural Order of Animals' of the *Philosophie Zoologique* where he would have found the general classification of the known animals from the invertebrates onwards to the mammals. He would even have come across the class of *Cirrhipedes* with which later on in his life he was to spend seven years as a taxonomist. Why so long on invertebrates? Did that experience with invertebrates with Robert Grant condition him in later life? The vertebrates he did work with – domestic pigeons – I have suggested might have been under Blyth's influence. During those last seven years the intelligent rising middle class was being introduced to the concept of evolution by the several editions of *The Vestiges of the Natural History of Creation*. About that subject Darwin had not yet published one word or produced privately any addition to his 1844 essay. In spite of Grant's kindness, Darwin in his autobiography states he could not remember how he met him.

Darwin also attended courses in geology and would have been instructed by Jameson himself. As a member of Jameson's course he was able to spend much time in the magnificent museum. In later life Darwin kept quiet about all this and let it be known that all the lectures at Edinburgh were boring and that he learnt nothing. Taking this at face value historians could only come to the conclusion that Darwin's time at university was a complete waste of time. Here is his statement in the autobiography: 'During the three years which I spent at Cambridge my time was wasted, as far as academical studies are concerned, as completely as at Edinburgh and at school.'

The facts are that at Cambridge he collected beetles and went on botanical trips with Henslow, the Professor of Botany. He also went on a geology expedition with Sedgwick, the Professor of Geology. Darwin found Sedgwick's lectures more interesting than Jameson's at Edinburgh although in his autobiography he wrote: '. . . but I was so sickened with lectures at Edinburgh that I did not even attend Sedgwick's eloquent and interesting lectures.' Henslow also persuaded him to study geology. His cousin Darwin Fox introduced him to entomology. It was nigh on personal tuition at a time when Sedgwick and Murchison were making great strides in identifying the geological strata. And yet, in spite of all this experience and kindness, Darwin maintained that he learned nothing and the whole of university life was a bore. Yet on 6 October 1858 he had written to Lubbock, after the 'delicate arrangement', *Floreat Entomologia!* – to which toast at Cambridge I have drunk many a glass of wine.' That does not sound like a man who had a boring academic time at Cambridge. He had also forgotten that, in the preface to the 1845 edition of the *Journal of Searches*, he had written, '. . . but I must here be allowed to return my most sincere thanks to the Reverend Professor Henslow, who, when I was an undergraduate at Cambridge, was one chief means of giving me a taste for natural history.'

If he had learned nothing at university why was he recommended by the Professor of Botany at Cambridge as naturalist for the voyage of the *Beagle*? For the rest of his life Darwin was bent on telling the world that he owed nothing to his predecessors. Darwin's autobiography is about as misleading as that of Rudyard Kipling.

It is not quite accurate to say that Darwin was appointed as official naturalist to the *Beagle*. Originally, the official naturalist was Dr Robert McCormick who fell out with Captain Fitzroy early in the voyage and was sent home. Even so, from the very first landing Darwin behaved as if he were the official naturalist and not just a companion to Captain Fitzroy with whom, it would seem, he had nothing in common. Captain Fitzroy had intimated to the Admiralty that although he wished to have a well-bred gentleman as his companion on the *Beagle*, it would be an advantage if he were interested in natural history. It was made clear that there would be ample opportunity to pursue such interests. Professor Henslow was well aware of Darwin's aptitude for specimen collecting and who was also well tutored in botany, zoology and entomology; this was the reason for recommending his bright pupil. At Cambridge Darwin was advised by Professor Henslow to combine the study of botany with Lyell's geology. Darwin also set off with one volume of the first edition of Charles Lyell's *Principles of Geology*. As far as Darwin was concerned he was not on the *Beagle* just for the ride. The way he made exhaustive notes on all he saw and the numerous specimens he carefully collected demonstrated he was already a trained scientist which rather contradicts his own statements that he learned nothing at university.

Professor Henslow wrote to Darwin on 24 August 1831, 'I have been asked by Peacock, who will read and forward this to you from London, to recommend him a Naturalist as companion to Captain Fitzroy, employed by the Government to survey the southern extremity of America. I have stated that I consider you to be the best qualified person I know of who is likely to undertake such a situation. I state this not in the supposition of your being a finished naturalist, but as amply qualified for collecting, observing, and noting anything worthy to be noted in Natural History.'

Darwin's indifference to people who aided him can be seen from the beginning of his writings in the post-*Beagle* period. The preface to the 1839 edition of the *Journal of Researches* contained no acknowledgement of those who helped him collect specimens on the *Beagle*. When Captain Fitzroy received his copy he immediately sent off a very stiff reprimand to Darwin. The effect of this can be seen in the preface to the 1845 edition: 'As I feel that the opportunities which I enjoyed of studying the Natural History of the different countries we visited have been wholly due to Captain Fitzroy, I hope I may here be permitted to repeat my expression of gratitude to him; and to add that, during the five years we were together, I received from him the most cordial friendship and steady assistance. Both to Captain Fitzroy and to all the Officers of the *Beagle* I shall feel most thankful for the undeviating kindness with which I was treated during our long voyage.'

By the time Darwin returned home he had studied the first volume of Lyell's *Principles*. He would not have found himself in a strange world of Uniformitarianism. The geological theory to which most naturalists adhered before Darwin set out in 1831 was Catastrophism. Lyell had now shown that what was going on in the inorganic world today was similar to what went on in ages past. Lyell's rejection of the organic world and mutation of species was based on the fact that new species could not be demonstrated arriving today. That the inorganic world had evolved seemed quite evident to those who accepted Lyell's new system but they jibbed against evolution in the organic world and, as was being argued in Paris, man himself had evolved from lower animals. Lyell who had spent some time in Paris himself had returned to England and, horrified by the bleak materialism of Lamarck introduced his condemnation in volume 2 of his *Principles*. For example: man was just a class of mammal! Thus French science was introduced to an English audience in a manner quite different to that advocated in 1826 by Robert Grant. Grant, now the Professor of Zoology in London, together with his radical followers continued to voice their admiration for Lamarck. (Desmond, 1989). Darwin certainly did not ally himself with the radicals although he was developing a radical theory himself.

There have been several theories attempting to explain why Darwin took so long to publish his theory of Natural Selection. One clear fact is he took seven years away from the subject and another is that he was not ready. To get a clearer picture of this problem one has to take the attitude of the contextual historian and examine the social and political conditions obtaining in England right up to 1859.

One aspect of life in London in the 1840s which could have disturbed the very comfortably well-off country gentleman was the Chartist Movement (Wilson, A., 1970). Some sections of the rising middle class together with the labouring classes were bent on gaining more franchise and a better quality of life. In contradistinction to Darwin, Patrick Matthew was concerned, as demonstrated in the *Appendix,* with Natural Selection in the world of plants and animals but also with man as a social animal. The law of entail he considered an outrage on the universal law of Natural Selection. Matthew was well to do and enjoyed a financially comfortable life. His concern for the less better off classes forced him to engage in politics and the Chartist Movement suited his ambitions. This, then, is perhaps an appropriate time to introduce Patrick Matthew to this particular discussion. As we have previously noted news of the 1830 French Revolution which removed Charles X from the throne of France arrived when Matthew had just finished writing the *Appendix*. He now immediately decided that his theoretical work must give way to practical politics. He was involved in the Chartist Movement all through the 1830s. He became an elected representative for his area in Scotland for the Great Convention in London in 1839. However, the leader of the Movement by this time was an Irishman Feargus O'Connor. He was something of a firebrand and, nurtured in Irish revolutionary traditions, was now urging the members to take to the barricades. Patrick Matthew, in spite of his previous lauding of war, withdrew from the Movement as he and his constituents judged O'Connor's tactics unwise (Wilson,

1970). The government did not play around with the Chartists: their meetings were broken up, masses arrested, some killed, imprisoned or transported. The failure of the Movement was due to the immaturity of the labouring classes; confusion and weakness of the various factions became confounded by their different interests and aims (Gamage, 1894). Struggles, however, continued throughout the 1840s including the agitation against the hated Corn Laws. Matthew, as an heir to the Free Trade policy of Adam Smith, joined in the protests of the Anti-Corn Law League. At the end of the 1840s there was beginning a long spell of trade expansion and prosperity; enough prosperity to enable the owning class to buy off violent labouring-class demands. By 1858 Marx wrote, '. . . the English proletariat is becoming more and more bourgeois.' The year 1859 was a reasonably stable political time for publishing the *Origin*. Back in Scotland Matthew had been planning his own solution to the mass unemployment prior to the break up of the Chartist Movement. That Movement was in no position to solve unemployment and in 1839 Matthew published *Emigration Fields*. Critics usually criticize Matthew for not continuing the debate on speciation. These critics forget that the *Appendix* had a political as well as a biological aspect to it. Matthew now devoted his spare time to politics. This aspect of Matthew's life is discussed elsewhere.

Darwin now settled in London was soon interested in accumulating facts about species and varieties in addition to his other work at the Geology Society. Eiseley (1959) suggests that soon after his return to England Darwin came across Blyth's essays. Darwin certainly met breeders who may have directed his attention to those essays in a magazine edited by Julius Loudon. This same Loudon had reviewed Matthew's *Naval Timber* in 1832 and he made a point of including in the review what was in the appendix.

So far as the *Origin* is concerned there are references to other aspects of Blyth's work but no mention of these essays of 1835–37. Although Eiseley has been much criticized, for his study of Blyth and Schwartz (1974) is particularly scathing, there is a great deal of evidence in favour of Eiseley's contention. Schwartz (1974) takes Darwin's statement of the influence of Malthus at face value which is always unwise; Darwin frequently gave different statements to different people. It was after the *Origin* was published that the Malthus influence appears. This has been accepted as the real state of affairs in spite of his close friend Joseph

Hooker who, in 1863, specifically wrote him to ask if he had ever read
Malthus's miserable book. Hooker had checked the proofs of the *Origin*
and had read it several times because it was the most difficult book he
had ever read. He never got the impression that Malthus had any influence
on Darwin and there is no evidence this subject cropped up again.
Schwartz feels confident that Blyth's essays played no part in Darwin's
thinking and quotes De Beer (1960): 'Bearing in mind that Darwin was
after one thing: how species became modified, it may be asked what
Darwin's debt to Blyth was? So far as the construction of his theory is
concerned is probably nothing at all.' How De Beer can make such a
statement and, what is worse, have it believed is baffling. The first two
chapters of the *Origin* are concerned with varieties under domestic
conditions and in the wild. Anyone seeking information on varieties
could hardly avoid finding some information in these essays, with similar
titles, published in recent numbers of a top journal.

The facts are that the personal copy of the *Magazine of Natural History*
containing the 1835–37 essays have been found with comments made
by Darwin. The question was when did Darwin read them? The question
should be what did he get out of them? Young (1992) points out that
prior to 1844, '. . . variability was thought to be comparatively rare and
unimportant, and not to affect the essential character of a species.' Young,
then, notes that Darwin is in agreement with this in his 1844 essay. There
are several comments one can make about Young's idea of the history
of varieties prior to 1844. Firstly, it would appear that Young has not
read Blyth's seminal essays on varieties (1835–37) or realized he had
classified them. The other point is the unreliability, once again, of the
Darwin notebooks and early essays as prototypes for the *Origin* because
the first two chapters in the *Origin* discuss varieties. If one reads Blyth's
essays and then the two chapters in the *Origin* one can appreciate where
Darwin gained his ideas. In Young's *History of Evolution* there is no place
for Blyth, Robert Grant or Patrick Matthew!

All the magical words which were to be part of Darwin's life are in
these essays: instinct, select, varieties, sexual selection, hybridization,
design, radiation, moulting and double moulting, isolation, geographic
isolation, divergence and ramification, diversity and structural change,
colour changes, concealment, balance of nature, struggle for existence,
descent from a common ancestor and even domestic pigeons!

Any naturalist seeking information on species and varieties would receive a good grounding from Blyth's essays and the second volume of Lyell's *Principles*. Blyth refers his readers to this volume. Darwin had received the second volume by 1836. All the subjects discussed in the *Origin* are contained in these two references. Few science historians have heard of Blyth's essays and so fall back on Malthus as the inspirer. Volume 2 of the *Principles* gave a detailed account of Lamarck's writings and Lyell in later life pointed out that what he had written in 1832 was being confirmed by Darwin. The tragedy is that no one seems to have taken any notice.

The chapters in the *Origin* discuss subjects which were discussed by Lyell (geology and Lamarckism; key points noted by Lyell – struggle for existence, descent from common ancestor, evolving species), Blyth (varieties, instincts, hybrids, struggle for existence, descent from a common ancestor, geographical distribution) and Matthew (Natural Selection, divergence, catastrophes, struggle for existence, steady state, descent from a common ancestor, human involvement and political consequences of Natural Selection). Here are the chapters of the *Origin*: Variation (2 chapters), Struggle for existence, Natural Selection, Laws of variation, Difficulties of theory, Instinct, Hybridism, Imperfection of the geological record, Geological succession of organic beings, Geographical distribution, Mutual affinities of organic beings, Recapitulation.

That Darwin collected a vast amount of data from the published work of other naturalists and produced a strong body of evidence in favour of ideas expressed by these three naturalists is not in dispute. The dispute is about Darwin's claim to owe nothing to his predecessors. Lyell, himself, wrote in the later editions of his *Principles* that what Lamarck had written in the early part of the nineteenth century Darwin was now confirming. Confirming was hardly the correct word because Darwin did not introduce any new information establishing the fact of evolution. Natural Selection, on Darwin's own admission, was picked up from the breeders and when the *Origin* was published the term had a lukewarm reception. Edward Blyth had presented, in his essays, most of the concepts that appeared in the *Origin*.

In the *Origin* Darwin got around to the classification of varieties, which I found more difficult to understand than that of Blyth, but in chapter 13 we come across this: 'We can understand, on these views, the very important distinction between affinities and analogical or adaptive resemblances. Lamarck first called attention to this distinction.' It was noted elsewhere that Darwin had told Lyell that he had not got one fact or idea from Lamarck!

In discussing the same subject Blyth writes: 'Every vertebrate animal is, therefore, allied to every other vertebrate animal by what, to specify numbers, may be expressed as three degrees of affinity . . .' And later on: 'The Ornithorynchus, among mammifers, approximates very remarkably towards birds, but it exhibits less analogy with them.'

In *The Descent of Man* (1871) Darwin introduced the ornithorynchus: 'Breaks occur in all parts of the series, some being wide, sharp and defined, others less so in various degrees; so between the Orang and Lemuridae – between the elephant and in a more striking manner between the Ornithorynchus or echidna and other mammals.'

It should be pointed out at this stage that the ornithorhyncus and echidna were discovered in Australia at the end of the eighteenth century. Lamarck was aware that no link had been found between birds and mammals until these species had been discovered. He judged them to be a special class – the monotremes – for the following reasons: they were not mammals because they had no mammae although they were quadrupeds; they were not birds because their lungs were not pierced through and their bodies were covered with hair, and they had no limbs shaped as wings; they were not reptiles because their two ventricle hearts separated them from this category. Lamarck discussed this subject in the chapter 'Degradation of Organization.' So, it would seem that Blyth noticed the importance of the nature of these species and later on Darwin in the *Origin* and *The Descent of Man!*

On this occasion there is no reference to Blyth because the only reference would be the 1835–37 essays or Lamarck. In other instances where these essays are the source Darwin writes, 'Mr Blyth informs me . . .' There are 42 references to Blyth in *The Descent of Man* but not one to these essays. Blyth spends a long time on bird plumage and so does Darwin in the second edition of *The Descent of Man* (1874). Here is a statement from the second edition: '. . . coloured pipits (anthus) have a double, whilst others have only a single annual moult.' The reference given is Blyth, Ibis 1867. Here is Blyth in the 1835 essay: '. . . but, there are various other tribes (as the wagtails and pipits, Motacillinae, and most of the aquatic races) which regularly undergo another general moulting in the spring.' Pipits are rare visitors to this country but recently one bird was sighted near Felixstowe. It was only the third time Blyth's pipit has been reliably sighted in England. A note in a national newspaper recorded what happened: 'As the scores of bird-lovers marvelled at the sighting, their excitement turned to horror as a kestrel swooped down and dived on the unsuspecting pipit. The bird of prey snatched it up in its claws and flew off.'

Edward Blyth, had he observed this raw side of nature, would have added this event to his stores of observations. The unsuspecting bird was snatched by a kestrel so Blyth would have interpreted this event, as he had written it precisely in his essays, as proof that any aspect out of ordinary would be dealt with as a means of stabilizing the species. Blyth drew attention to the bird with abnormal plumage or any creature not able to look after itself would 'go to the wall'. This, Blyth maintained, was the localizing principle which maintained the stability of the species. Blyth had personally seen a falcon swoop down on an unsuspecting bird. Darwin turned this reasoning around so that any favourable change promoted a gradual change in the species. Lamarck was convinced that the inheritance of minute variations was the way nature worked towards a gradual and imperceptible development. It was when Lamarck tried to explain the causes of evolution that he became involved with the inheritance of acquired characteristics. It should be realized that this subject occupies a small part of *Philosophie Zoologique*. The chapter headed 'Influence of the Environment', in which this speculation is discussed, is only 20 pages long in a book of 400 pages.

It would seem that these early essays of Blyth were an everlasting embarrassment to Darwin and had to be ignored at all costs. Blyth had translated Cuvier's seminal work *La Regne Animale* so, occasionally, Darwin will give a reference to Blyth's translation of that work. Poor Blyth had died by the time the second edition of *The Descent of Man* was published. All his days Blyth had sent Darwin everything he observed; nothing was thrown away and Darwin never extended any kindness to Blyth.

Blyth discusses the various means of concealment. He pays quite a lot of attention to concealment by change of colour: 'Grouse are brown heather, black game are peat black and single.' Darwin discusses the same subject: 'Hence I can see no reason to doubt that natural selection might be most effective in giving the proper colour to each kind of grouse and in keeping that colour, once acquired, true and constant.' Once acquired? That sounds like inheritance of acquired characteristics.

Poor Blyth sums up: 'I think it is not too much to infer, that the changes of colour in many arctic animals were intended by Providence for the double role of preserving their bodily heat and of enabling them to elude the observations of their enemies.'

There was nothing new in what Blyth and Darwin spent so much time on for Matthew had it covered: 'This principle is in constant action, it regulates the colour, the figure, the capacities, and instincts; those individuals of each species, whose colour and covering are best suited to concealment or protection from enemies, of defence from vicissitude and inclemencies of weather . . . those only come forward to maturity from the strict ordeal by which Nature tests their adaptation to her standard of perfection and fitness to continue their kind by reproduction.'

Brief? Perhaps Darwin and Blyth were too prolix.

By substituting Natural Selection for: Supreme Omnipotence, Ever-glorious Being, Him, Awful Being, Great First Cause, Providence, All-wise Creator, Darwin could, like Marx standing Hegelian Philosophy on its feet, stand Blyth's observations into a correct posture. Darwin must have been one of the few people at that time to realize the worth of these essays. All praise to Darwin for his prescience.

Schwartz (1974) does not seem to be aware how devious a character Darwin was. Just because Blyth's name does not appear in the first two chapters of the *Origin* does not mean that the influence of Blyth was nil. Darwin was very careful with his sources. As will be shown later the very first sentence of the *Origin* was lifted from the 1835 essay.

If Darwin was bent on absorbing all the latest data on varieties what better starting point than these essays in the *Magazine of Natural History*? And why not? The problem is that so many Darwin enthusiasts wish to establish that all the biology in the *Origin* was thought up by himself; since Darwin gave very few of his sources a good case could be made that it was all his own work. He did admit that from the beginning he had read widely in agricultural and horticultural journals but still made out that he owed nothing to his predecessors.

If we doubt that Blyth had any influence on Darwin is it a coincidence, then, that the very first sentence of the *Origin* runs as follows: 'When we look to the individuals of the same variety or sub-variety of our older cultivated plants and animals, one of the first points which strikes us is, that they generally differ more from each other than do the individuals of any one species or variety in a state of nature.' Blyth's essay begins with a classification of varieties – simple, acquired, breeds and true. In the first paragraph of his discussion of simple varieties is this sentence: 'These simple variations occur both in wild and in domesticated animals, but are much more frequent in the latter, and are commonly observed in all breeds and true varieties.' This observation was clearly well established years before because Matthew had this to say on the subject in *Naval Timber and Arboriculture* (1831): 'Man's interference, by preventing this natural process of selection among plants, independent of the wider range of circumstance to which he introduces them, has increased the difference in varieties particularly in the more domesticated kinds.' And yet, Darwin in his *Historical Sketch* stated Matthew's book was on a 'different subject'!

There then follows in both essays discussions on breeds, plumage of birds (particularly grouse and domestic pigeons), albinos, variations brought about by confinement, foodstuffs including those foods, like madder, that cause colour changes. Other colour changes are introduced all to explain concealment or responses to temperature changes.

Blyth continues with observations which readers of the *Origin* will recognize: 'Taking a series of species, we have every grade of diversity, from the obviously distinct Japanese Peafowl to the mealy linnet.' 'Of course, all the various facts lead us to the important consideration of, what is a species?' 'The bearings of this law [i.e. the ability to migrate and return] on the geographical distribution of species do not appear to have been sufficiently taken into consideration.' 'Breeds are my third class of varieties, and though these may possibly be some times formed by accidental isolation in a state of nature, yet they are, for the most part, artificially brought about by the direct agency of man.'

The big debate on geographic isolation in relation to speciation came later with Darwin and Moritz Wagner in constant disagreement. Blyth gives no reference and so it is impossible to detect his sources, but it is probable that it was the essay by Von Buch published in 1825. It was taken up by Darwin in his notebooks of 1842 and 1844. It is obvious that this observation had been made long before Blyth came to study it. Only gradually did naturalists come to realize that mountains, rivers and seas would separate animals and plants and so inhibit variety formation.

This finally led to recognizing the relation of geographic isolation to species formation.

Blyth discusses domestic pigeons in these essays so much one wonders if they had a subliminal effect on Darwin and some years later, when well established at Downe, he set about breeding domestic pigeons and joined two pigeon fancier clubs. Why domestic pigeons? Why not chickens, rabbits, mice?

Blyth introduces 'the struggle for existence' which was probably lifted from volume 2 of Lyell's *Principles* but the phrase goes back to Lamarck. In support of his anti-mutationism Blyth interprets any deviation from the norm, any weakness and any slight difference in colour as leading to the demise of those animals but those that are strong, have correct plumage survive and so maintain the species: '. . . and which, consequently, in the struggle for existence, was the best able to maintain his ground, and defend himself from every enemy.'

Blyth chose to stress only one aspect of the species problem; Matthew referred to this aspect as species being 'steady' during long periods in any epoch. Darwin stressed the other side of the coin: 'Natural selection can act only by the preservation and accumulation of infinitesimal, small, inherited modifications, each profitable to the preserved being . . . I have called this principle, by which each slight variation, if useful, by the term natural selection, in order to mark its relation to man's power of selection.' It seems clear that Darwin's continual reference to the significance of changes in an animal which were favourable was based on Lamarck's original concept of the mutability of species in contrast to Cuvier's fixity of the species. The *Origin* owed a great deal to Lamarck's *Philosophie Zoologique*. Matthew added this aspect as well: '. . . a power of change, under a change of circumstances, to belong to organized existence . . . affording us proof of the plastic quality of superior life.' Early on in the *Origin,* when he is discussing varieties, Darwin states a similar view: 'The whole organization seems to have become plastic, and tends to depart in some small degree from that of the parental type.'

Darwin would have had no difficulty in turning this sentence into Natural Selection terms: 'the same laws, therefore, which was intended by Providence to keep up the typical qualities of a species, can be easily converted by man into a means of raising different varieties.'

Blyth describes how, by constant selection, a breed may be formed: '. . . and only those in which the same peculiarity is most apparent, be selected to breed from, the next generation will possess it in a still more remarkable degree . . . till at length, the variety I designate a breed, is formed . . . which may be very unlike the original type.' (Note the title of Wallace's 1858 paper: 'On the tendencies of varieties to depart indefinitely from the original type'.)

Many years later Darwin wrote in the *Origin*, 'Breeds have improved over the years. The key is man's power of accumulative selection, nature gives successive variations; man adds them up in certain directions useful to him.' Then in a few pages further on: 'The whole organization seems to have become plastic, and tends to depart in some small degree from that of the parent type.'

Blyth deals with instincts but has little to offer on this subject. Although Darwin spends a whole chapter on instinct he found it difficult to involve Natural Selection. Blyth was of the opinion that instincts were adapted to the mode of life of animals. 'They evince superhuman wisdom, because it is innate, and therefore, instilled by an all-wise Creator.' Instinct was not a reasoning process, Blyth argued, because beetles, just emerged from the pupa stage, can simulate death like the wiles of the fox (shades here of Matthew's Universal Law). If Darwin did pick up anything for his chapter in the *Origin* it would be the substitution of Natural Selection for 'Providence has conferred instinctive wiles on animals as a resource against contingencies'.

Blyth and later Darwin were concerned with many ways of concealment by wild animals: the colour of coats or feathers (both Blyth and Darwin consider the colour of the grouse feathers in relation to concealment), the time of day some wild animals search for food, the constant vigilance and any deviation from the species norm as a means of maintaining the species. Darwin turns this round so that any favourable deviation is the means by which variation and so change occurs. Cuvier could not accept that transitional varieties could subsist and Blyth went along with this as any anti-mutationist would argue.

Darwin would have had no difficulty in dealing with, 'But to return to that mysterious guiding principle, so important, as we have seen, in regulating the distribution of species.'

It is a curious fact that after Blyth arrived in India and set about observing and collecting facts about animals and plants in Asia he seems to drop all the religious trappings in his reports to Darwin; reports so accurate and wide-ranging that in *The Descent of Man* his works are referred to more than any other naturalist.

Blyth and before him Lyell summed up the various points that were being and had been discussed. By 1836, Darwin arrived back and quickly got down to work on selection after a very busy period in London was over. However, by 1836 there was only one author, Patrick Matthew, announcing the universal law of nature – Natural Selection. Anyone reading Blyth's papers carefully – and, like the *Origin*, they require several readings and bring on the reader the fatigue which Sir Arthur Keith complained about on reading the *Origin* – they will realize that 24 years later Darwin set about, what Lyell and Blyth had done in their early days, collecting and wrote up the available data of his day.

Eiseley (1958) did not seem aware of the social and political turbulence of the 1830s and 1840s which have been mentioned before. The Chartist Movement was in full swing and there were riots; even riots against the clergy who were gaining more and more influence, many of whom were becoming magistrates. French science was now being taught by university lecturers like Robert Grant and other radicals. Lamarckism was loudly professed by the radicals in London and Edinburgh. The reason why French science had taken hold in England in the 1830s is due to all those students flocking to Paris to follow the courses in medicine and natural history. All the people who were to figure in the great species debate during the next few decades had made the pilgrimage to Paris. Richard Owen was there attending the course given by Cuvier and remained faithful to Cuvier for the rest of his life. Robert Grant went annually to Paris and helped the young Richard Owen as he had helped the young Darwin. Like Darwin, Owen had little good to say about Grant in later years and even conspired against him. But why Paris? On the eve of the French Revolution France possessed the most highly institutionalized and productive scientific community in the world. Religion had been abolished and, although brought back by Napoleon who realized its opiate value, religion was never again permitted to interfere with scientific ideas. Atheism was the basis of all intellectual thought in France. Charles Lyell also spent time in Paris in the 1820s and came away horrified by the materialist basis of Lamarckian evolution. The English government had tried to stem the tide of French science with the Seditious Acts but by the 1830s no one paid any attention to them.

Darwin would be out of sympathy with this social and political situation in London on his return. The Darwin family were anti-radical; his mother and his cousin's wife came from the wealthy Wedgewood dynasty. The anti-radical opposition were prepared to use any means to control the radical movement and the struggle would continue for the rest of the century. For anyone to publish an atheistic book into this atmosphere would be in danger of his life and property. Even if Darwin were ready to publish in the 1840s, which he was not, he would not have dared to publish anything like what appeared in 1859. Even then he was virulently attacked for his irreligiousity. So when Eiseley states his theory why Darwin delayed publishing earlier because, '. . . he had his secrets . . . and he had his justification', Schwartz jumps on this to ask, quite rightly, 'What were those secrets and what is the justification for them?' Schwartz had no idea either why there was delay. We know that by 1842 Darwin was now an 'aged, haggard, ailing man'. He was not much better in 1859. The delay in publishing was a combination of long-standing debility, inability to get his data together, the long desertion of the species problem for seven years' classifying barnacles, and the unstable political situation. In the 1840s *The Vestiges of the Natural History of Creation* was published, became popular with the more intelligent of the middle classes and ran on into the 1850s with ten editions; the tenth arrived in 1855. There was still no mention of Natural Selection but evolution was 'in the air' as the saying goes. Herbert Spencer also had a hand in making people aware of evolution. He produced a philosophy of evolution as a process of progressive differentiation from simple to complex. Evolution, no doubt, was being discussed in scientific circles; Natural Selection came later with the *Origin*; soon after publication Matthew let it be known that he had introduced Natural Selection as a universal law of nature many years before. This is why English historians consider that evolution was in the air by 1859. This point has been overlooked by some American historians, for example, Cohen (1982) indignantly asserting, 'The analysis of these episodes also shows the shallowness of those who would denigrate Darwin's great and original contribution simply because it was in the air.' Evolution was in the air all right but that was not the reason why the *Origin* was published; it is the reason why the book, when published, was bought in hundreds of copies. The reason the *Origin* was published in 1859 was the essay arriving on Darwin's desk in 1858 from Wallace and the demands to publish forced on Darwin by Sir Charles Lyell and Joseph Hooker.

As soon as the *Origin* was published and then reviewed by Thomas Huxley in *The Times* the long-ignored Patrick Matthew briefly took the stage. A damning and untruthful letter in *Gardeners' Chronicle* from the enraged Darwin sunk Patrick Matthew almost without trace.

Back in 1858 Thomas Bell, President of the Linnean Society, wrote in his report: '. . . there are, perhaps, few striking facts to record of particular interest . . . There has been no very important discovery enunciated, of a character to impugn former theories or systems, or to establish new ones.' There was plenty to report after November 1859. Although evolution, as a concept, had become widely discussed, thanks to the *Vestiges,* the utter irreligiousness of the *Origin* shattered what had previously been a bitter but relatively peaceful debate between the radicals supporting Lamarckism and the conservative opposition refuting mutation of species. The debate was now taken up by the clergy and the devout sections of the population. The concept of Natural Selection, although just an incremental advance, was to hold centre stage for the rest of the century.

If we introduce Patrick Matthew at this stage it is to inform readers that much of what Blyth discussed was contained in Matthew's *Appendix.* So before we proceed to investigate what influence Blyth had on Wallace we may first note a disagreement between Matthew and Wallace. In the 1855 paper Wallace introduced a law which he had deduced from the evidence he provided: 'The following law may be deduced from these facts; every species has come into existence co-incident both in space and time with a pre-existing closely allied species.' We are obliged now to bring Wallace into the discussion.

This so-called new law was old hat because it was disposed of in the *Appendix* (1831): 'It is improbable that much of this diversification is owing to commixture of species nearly allied, all change by this appears very limited, and confined within the bounds of what is called species; the progeny of the same parents, under great influence of circumstance, might in several generations, even become distinct species, incapable of co-reproduction.' This is the line Darwin would support as we read the *Origin* today.

It is clear from his statement that Matthew correctly envisaged that the driving force of diversity was by 'sports' or, as one says today, genes.

Wallace's 1855 essay was published in *The Annals and Magazine of Natural History* which was a continuation of the Loudon and Charmsworth's *Magazine of Natural History!* This was the magazine in which Blyth's essays were published in 1835–37. So Wallace must have had an opportunity to read them. Evidence will be presented later that indicates Wallace must have read Blyth's essays.

Now that diversification has been mentioned it is clear that this phenomenon had been discussed prior to 1836. There is a very odd article in the recently published *Encyclopaedia of Evolution* which discussed diversification as if it had been invented by Darwin: 'There has been much debate among scholars about why Darwin came to understand divergence so late in the day, or even whether he might have lifted diversification from Wallace.' Why should Darwin lift divergence from Wallace when he could have lifted it from Blyth or even Erasmus's *Zoonomia?* There may be a case to be made that Wallace lifted divergence from Blyth. In Darwin's 1837 notebook there is a diagram of a branching tree. This idea must have been derived from Blyth's essays and it certainly was not lifted from Wallace. In Wallace's 1855 essay Darwin found nothing new and noted that Wallace had described a branching tree similar to his 1837 diagram. Nevertheless, Darwin wrote to Wallace in 1857 agreeing with his 'Sarawak' law. (Wallace, 1916). Darwin was right to comment that there was nothing new in Wallace's essay if for no other reason than the tree of life was commonly discussed in the 1850s by naturalists. But Blyth's 'reiterate diversity' in his 1830s essays must have caught Darwin's roving eye very early. So the idea that diversity came to Darwin late does not seem to fit the facts. But why would Darwin agree with the 'Sarawak' law when he had by 1844 accepted descent from a common ancestor? Was Darwin, perhaps, prepared to allow Wallace to continue on the wrong track? If we do not wish to impugn the honour of Darwin the only other alternative is that Darwin had changed his mind about descent from a common ancestor for which I can find no evidence. Darwin's letter to Wallace on 1 May 1857 opens: 'I am much obliged for your letter of October 10th from Celebes, received a few days ago; in a laborious undertaking, sympathy is valuable and real encouragement. By your letter and even still more by your paper in the *Annals*, a year or more ago, I can plainly see that we have thought much alike and to a certain extent have come to similar conclusions. In regard to the paper in the *Annals*, I agree to the truth of almost every word of your paper . . .' How different was his tone towards Patrick Matthew some four years later.

Although there is evidence that Darwin thought hard about the so-called 'Sarawak' law, Young (1992) does not appear to realize the significance of what he has quoted, without comment, from Wallace's essay.

Matthew, like many generations before him, had noticed 'sports' by which was meant varieties; centuries of hybridization had shown continued breeding, as in modern F2 parlance, would produce some reversion to the parent form; without the ratios there seemed to be chaos. It was this chaos which Mendel made sense of and with the principle of heredity the miraculous birth of species could be abandoned even by the most devout. For Wallace in his 1858 paper to claim that he had discovered this principle was as inaccurate as the law which he professed to have discovered in 1855.

It is quite clear from what Matthew stated in the *Appendix* that there had been wide discussion and some disagreement in the period prior to 1831. We can appreciate that Matthew took what would be referred to as a 'Darwinian line' in this debate. He introduced the problem thus: 'In endeavouring to trace, in the former way, the principle of these changes of fashion which have taken place in the domiciles of life, the following questions occur: Do they arise from a mixture of species nearly allied producing intermediate species? Are they the diverging ramifications of circumstance? Or have they resulted from the combined agency of both?' His answer was given on a previous page.

So 25 years after this kind of statement in the *Appendix* Wallace produced a law which he presents as something new. How is it that Charles Lyell did not recognize that the law was not new? Darwin and he met together to discuss the paper. We will continue to follow Wallace up to his 1858 essay in order to demonstrate that data which were available in 1836 are to be found in that essay.

We come now to the title of Wallace's essay of 1858 which came to rank him along with Darwin as the co-founder of the origin of species by Natural Selection: 'On the tendency of varieties to depart indefinitely from the original type'. Wallace ends his essay: 'We believe that we have now shown that there is a tendency in nature to the continued progression of certain classes of varieties further and further from the original type.'

Now Blyth: '. . . and only those in which the same peculiarity is most apparent, be selected to breed from, the next generation will possess it in a still more remarkable degree . . . till at length, the variety I designate a breed, is formed which may be very unlike the original type.'

Could Darwin have missed this when he was searching through the journals in the 1840s? The individual has now developed into a breed. We see here a difference which Bowler (1976) has stressed when discussing the Wallace 1858 essay and the *Origin*. Wallace is discussing varieties departing from the original type whereas Blyth (and later Darwin) indicates how a selected individual can be made to develop into a distinct variety – a breed.

Now Wallace: '. . . a struggle for existence in which the weakest and least perfectly organized must always succumb.'

Now Blyth: '. . . so that all the young which are produced must have had their origin from one which possessed the maximum of power and physical strength, and which, consequently, in the struggle for existence was the best able to maintain his ground and defend himself from every enemy.'

This was old hat as well and the sentiment is in the *Appendix* and probably elsewhere: '. . . even in man himself, the greater uniformity, and the more general vigour among savage tribes, is referable to nearly similar selecting law – the weaker individual sinking under the ill-treatment of the stronger or under the common hardship.' The only difference here is the introduction of the universal law of Natural Selection.

Now Wallace: '. . . There is a general principle in nature which will cause many varieties to survive the parent species.'

Now Blyth, dealing with what he called True Varieties, discusses variants which could not be perpetrated in the wild, '. . . but which, by man's agency, often became the origin of a new race.' He then described how the Ancons sheep appeared: 'A ewe produced a male lamb of peculiar form, with a long body, and short and crooked legs . . .' A sheep breeder, as a part of nature, then selected this favourable mutation and continued breeding from this male sheep. The 'favourable mutation', so far as the breeder was concerned, was the reduced ability of these physically impaired sheep to jump fences. We can see here that Blyth stresses the individual and not a group to be involved; it was 'a ewe' that produced the variation. But it was obvious that this variety of sheep could never survive in the wild.

Now Wallace: '. . . Varieties produced in a state of domesticity are more or less unstable, and often have a tendency, if left to themselves, to return to the normal form of the parent species.'

Now Blyth: 'The same law, therefore, which was intended by Providence to keep the typical qualities of a species, can be easily converted by man into a means of raising different varieties, but it is also clear that, if man did not keep up these breeds by regulating the sexual intercourse, they would all naturally soon *revert to the original type*.' In using the term 'revert to the original type' Blyth reveals that the role of heredity was not quite appreciated in his day. Until Mendel brought the ratios in to the assessment of progeny of successive generations, breeders were baffled by the appearance of the original type amongst the other varieties.

It is clear that Blyth is not claiming that he is saying anything new; it was all known ages before. For Wallace to put it about that this essay was something out of his own brain, an original thought and a gem of invention is difficult to explain. Perhaps it was because he had just recovered from another bout of malaria; he wrote the essay from the other side of the world.

As one goes through the 1858 essay one can see that all the points Wallace makes about the effects of colour, methods of concealment in the wild, the effect of varying the food supply and its effect on determining procreative power, the precarious nature of food in the wild, that carnivores are always less numerous than the herbivores, the effects on species of changes in physical conditions, that in the wild varieties may be favourable or unfavourable, the differences between domestic and wild species in relation to food supply and concealment – and much else is covered in Blyth's essays of 1835–37. And a fair amount of the relevant data introduced was in the *Appendix*. Here, for example, is almost word for word what Blyth wrote: 'Even a change of colour might, by rendering them more or less distinguishable, affect their safety.' Again, Blyth writes: '. . . if man did not keep up these breeds by regulating the sexual intercourse, they would all naturally soon revert to the original type.' Here is Wallace: '. . . and the same principle which produces this result in the state of nature will also explain why domestic varieties have a tendency to revert to the original type.'

Wallace's opening statement in his 1858 essay, is as follows: 'One of the strongest arguments which have been adduced to prove the original and permanent distinctness of species is that varieties produced in a state of domesticity are more or less unstable, and often have a tendency, if left to themselves, to return to the normal form of the parent species.'

Here is Matthew's statement: '. . . man had already had considerable influence . . probably occasioning the destruction of many species, and the production and continuation of a number of varieties or even species, which he found more suited to supply his wants, but which, from the *infirmity* of their condition – not having undergone selection by the law of nature, of which we have spoken, cannot maintain their ground without his culture and protection.'

Wallace continues to write about varieties using Blyth's classification but not mentioning that source. Then comes an extraordinary statement: 'It will be observed that this argument rests entirely on the assumption that varieties occurring in a state of nature are in all respects analogous to or even identical with those of domestic animals, and are governed by the same laws as regards their permanence or further variation. But it is the object of this paper to show that this assumption is altogether false, that there is a general principle in nature which will cause varieties to survive the parent species, and to give rise to successive variations departing further and further from the original type, and which also produced, in domestic animals, the tendency of varieties to return to the parent form.'

Why Darwin became so depressed by this essay and not the 1855 essay was the struggle for existence which Wallace introduced. Darwin must have known that the struggle for existence was in Blyth's essays and Lyell's *Principles*. Still, here it was and no source given. Those ignorant of Blyth and Lyell would regard this as something novel. But struggle for existence, which goes back to Lamarck, was coming dangerously close to his own struggle for existence and Natural Selection. That was enough to start the alarm bells ringing and Darwin took immediate action in writing to Lyell.

There was nothing new either in the assumption or the object of Wallace's paper. Matthew and Blyth had clearly stated the difference between domestic and wild varieties. Blyth had gone on to attempt to classify them; there is some evidence that Wallace used Blyth's classification of varieties. As we have indicated elsewhere Naudin (1852) was of the opinion that the hybridist just copied nature. We can go further: we have shown that Wallace, in his essay, repeated nearly every difference between wild and domestic varieties which Matthew and particularly Blyth had noted and commented on twenty years before. How Wallace came to be regarded as the co-founder of the principle of Natural Selection without ever using the term in his essays is one of the mysteries of the history of biology.

But the object of Wallace's paper was nothing more than what came to be known as the F1 and F2 Mendelian laws. Before Mendel made sense of the F2 progeny the results were regarded as chaotic. Darwin experienced this with his domestic pigeons; in the *Origin* he drew attention to Sebright's experiences with mongrel dogs in the eighteenth century. When Mendel showed that the F2 results – 50% reversion to the parents and 50% were combination of the parents – all was revealed. Before the ratios were established chaos reigned. In the *Origin* Darwin states, '. . . but when these mongrels are crossed one with the other for several generations, hardly two of them will be alike, and then the extreme difficulty, or rather utter hopelessness, of the task becomes apparent.' This was the very problem he should have addressed.

This breeding problem still frustrates the amateur breeder today. A well-known amateur breeder of lurchers (Gazdar, 1995) recently described her results: 'But lurcher breeding is fraught with the incidence of throw-backs, uneven pup sizes heights and builds. It is not uncommon to find raving beauties and ugly ducklings suckling side by side when both parents were of similar types.' Another amateur breeder, Charles Darwin, encountered the same experience with domestic pigeons but failed to shed any light on the chaotic results.

Although Cuvier's Catastrophism had been rejected by 1836 his influence on other aspects of natural history was carried on by his pupils – notably Richard Owen. The reason why Cuvier is introduced now is because if we are to discuss diversity in nature it will not be possible to ignore his great contribution to that subject.

Cuvier appears to some people as a rather remote character in Paris. He was well known in surgical circles in London. He visited the College of Surgeons in London in 1817. He claimed to have discovered the red-blooded worm but John Hunter had described it many years before. Richard Owen pointed out this fact in his critique of Cuvier's history of natural science in the eighteenth century. Owen went on to criticize Cuvier who had assessed Vicq d'Azyr as the greatest dissector of the eighteenth century; he only dissected vertebrates whereas Hunter had dissected 315 animals covering the whole range from human to Polype. When Owen was in Paris in 1832 he found Delpech and Coste claiming to have discovered the late appearance of red blood cells in the chick embryo. Hunter had demonstrated this 50 years before. A demonstration of avian bones was given by Hunter in 1758 but the French contribution came in 1776. Cuvier was not the first naturalist to include fossils in his classification of animals. He was only 24 years old when John Hunter died in 1793. In Hunter's museum were several fossils laid beside, wherever possible, similar specimens of extant species. The majority of this collection was destroyed in a fire at the College of Surgeons during the London raids in the Second World War. Darwin, himself, added to this collection on his return from the voyage. Most of the fossils brought back by Darwin were identified by his future antagonist Richard Owen. It was in Hunter's museum that he came to realize that the extinct specimens and similar living forms he saw in South America denoted evolution. Hunter continued the development of comparative anatomy started by Buffon and with his collection of fossils and his deep interest in geology it is quite clear that what Hunter meant by adaptation was evolution. Darwin had little to say about Hunter's fossil collection or his museum of comparative anatomy or the influence it had on what he called 'my theory'. No one praised the work of John Hunter more than Richard Owen: for this reason alone Darwin would dismiss his debt to Hunter's museum.

When John Hunter died in 1793 his papers were taken into the care of Sir Everard Home, his brother-in-law. A Trust was set up to administer Hunter's affairs and the disposal of his huge specimen collection. The Trust consisted of three members: Hunter's wife, Matthew Baillie (a friend) and Sir Everard who was a practising surgeon.

By 1823 Sir Everard was the only living member of the Trust. Volume 4 of his *Lectures in Comparative Anatomy* was published in that year. Sir Everard then proceeded to destroy Hunter's papers and notes. So much material was cast to the flames that the primitive Fire Brigade, of the period, was called to help put out the fire in the house.

The Council of the Royal College of Surgeons investigated the matter but Sir Everard maintained that Hunter had told him to destroy all his unpublished work. No one believed him but the Council could only reprimand him. It is now clear that all four volumes of the *Lectures in*

Comparative Anatomy consist of Hunter's voluminous papers and notes. The burning of Hunter's papers was soon forgotten and so, quite naturally, present day scientists consider Home an important marine naturalist!

John Hunter was greatly respected by Erasmus Darwin. It was probably from Hunter and Buffon that Erasmus gained information about the new developments in natural science. Erasmus was a practising physician but also very interested in natural science. He did not carry out practical work like Hunter who dissected, devised physiological experiments, collected fossils and wrote essays on many subjects including geology. Since Hunter and Lamarck were linked scientifically to Buffon and so were on the same evolutionary trail it is not surprising that they produced similar ideas picked up by Erasmus. Lamarck differed from Erasmus as well because it was only after years of practical laboratory investigation he was able to publish his books – *Animaux sans Vertèbres* and *Philosophie Zoologique*. Erasmus had no practical scientific experience but, like Herbert Spencer in the next century, he was able to pick up the latest scientific ideas and theories and commit them, in a philosophical manner, to his poems and essays. John Hunter carried on a busy hospital and private surgical practice, founded scientific surgery, revolutionized military surgery in addition to his natural history studies but, through sheer lack of time, never got an opportunity to commit to publication many of his essays. Richard Owen did that for him in the next century when the governmental strictures on publishing anything contrary to Holy Writ had been abandoned. Hunter died aged 65 in 1793. To conclude, as Thomas Huxley did, that Lamarck was merely a trumpeter of Erasmus Darwin's music was scientific deception at its worst. For Charles Darwin to hint in the *Historical Sketch* that Erasmus was the anticipater of Lamarck was little better.

So we can see that Cuvier was not too dispassionate when it came to fair assessment of other people's work. Cuvier was jealous of Hunter and indicated that he had no time for Hunter's geology. Hunter wins the day, however, because in his geological essay Noah's Flood is dismissed whereas Cuvier accepted the biblical account. It is said that progress in natural science was held up for some time in the nineteenth century because of the 'baleful' influence of Cuvier (1769–1832).

But it is for his views on diversity that Cuvier deserves full praise; that nature was orderly but diverse was his great contribution. The type concept destroyed the possibility of a simplistic representation of organic nature. His palaeontological evidence demonstrated a definite faunal succession but Cuvier denied that the various fossil groups were genetically related so that there could be no transmutation of species. Having destroyed the zoological *série* Cuvier would not allow even a partially ramified line reaching from the simplest to the most complex. There were no ramifications in Cuvier's organic world.

Typologists, like Cuvier and his pupil Richard Owen, were unable to visualize how one type became converted into a new type. That was because they were unable to visualize intermediate stages because it was considered that this would involve uncorrelated parts; any evolutionary change would require, in their view, synchronous changes (Ridley, 1982). Matthew did not use the term 'type' but supported a Lamarckian concept of change. He then conceived of change by the process of Natural Selection; as an active breeder of fruit trees this was just an obvious conclusion to Lamarckian concepts of change through time.

Bowler (1976) makes an extraordinary statement: 'It was only at a stage in his thought – after he had discovered the principle of divergence – that Darwin actually came to realize that varieties would at some stage have to compete with one another.' Darwin discovering divergence? The first written account of diverging ramifications I have not discovered but it is in the *Appendix* of 1831; Blyth followed up a few years later. It would seem that these two authors extended markedly the collaterals which Lamarck (1914) accredited to the linear series.

The article in the *Encyclopaedia of Evolution* (Milner, 1990), which was introduced earlier, gives one the impression that divergence was a new phenomenon introduced by Wallace and Darwin. The fact is that divergence had been discussed well before Matthew's publication of 1831. Here is what Blyth had to say: 'The true physiological system is evidently one of irregular and indefinite radiation, and of reiterate divergence and ramification from varying number of successively subordinate plants; . . . the modifications of each successive type being always in direct relation to particular localities . . . It cannot be too often repeated that, upon whatever plan a species may be organized, its true relation the reason for its existence at all is solely connected with its indigenous locality.' Darwin ends the chapter on Natural Selection in the *Origin* with a discussion on divergence. He could not have gained a better introduction to that subject than Blyth's foregoing statement involving '. . . indefinite radiation . . . reiterate divergence and ramification . . . successively subordinate plants . . .' Here is Darwin's concluding statement: '. . . and this connection of the former and present buds by ramifying branches may well represent the classification of all extinct and living species in groups subordinate to groups.' Then Darwin closes the chapter with some rhetoric which he passes off as something only thought out by himself: 'As buds give rise by growth to fresh buds, and these, if vigorous, branch out and overtop on all sides many a feebler branch, so by generation I believe it has been with the great Tree of life, which fills with its dead and broken branches the crust of the earth, and covers the surface with its ever branching and beautiful ramifications.' Would it be fair to say that Blyth stated the subject more succinctly? Matthew's diverging ramifications would express the teeming variations of life more vividly than Darwin's rhetoric. Had Darwin been less prolix he may not have complained about Matthew's brevity.

Blyth's view of 'locality' would conflict with Matthew's statement in *Emigration Fields* that a change of place can be beneficial; this was apropos of emigration. But in the *Appendix* he states: '. . . most wonderful variation of circumstance parallel to the nature of every species, as if circumstance and species had grown up together.' And in another section: '. . . the breed acquiring the very best possible adaptation of these to its condition which it is susceptible of, and when alteration of circumstance occurs, thus changing in character to suit these as far as its nature is susceptible of change.'

Always aware of past catastrophes and the life which followed Matthew proposes, '. . . an unoccupied field would be formed for new diverging ramifications of life, which . . . would fall into specific groups, these remnants, in the course of time, moulding and accommodating their being anew to the change of circumstances.'

It would seem that 'diverging ramifications' was a popular term in the 1830s. Diverging ramifications, as far as I can determine, was introduced by Patrick Matthew in 1831. A few years later Edward Blyth is employing the term. Charles Lyell started his first notebook on the species problem in 1837 so he can not be the source of Blyth's 'reiterate divergence'. Did Lyell lift divergence from Blyth? After 1837 Darwin could pick up this term from Lyell and there is evidence that he did. Young (1992) makes the point that in Darwin's copy of Lyell's fifth edition of the *Principles* (1837) there were comments about divergence. This is another instance proving how wrong some American authors are in maintaining that Darwin discovered divergence or came to divergence late and could have lifted the concept from Wallace. Another point: the 1837 notebook has Darwin's first branching tree of life. Bronn's essay was published in 1858 (in German) with an illustrated tree of life.

Whatever speculations authors may make about when Darwin came to absorb divergence into his book, one should not forget that Darwin was well acquainted with Cuvier's writings. He quotes from these writings in several places in the *Origin*. The fact that Cuvier had introduced divergence in the early nineteenth century would surely not be lost on Darwin. It is odd, however, that Darwin came to embrace Cuvier–Lamarckian divergence so late; if, in fact, he did because Matthew (1831) and Blyth (1835–37) have quite clearly picked up and recognized the significance of divergence. On his own submission Darwin admitted he was slow to see the importance of divergence. In a letter to Lyell, 30 September 1859, he wrote to say that the last sheets of the *Origin* had been sent off. He continued, 'I suppose that I am a very slow thinker, for you would be surprised at the number of years it took me to see clearly what some of the problems were which had to be solved, such as the necessity of the principle of divergence of character . . .' What Darwin placed in the *Origin* on divergence does not make compelling reading.

Stauffer (1972) notes that Darwin returned to Chapter 6 in 1858 and expanded it by interpolating a new discussion on divergence. If he did that then he changed his interpolation in the *Origin* to Chapter 4 dealing with Natural Selection under the heading 'Divergence of Character'. Darwin closed that chapter with divergence and so linked it with Natural Selection. Patrick Matthew did the same.

It has been said that Darwin was the first to consider evolution of varieties and species as a branching tree. Ramify means to divide into branches; the word is derived from the Latin 'ramus' meaning a branch.

Darwin continues his discussion of diversification by introducing, like Blyth, in a previous passage, physiology into the argument: 'The advantage of diversification in the inhabitants of the same region is, in fact, the same as that of the physiological division of labour in the organs of the same individual body . . .' Darwin continues: '. . . we may, I think, assume that the modified descendants of any one species will succeed by so much the better as they become more diversified in structure and are

thus enabled to encroach on places occupied by other beings.' This, by
the way, was exactly the argument Matthew had used about the Caucasians, being better structured, and so would be able to take over other
lands from savages less structured (Matthew 1839). Having introduced
the subject of diversity Darwin proudly invites the reader to consult his
diagram of the branches of a tree of evolution of species. Diverging
ramifications had said it all long before! The evolutionary tree has now
become a branched bush!

Mayr (1982) had obviously missed all these diverging ramifications of
Matthew and Blyth otherwise he could not have written this: 'Darwin,
curiously, was the first author to postulate that all organisms have
descended from common ancestors by a continuous process of branching.'
Darwin has no better public relations consultant.

Blyth's concept of species related to their indigenous locality was
concluded with: '. . . just, therefore, as the surface varies, so do its
productions and its inhabitants.'

Darwin in his turn took up the problem of diversification of structure.
Here is what influenced him: 'The truth of the principle, that the greatest
amount of life can be supported by great diversification of structure, is
seen under many natural circumstances. I found that a piece of turf, three
feet by four, which had been exposed for many years to exactly the same
conditions, supported twenty species of plants . . .'

But clearly this happy situation did not last because in apparently the
same piece of turf: '. . . out of twenty species growing on a little plot
of turf (three by four) nine species perished from the other species allowed
to grow up freely.'

Clearly, the best circumstance-suited survived and the least suited
perished. Matthew had the same view of nature with his best suited tree
smothering the rest and so gaining dominance.

Darwin would have been able to describe a far better example of plant
biodiversity than the number of plants growing on his piece of turf had
he visited the right part of the wild lands of the Cape of Good Hope.
In his *Journal of Researches* (1845) he recounts that the *Beagle* landed at
Cape Town. 'I made an excursion of some days' length into the country.'
He formed the strong impression that the country was infertile and so
he disputed the belief that large quadrupeds required luxuriant vegetation.
'With regard to the number of large quadrupeds, there certainly exists
no quarter of the globe which will bear comparison with South Africa.

After the different statements which have been given, the extremely desert character of that region will not be disputed.' 'Dr Andrew Smith . . informs me that, taking into consideration the whole of the Southern part of Africa, there can be no doubt of its being a sterile country.' (Darwin, 1845.) This makes strange reading today. The excursion Darwin went on obviously missed those wild areas of the Cape where the fynbos supports more species per square metre than anywhere else on earth. The fynbos has a total of 8,574 species; of these 68% grow nowhere else. Mass biodiversity in some regions has a great bearing on the amount of rain run off into streams and rivers. This is the problem facing the water supply to Cape Town today.

So, what we can gather from Blyth and Matthew is that diverging ramifications was a well discussed subject long before they started writing. Indeed, it was! Lamarck imagined the linear series with collateral branches (Lamarck, 1809). These collateral branches became the diverging ramifications of Matthew and the reiterate diversity of Blyth. Coming to the problem in 1837 Darwin sees all this as a tree of life. From 1837 onwards Darwin was to absorb Lamarckism and be influenced by it but at the same time ridiculed it until in old age he could no longer slander the man who had played such a large part in his life.

In a letter to Joseph Hooker way back in 1844 Darwin, unwittingly, let the cat out of the bag: 'At last gleams of light have come, and I am almost convinced (quite contrary to the opinion I started with) that species are not (it is like confessing a murder) immutable. Heaven forfend me from Lamarck nonsense of a 'tendency to progression', 'adaptations from the slow willing of animals', etc! But the conclusions I am led to are not widely different from his; though the means of change are wholly so.' (Darwin, F., 1902.) This last remark was fair comment if by the 'means of change' Natural Selection was intended. Lamarck's idea was that life forms change over immense time. Lamarck was not a breeder and so selection would not occur to him. Indeed, it was only when a breeder with a philosophical turn of mind came to study the species problem that 'the natural process of selection' was added to what Cuvier and Lamarck had started. That breeder was Patrick Matthew.

A year later Darwin wrote to L. Jenyns (12 October 1845): 'The general conclusions at which I have slowly been driven from a directly opposite conviction, is that species are mutable, and that allied species are co-descendents from common stocks. I know how much I open myself to reproach for such a conclusion, but I have at least honestly and deliberately come to it. I shall not publish on this subject for several years.' No one would suspect from this baring of a troubled soul searching for truth that Lyell in Volume 2 of his *Principles* had set out the basis of Lamarckism in 1832. Towards Lamarckism Darwin steadily veered throughout his life.

So there we have it. Lamarck 40 years before had spent most of his life in teaching the mutability of species. Patrick Matthew had offered the possible means of change in 1831 with 'the natural process of selection'. Furthermore, in London since 1828 Robert Grant of University College (Darwin's teacher in Edinburgh) had vigorously preached Lamarckism and the mutability of species.

The whole story throughout the generations has been confused by authors in their deep and sincere devotion to Darwin stressing 'the Lamarck nonsense' in the letter which has just been quoted but leaving out the sentence '. . . but the conclusions I am led to are not widely different from his . . .' And Darwin himself confuses the picture by asserting that Matthew had 'merely enunciated' the theory and yet on other occasions states Matthew's views are not much different from his. How could this be so if Matthew merely enunciated the theory? Darwin fans even in recent times have dug up the 'mere enunciation' side of the story and so have perpetuated the confusion. Furthermore, by reducing Lamarckism to nothing more than the inheritance of acquired characteristics, Darwin enthusiasts have distorted the history of the idea of evolution.

7

Charles Darwin's Predecessors

It appeared to me extremely poor; I got not a single fact or idea
from it.

(Charles Darwin to Charles Lyell on Lamarck's book)

We can understand, on these views, the very important distinction
between real affinities and analogical or adaptive resemblances.
Lamarck first called attention to this distinction, and he has been
ably followed by Macleay and others.

(Chapter on Classification in
The Origin of the Species. Charles Darwin)

Darwin let it be known that he owed nothing to his predecessors.
Although this might seem the height of arrogance most fans of
Darwin still believe this.

In 1860 Darwin wrote to Professor Baden-Powell, the professor of
geometry at Oxford, and amongst other remarks included this: 'The only
novelty in my work is the attempt to explain how species become
modified, and to a certain extent how the theory of descent explains
large classes of facts; and in this respect I received no assistance from my
predecessors.'

But the Oxbridge academics, like Baden-Powell, were not to know
that when Darwin was in Edinburgh there was great discussion about
the mutability of species. Edinburgh was linked to Paris scientifically and
although the English Government tried desperately to prevent French
atheism gaining access to these shores their efforts were in vain. Many
academics were pouring into Paris and returning with all the evolutionary
ideas which were circulating freely now that religion had been abolished;
although Napoleon had brought it back there were no priests in the
Sorbonne any more.

Darwin's statement together with statements from authors with their

'Darwin tale' continued the widespread belief that the *Origin* was all Darwin's idea. Even present day authors are guilty of presenting their tale in a way which continues the mystique surrounding Darwin. For example this: 'From behind his great wall at Down he plucked up courage and confessed his awful secret, his belief that all animals were descended from common stocks.' (Desmond and Moore, 1991.) To begin, there is no 'great wall' at Down House. Presented in such a way the ordinary reader gets the impression that descent from a common ancestor was Darwin's discovery. Descent from a common ancestor was not a secret. It was in Blyth's essays and dismissed on religious grounds. It was in Lyell's *Principles of Geology* and dismissed as being contrary to Christian doctrine. Matthew had it in the *Appendix*. Above all it was in the writings of Lamarck. For Darwin to impress the young Hooker with 'his awful secret' was very easy. The young Hooker was 25 years old and had just returned in 1843 from four years at sea. He was not to know what was already in the journals.

Like Hooker most people were and are quite unaware of what was in the literature which Darwin had been reading between 1837 and 1858. One can understand how, as intended, people got the impression that the *Origin* was all Darwin's idea. By leaving out his sources in the *Origin* who was to know what was second hand or original? Even Huxley, who had not followed the species problem prior to 1859, had to ask Darwin for advice about how to get more information. When Murray, the publisher of the *Origin,* received Darwin's manuscript marked *An Abstract* he objected to such a title and wrote Darwin to tell him so. Darwin then appealed to Lyell who forced Murray to withdraw his objection. Darwin was quite open about omitting references and in a letter to Lyell (30 March 1859) wrote, 'I am sorry about Murray objecting to the term Abstract, as I look at it as the only possible apology for not giving references and facts in full . . .' And Darwin got away with it.

If we study carefully the naturalists Darwin introduced to his *Historical Sketch* in the third and sixth and final edition (1872) of the *Origin*, together with remarks made many years before, one can see that anyone who was or could be traced as a possible influence was systematically made out to be unimportant or ignored or slandered. This chapter is included because Patrick Matthew was introduced into the *Historical Sketch* and the derogatory remarks written twelve years before were reproduced in 1872.

The very first paragraph of the *Sketch* is full of misleading statements: 'Until recently the great majority of naturalists believed that species were immutable and had been separately created . . . Some few naturalists, on the other hand, have believed that species undergo modification, and that the existing forms of life are the descendants by true generation of pre-existing forms.' This statement passes over the fact that between 1844 and 1855 ten editions of the *Vestiges of the Natural History of Creation* had stimulated the intelligent section of the rising middle class. This book set out to show that the Creator had produced a forward moving series of animals from fish to amphibians to reptiles to mammals which indicated an evolution of animal life had taken place. How those changes had taken place was not discussed and there was no hint of Natural Selection. Darwin continues, '. . . the first author who in modern times has treated it in a scientific spirit was Buffon. But as his opinions fluctuated greatly at different periods, and as he does not enter on the causes or means of the transformation of species, I need not here enter on details.'

From this apparently innocent and truthful statement one is not to know that everyone was aware at the time Darwin was writing that Buffon (1707–1788) all his life was under the heel of the clerics of the Sorbonne. When ever he made a scientific statement which was not in accord with Holy Writ the clerics forced him to recant. Recant he did but with tongue in cheek. He died in 1788 one year before the French Revolution which immediately abolished religion. Had Buffon lived longer his 'fluctuating opinions' would have ceased to fluctuate.

It is clear from this curt dismissal of Buffon that Darwin was in no mood to mention that Buffon had considered varieties as alterations of species and so their mutability. Buffon was the first to react against fixity of species announced by Linnaeus. Nor would Darwin's statement lead one to conclude that Pangenesis was lifted from Buffon. It was Thomas H. Huxley who pointed out to Darwin that Pangenesis was similar to an idea of Buffon 100 years before. Huxley did not incriminate Lamarck although he has taken the blame ever since for the inheritance of acquired characteristics. Lamarck as a dutiful pupil of Buffon continued to include Buffon's ideas in his list of laws controlling change over time.

Unfortunately, Buffon used terms which were not well understood. Instead of variety he used 'degeneration'. That there was descent from a common ancestor to related species Buffon considered to be by 'degeneration'. An unhappy term but it really meant divergence and so variety.

Lamarck in his *Philosophie Zoologique* uses this term as well. 'We have to distinguish the degradation of organization which arises from the influence of environment and acquired habits, from that which results from the smaller progress in the perfection or complexity of organization.' In fact, the sixth chapter is headed 'Degradation of Organization'. Buffon went on to question the Churches' teaching on the age of the earth. To all his scientific ideas he had to recant if they did not square with Church authority; they seldom did. So, fluctuations, as Darwin referred to them, were merely recantations of genuinely scientific observations. As for the Flood there was no evidence. Darwin must have been well aware of this.

Nor would Darwin's comments lend a clue to the tremendous contribution to comparative anatomy which Buffon carried out in his lifetime although Daubenton did most of the work published in the first fifteen volumes. His fifteen volumes of comparative anatomy were in the library of John Hunter who was the only one in Europe, after Buffon, to realize the importance of comparative anatomy even for clearing up some errors of the past regarding human anatomy. Without this development in comparative anatomy Cuvier's palaeontological studies would have been very limited. With the background of comparative anatomy Cuvier divided animal life into four main branches. But after establishing these branches Cuvier would only see lines that did not branch.

Had Darwin given the reader a fuller account of Buffon's ideas over the years when he had to contend with the clerics of the Sorbonne, he would have betrayed the fact that Buffon questioned the fixity of species. Indeed, in his lifetime species were vague concepts. It was against Christian doctrine to deny the fixity of species but we find Buffon as early as 1766 in the fourteenth volume of his *Histoire Naturelle* posing the problem, 'After surveying the varieties which indicate to us the alterations that each species has undergone, there arises a larger and more important question, namely, how far species themselves can change . . .' If the clerics of the Sorbonne noted this then Buffon would somewhere state that what he said was all nonsense; fluctuations, according to Darwin. But Buffon came out with a definition of species which later naturalists confirmed: 'We should regard two animals as belonging to the same species if, by means of copulation, they can perpetuate themselves and preserve the likeness of the species; and we should regard them as belonging to different species if they are incapable of producing progeny by the same means.' The French Revolution liberated the French scientists from the fetters of the clerics and we can now see Lamarck placing his tutor's ideas into a firm scientific statement of evolution, the mutation of species and descent from a common ancestor.

Darwin then turns to Lamarck: 'This justly celebrated naturalist first published his views in 1801; he much employed them in 1809 in his *Philosophie Zoologique*, and consequently in 1815, in the introduction to his *Hist. Nat. des Animaux sans Vertèbres* In these works he upholds the doctrine that species, including man, are descended from other species . . . He first did the eminent service of arousing attention to the probability of all change in the organic, as well as the inorganic, being the result of law, and not of miraculous interposition.' Yet in 1859 Darwin wrote to Charles Lyell about Lamarck's publication: 'It appeared to me extremely poor; I got not a single fact or idea from it.' So that impression would imprint in Lyell's mind for some years to come that Lamarck was of zero significance. By 1863, however, Lyell began to see that he had done Lamarck an injustice in his volume 2 of the *Principles* when the first edition was published in 1833.

This rather meagre comment on Lamarck provided no real information about what advances Lamarck had made. Lamarck's studies of fossils and extant species led him to the view that the disappearance of old forms and the appearance of new ones was not a consequence of the total destruction of the organic life, but the formation of new species out of older forms which had most probably resulted from altered conditions of life. It was for this reason that, unlike Cuvier who described only four main branches of animal life, Lamarck envisaged a continuous but ever changing line of development; in other words evolution of all life forms. This is why he was accused of holding on to a 'ladder of life'. Cuvier could not accept branching from the linear series he had so well described. There was no hereditary link, he stubbornly maintained. Lamarck, however, envisaged what he referred to as collaterals. How extensive these collaterals were is not absolutely clear from his text; did collaterals mean branching of the branches? This point came clearer later and, as far as I can derive from the literature, Matthew was the first to commit to print 'diverging ramifications'; as we have related elsewhere Edward Blyth followed in his 1835–37 essays. It would seem that both Matthew and Blyth interpreted Lamarck's collaterals as branching of the branches. Darwin, who many people still regard as the originator of a branched tree of life, came much later in 1859 although in his notebook of 1837 he drew a diagram of a branched tree of life. Nowhere does Darwin try to establish a line of biological development in Europe; he had always to make people believe he owed nothing to his predecessors.

When the *Origin* was published, however, we find that Darwin did get a fact and a very good idea from Lamarck. In the chapter headed 'Classification' there is this statement: 'We can understand, on these views, the very important distinction between real affinities and analogical or adaptive resemblances. Lamarck first called attention to this distinction, and he has been ably followed by Macleay and others.' Macleay (1792–1856) was another English naturalist who made denigratory remarks about Lamarck: 'His peculiar and very singular opinions have never gained many converts in his own country and I believe none in this . . .' However, as we have shown for Darwin, the Reverend Fleming likewise accused Macleay of lifting several ideas from Lamarck! And Fleming, himself, had ambivalent attitudes towards Lamarck whom he admired for his biological contributions but who, '. . . substitutes conjectures for facts, and speculations for philosophical induction.'

Darwin continued his comment on what Lamarck had initiated: '. . . the resemblance, in the shape of the body and in the fin-like anterior limbs, between the dugong, which is a pachydermatous animal, and the whale, and between both these mammals and fishes, is analogical.' This was the basis of what Lamarck classified under the effect of conditions of life influencing structure. As the above example shows the body of any terrestrial animal returning to the sea has to take virtually the same shape as fishes if it is to propel itself quickly through the water. This, of course, takes unimaginable time. Recently a whole skeleton of an intermediate animal proceeding to be a whale has been found in Pakistan. It has four short feet, a serpentine tail and a long fish-like body. It was still a semi-terrestrial animal. This animal with four short legs, a serpentine tail and a strange head got along pretty well as half-ungulate and half-aquatic. One recalls Jay Gould's comment, 'What good is 40% of a wing?' The answer could be pretty well. The Cormorants cope very well under water with half-opened wings and totipalmate feet which do most of the work. The modern genus of Cormorants dates back 40,000,000 years.

Yet Darwin in his constant criticism of Lamarck seemed to ridicule the effect of conditions of life. We will return to this subject when we discuss Patrick Matthew. Elsewhere we will note that Blyth had absorbed Lamarck's message but rejected his materialist approach.

Instead of stressing what Lamarck had stressed all his life that animals and plants had changed (he used evolved) over millions of years, Darwin continued his statement with Buffon's idea of the inheritance of acquired characteristics. Lamarck was not a breeder and so Natural Selection does not enter his arguments. There is a footnote to the section on Lamarck which conveys the impression that Lamarck had lifted his ideas from those of Erasmus Darwin. Thomas Huxley was later to be influenced by the footnote and referred to Lamarck as a trumpeter of Erasmus Darwin's ideas.

In the introduction to *The Descent of Man*, having all his life ridiculed Lamarck, Darwin generously confessed: 'The conclusion that man is the co-descendant with other species of ancient, lower, and extinct forms is not in any degree new. Lamarck long ago came to the conclusion, which has lately been maintained by several eminent naturalists and philosophers.' This aspect of Darwin's writings is never alluded to by anti-Lamarckians like Richard Dawkins. The profound change of their opinion of Lamarck in the old age of Darwin and Lyell never reached the public at large. The damage had been done early on and continues today.

Dr W. C. Wells certainly had no influence on Darwin and so almost a full page is devoted to him. That Wells recognized the principle of Natural Selection is readily conceded by Darwin. That Wells knew, as Darwin was at pains to point out, that breeders improved their stock by selection of the best animals but this was nothing new. Wells discusses the well-known technique of hybridizing animals and concludes, 'But what there is done by art seems to be done with equal efficiency, though more slowly, by nature in the formation of varieties of mankind, fitted for the country which they inhabit.' This is a pretty pale anticipation of Matthew's 'universal law of nature' which was Natural Selection. Darwin knew this and every one else who had read the *Appendix* knew it. It is curious that the lead to downgrade Matthew by Darwin was continued over 100 years later by a Darwin enthusiast – Stephen Jay Gould (1983). On the basis of a very small knowledge of Matthew's writings and never having read *Naval Timber* or its appendix, having, like Darwin, apportioned the major part of the text to Wells, concluded, 'We have no indication that either Wells or Matthew recognized any of the revolutionary power behind his cleverness. Wells presented natural selection as an appendage to an essay he didn't even bother to publish until he lay dying. Matthew buried it among his trees and saw no forest (although he, unlike Wells, did advocate evolution as the cause of life's history).' Gould was ignorant of the fact that Matthew was not a planter of forest trees and his dismissive remark, I presume, supposed to be profound got it all wrong. As soon as Matthew finished the *Appendix* he straight away did what he said he would do and proceeded to put into practice the political aspect of the *Appendix*. As has been stated elsewhere he joined the Chartist Movement – a revolutionary political movement of some sections of the rising middle class. After that he set about arranging schemes of emigration. Some years later two of his sons emigrated and set up the first commercial orchards in the Antipodes. Gould's unfair remark with all its revealing ignorances is typical of the Darwin Industry; a label coined by Adrian Desmond.

Wells and Darwin considered that the black skin was an adaptation to climatic change and probably to combat diseases. It was appreciated by the time of the Second World War that a black skin sweats salt and water economically and that is the constant value of a black skin. Soldiers in the tropics during the last war were encouraged to have graduated sunbathing and compulsory salt at all meals. Once this principle was introduced heat exhaustion and sunstroke declined rapidly.

Professor Grant is allotted six lines, although one of the few mutationists since 1826. There is no doubt Robert Grant had a great influence on Darwin and hence he is doomed to the usual rubbishing treatment. Although Darwin points out that Grant had published a paper in 1826 in which, '. . . he declares his belief that species are descended from other species . . .' one would not gather from the six lines that Grant had befriended the young Darwin when he was in Edinburgh, instructed him in the rich fauna of the Firth of Forth and encouraged him to present short communications to the Pliny Society. In 1826, when Darwin was a student in Edinburgh, an anonymous article on geology was published in Edinburgh and it was widely suspected that Grant was the author. In this article Lamarck is extolled as the champion of evolution. 'Mr Lamarck, one of the most sagacious naturalists of our day . . . maintains that all other animals, by the operation of external circumstances, are evolved from these in a double series, and in a gradual manner . . . The doctrine of petrifactions, even in its present imperfect condition, furnishes us with accounts that seem in favour of Mr Lamarck's hypothesis . . . Mr Lamarck has expressed himself in the most unambiguous manner.' One may imagine that Grant's use of 'evolved' was a new concept in the species debate but he probably lifted the word from Lamarck. In the book dedicated to the doctrine of Descent and Darwinism, Schmidt (1881) quotes a section from Lamarck's writings *La Philosophie Zoologique* (1804), '. . . all organizations are true productions of Nature, gradually evolved in the course of a long succession of ages.' Although Charles Lyell is credited with the introduction of the word 'evolution' he probably picked it up while researching Volume 2 of his *Principles* when he was in France.

In addition to the introduction of Lamarck to the Scottish readers for the first time, Grant introduces, but without naming him, France's greatest palaeontologist Cuvier, who had discovered evidence of a series of catastrophes, in this comment: 'May this destruction, as is commonly received, have been the result of violent accidents and destructive revolutions of the earth; or does it not indicate a general law of nature, which cannot be discovered by reason of remote antiquity?' Darwin would have been a poor student if he did not refer to this essay over the next ten years.

It was Eiseley (1958) who suggested that Robert Grant may have been the author of the anonymous article of 1826. In a recent study Secord (1991) gathered some evidence that suggests that Robert Jameson, the professor of geology and the editor of the journal, was the author. That the editor of the journal must have been privy to whoever the author was, so that one must consider this possibility. It was a very odd way of concealing the name of the author. Why have in the same journal an anonymous article on geology in 1826 eulogizing Lamarck and an open article by Cuvier in 1829? Cuvier's article was on the state of Natural History. It was loaded with 'sacred books' and 'the Creator'. Secord (1991) is of the opinion that Jameson had every reason to publish on the merits of geology because, 'Throughout 1826 he had been editing and annotating the latest edition of Cuvier's *Discours Preliminaire*.' This and other ideas suggested by Secord do not convince me that Grant was not the author of the article. Jameson was not a linguist, had not attended Parisian debates hence would not introduce 'evolve' into his essay; Grant with his knowledge of Lamarckian ideas would. The fact that Jameson repudiated Cuvier's support for Noah's Flood would not be remarkable for any scientist in Edinburgh of that time and remaining devout as Jameson was. The Reverend John Fleming had also in 1826 rejected the

Flood and criticized both Buckland and Cuvier for supporting it; the
Scottish divine rejected the Flood because it did not correspond with
the Mosaic account of gentle rain falling for 40 days and nights! There
must have been a clear case of collusion between Jameson and Grant. It
is known that both Jameson and Fleming, who were very close friends
were very respectful of Grant. That 1826 article contained the influence
of a Creator which would have pleased both Jameson and Fleming and
that was traded in exchange for a boost for Lamarck. Both parties would
be satisfied that geology would be advertised.

Grant continued his Lamarckian lectures when he became transported
to London. He taught that all the forces from Cambrian times through
all geological epochs were all part of one creation: 'The gradual transition
which connect the species of one formation with those of the next . . .
indicate that they form the parts of one creation, and not the heteroge-
neous remnants of successive kingdoms begun and destroyed.'

One would think that some one like Grant would be warmly praised
by Darwin. Not so. Grant had to get the treatment. Adrian Desmond
(1989) asks the question but provides no answer: 'Why this lack of
dialogue with the one man who had such an abundant enthusiasm for
transmutation, the man who had originally guided him, shared his
obsession for Flustra and the longer laws of life, and was teaching in the
University's cloisters, not a stone's throw from Darwin's Gower Street
house? The lack of hard evidence prevents any pat answer.' When the
treatment Grant received is placed in line with similar treatment of other
people in and out of the *Sketch* one is drawn to the conclusion that a
consistent strategy is at work. Grant was not a breeder and so selection
does not enter his writings.

In Darwin's autobiography (1876) Grant is written off as having done
nothing after coming to London. Besides being a full-time lecturer, which
Darwin was not, Grant wrote out about 25 publications involving
collected lectures, descriptive papers and monographs and including a
200-page monograph on Mastodons. He continued his Edinburgh interest
in sponges and was highly estimed by the French Academy, which Darwin
never was, and in addition to his zoology lectures he immersed himself
in the Geology Society, the Zoological Society and medical politics; a
detailed account of Grant in London is to be found in Desmond's *Politics
of Evolution* (1989). Above all Grant preached the virtues of Lamarckism
throughout his years in London. Grant was an excellent linguist, was a

great admirer of French science and involved the teachings of Lamarck and St Hilaire into his own lectures. As Desmond (1989) points out, despite the fact that Grant was a radical activist and had been described in these terms: 'whenever a good, honourable, generous and liberal cause was in agitation you would find the name of Professor Grant' (Marshall Hall), the good honourable causes were not Darwin's. Without checking Darwin's false and perverse comments Gruber (1974) repeats, 'Grant was not a productive scientist in later years.' In any case how many are? Grant up until 1859 was a far more highly regarded scientist internationally than Darwin. Gruber (1974) seems quite unaware of the soul-destroying conditions Robert Grant had to work under and the wonder is not that he did nothing in London but how much he achieved.

In Darwin's autobiography is this statement: '. . . but after coming to London as professor in University College, he did nothing more in science, a fact which has always been inexplicable to me.' If ever there was a prize for name dropping this autobiography would gain it. There were other contemporaries of Grant who had different memories of him in 1840: '. . . one of the most distinguished naturalists of his day, licensed in Edinburgh yet unable to prescribe in London.' Grant had arrived in London in 1828!

Grant is followed in the *Sketch* by Patrick Matthew. Now this individual really infuriated Darwin who had accepted Wallace's paper of 1858 calmly but with much chagrin and was always polite in his letters to Wallace. Although he was already a distinguished naturalist, Wallace was not a breeder and so Natural Selection does not appear in his paper; indeed Wallace for many years would have nothing to do with Natural Selection but by 1889 in the first edition of his *Darwinism* he is quite happy with the term: 'Although I maintain, and even enforce my differences from some of Darwin's views, my whole work tends forcibly to illustrate the overwhelming importance of Natural Selection over all other agencies in the production of new species.' Darwin could afford to be magnanimous towards Wallace but Patrick Matthew had written out the actual term 'Natural Selection' some 30 years before. One can sympathize with Darwin's disappointment but one cannot condone the kind of letter he sent to the *Gardeners' Chronicle* in reply to Matthew's long letter of the 17 April 1860.

Wallace points out in *Darwinism*, '. . . such eminent naturalists as Geoffroy St Hilaire, Dean Herbert, Professor Grant, Von Buch, and some others expressed their belief that species arose as simple varieties, and that the species of each genus were all descended from a common ancestor; but none of them gave a clue as to the law or the method by which the change had been effected.'

It is a curious fact that none of these people, or indeed Wallace himself, was a breeder and so selection or Natural Selection did not enter their arguments. But now this Patrick Matthew was employing Natural Selection as the great universal law of nature.

It is clear from this list of predecessors that Wallace had forgotten all about Patrick Matthew who was the first to enter the literature with Natural Selection. Wallace had heard all about Patrick Matthew decades before. Now that Wallace was a Natural Selectionist himself he would be no keener than Darwin to acknowledge Matthew. For what reason did he omit Matthew from his list?

Darwin was usually a mild mannered man but not averse to spreading false statements and what he said in public was not always what he said in private in his letters. When what he always referred to as 'my theory' was in any way threatened he became a different animal and this is reflected in his shameful reply to Matthew's letter. Unable to suppress his fury Darwin introduced a wild, unwarranted and irrelevant assertion: 'I think that no one will be surprised that neither I, nor apparently any other naturalist, had heard of Mr Matthew's views, considering how briefly they are given, and that they appeared in the appendix to a work on *Naval Timber and Arboriculture* . . . if another edition of my work is called for, I will insert a notice to the foregoing effect.' One can appreciate that because the second edition appeared about three weeks later that Darwin could hardly keep his promise. However, in 1863 the third edition appeared and included the first edition of the *Sketch*. We are considering now the *Sketch* as it appears in the sixth edition, which was published in 1872. In the previous year *The Descent of Man* had been published and was favourably reviewed by Patrick Matthew in the *Scotsman* newspaper. Matthew sent a letter (March, 1871) and a copy of the review to Darwin who replied with a six-line letter, two lines of which were about the state of his health, one and bit about the quantity of letters he had to write and the review is referred to as 'the newspaper article'. Anyone reading this letter would not conclude that 'the newspaper article' was a long and favourable review of *The Descent of Man*. When we return to the *Sketch* in the sixth edition of the *Origin* published barely a year later in February 1872 we find that Darwin did not let up on what he had written in 1860: 'Unfortunately, the view was given by Mr Matthew very briefly in scattered passages in an appendix to a work on a different subject, so that it remained unnoticed until Mr Matthew himself drew attention to it in the *Gardeners' Chronicle,* on April 17th 1860.' The 'different subject', *Arboriculture* as written in Matthew's book, was as valid an introduction to a philosophical discussion about species and Natural Selection as Darwin's inclusion of geology in the *Origin.* The several favourable reviews of Matthew's book are discussed elsewhere.

Darwin knew very well that the subject of Matthew's book was not about a different subject. In 1868 Darwin published *Variations in Animals and Plants under Domestication* and actually quotes from *Naval Timber and Arboriculture*: 'Our common forest trees may be seen in every extensive nursery-ground; but as they are not valued like fruit trees, and as they seed late in life, no selection has been applied to them; consequently, as Mr Patrick Matthew remarks, they have not yielded different races . . .' Darwin's statement is a direct quotation of Matthew's comment in the chapter on Nurseries page 107 of *Naval Timber and Arboriculture.* Yet, in 1872 Darwin asserts that the subject was different from that in the *Appendix*; at face value it seemed a truthful statement and, of course, was believed. A century later Mayr (1982), having never read a word of *Naval Timber and Arboriculture* or its appendix, accepts Darwin's statement and repeats, 'These notes have virtually no relation to the subject matter of the book, and it is therefore not surprising that neither Darwin nor any other biologist had ever encountered them.' Mayr had plenty of time in his long life to have glanced through *Naval Timber and Arboriculture* but he never did. His assertions which have just been quoted above were mere repeats of inaccurate statements made by Kentwood Wells (1973). In reviewing Matthew's book John Loudon certainly made the point that the book and its appendix were linked.

Eiseley (1959) made this assertion about the above quotation from Darwin's book of 1868: 'This statement appears to be a shortened version of the 1844 comment placed in a new setting with some additional comment from another page of Matthew added. The re-emergence of this discussion of the variability of forest trees in nurseries suggests that Darwin was aware of Matthew in 1844.'

Darwin continues, '. . . the difference of Mr Matthew's views from mine are not of much importance: he seems to consider that the world was nearly depopulated at successive periods, and then restocked.' Was this one of the differences? If so, Matthew's view is the modern view that extra-terrestrial catastrophes had wiped out large masses of plant and animal life and those that had survived carried on life until the next catastrophe. The history of the organic world according to Matthew was a steady state interrupted by catastrophes. Cuvier had evidence of the catastrophes but believed that new life had been created miraculously. Matthew did not accept the latter aspect of Cuvier's catastrophism.

Darwin continues, '. . . and he gives as an alternative that "new forms may be generated" without the presence of any mould or germ of former aggregates.' This was an idea that had done the rounds in Paris. There is a chapter in Lamarck's *Philosophie Zoologique* on spontaneous generation. It would appear that Matthew was not impressed. Since Darwin gives only half of Matthew's sentence the inclusion of this section could only serve to make Matthew look ridiculous. In fact Darwin stops half-way in the sentence which continues, '. . . but this scarcely differs from new creation, only it forms a portion of a continued scheme or system.' Since Matthew ruled out 'new creation' it was obvious that he did not accept what amounted to miraculous birth.

Darwin continues, 'I am not sure that I understand some passages; but it seems that he attributes much influence to the direct action of the conditions of life.' The uninformed reader by the time the last sentence is reached has already written off Patrick Matthew. Is Darwin saying that he does not understand 'the influence of the direct action of the conditions of life'? Is this another of the differences? Matthew certainly did take into consideration the direct action of the conditions of life. The modern concept of convergence fits the concept of the direct action on the conditions of life. Indeed it would accord with Lamarckian concepts of change. That Darwin in 1872 did not care about this influence becomes clear in a letter to Professor Semper on 19 July 1881: '. . . no doubt I originally attributed too little weight to the direct action of conditions.' If we turn back to the section on Lamarck we will see how confusing Darwin could be.

It is odd that Darwin should show apparent surprise that Matthew should take 'the conditions of life' into consideration. This, of course, was one of Lamarck's ideas, and hence of doubtful value in England at that time. It is odd because from the very first edition of the *Origin* in the chapter on 'Hybridism' several pages are devoted to the 'conditions of life': 'It is an old and almost universal belief, founded, I think, on a considerable body of evidence, that slight changes in the conditions of life are beneficial to all living things.' In these pages Darwin makes the point that slight changes in the conditions of life are beneficial whereas greater changes are not. When Matthew used this 'universal belief' to predict that a change of conditions for the British unemployed would be beneficial he was not stating anything new except that he now included man, himself, among 'all living things'. (*Emigration Fields*, 1839.)

In the summary of the chapter on 'Hybridism' Darwin did not forget to introduce the conditions of life aspect. So what was Darwin's motive in pointing out that Matthew believed that a change of conditions could be important? Could it be that the conditions of life was a well known Lamarckian concept? In fact, Lamarck devoted a whole chapter to 'Influence of Environment' in *Philosophie Zoologique*. To be a Lamarckian was not at that period considered to be scientifically correct! Like Darwin's original reference to Matthew's mass extinctions this other example of Matthew's 'nonsense' would be understood. But Lamarck made distinctions between what was and what was not influenced by the environment: 'But the birds when compared with the mammals display an obvious degradation of organization which has nothing to do with the influence of the environment.' If one examines the 'Comparisons of Editions' of the *Origin* (Oxford University Press) there are only a few words that were changed over the years in that particular chapter. Whatever Darwin's motive may have been the short note about Matthew in the *Historical Sketch* did not do Matthew's reputation any good.

One should not forget that Darwin was also well aware that Cuvier was concerned with the conditions of life or, as Cuvier expressed it, 'conditions of existence'. 'The expression of conditions of existence, so often insisted by the illustrious Cuvier, is fully embraced by the principle of natural selection. For natural selection acts by either now adapting the varying parts of each being to its organic and inorganic conditions of life or by having adapted them during long-past periods of time; the adaptations being aided in some cases by use and disuse, being slightly affected by the direct action of the external conditions of life. Hence, in fact, the law of the Conditions of Existence is the higher law; as it includes,

through the inheritance of former adaptations, that of the Unity of Type.'
And there Darwin closed chapter 6 of the *Origin* – Difficulties of Theory.

So what was Darwin on about with, '. . . it seems that he attributes
much influence to the direct action of the conditions of life'? This
Cuvier–Lamarckism in its many distorted forms was by then considered
to be scientifically incorrect. No one more than Darwin knew that
Matthew was not voicing anything new. The effect of 'conditions of
life' runs through the French naturalists' writings of Lamarck, Lacépède
and others back to Buffon himself. Nowhere, on the other hand, does
Darwin mention that Matthew attributed much influence to Natural
Selection. And nowhere in the *Origin* is the 'illustrious Cuvier' presented
as the naturalist who helped to prepare the climate for the development
of organic evolution.

Although Darwin ended his short note that Matthew, 'saw clearly the
full force of natural selection', he had so belittled Matthew earlier on
that the importance of the last sentence was dissipated. In any case, what
did the full force of Natural Selection mean if Matthew had written so
briefly? Had Darwin told the truth the statement would have read thus:
Matthew introduced the concept of Natural Selection as a fundamental
law of nature, in addition he discussed divergence in terms of diverging
ramifications, the mutability of species, rejected the miraculous birth of
new species following catastrophes, held to a steady state in nature
interrupted by catastrophes, rejected development from nearly-allied
species in favour of descent from a common ancestor, recognized the
difference between domestic and wild species, and recognized what
constituted a species.

Had Darwin reduced the *Origin* to the size of the summaries of each
chapter the *Origin* would still have retained its full flavour. Darwin should
have written the *Origin* as an encyclopaedia.

Darwin did not comment on a passage a few lines further on in the
Appendix. This can only be described as inspired speculation: 'Does
organized existence, and perhaps all material existence, consist of one
proteus principle of life capable of gradual circumstance-suited modification and aggregation . . . ?' The current belief following the discovery
of the double helix is the apparent universality of DNA as the hereditary
material and the universality of the genetic code from bacteria to man,
indicate a common origin of all living things.' (Smith, 1974.)

Darwin does not mention whether there were any differences with

Matthew over the subject of Natural Selection itself. Darwin kept on defining what he meant by Natural Selection in the chapters devoted to the struggle for existence and Natural Selection. Here are some of these definitions:

'But natural selection, as we shall hereafter see, is a power incessantly ready for action, and is as immeasurably superior to man's feeble efforts, as the works of Nature are to those of Art.'

'Natural selection can act only by the preservation and accumulation of infinitesimal small inherited modifications, each profitable to the preserved being.'

'I have called this principle, by which each slight variation, if useful is preserved, by the term Natural Selection, in order to mark its relation to man's power of selection.'

Matthew defines the Natural Selection once: The principle of Natural Selection,

'. . . is in constant action, it regulates the colour, the figure, the capacities, and instincts; those individuals of each species, whose colour and covering are best suited to concealment or protection from enemies, or defence from vicissitude and inclemencies of climate, whose figure is best accommodated to health, strength, defence, and support; whose capacities and instinct can best regulate the physical energies to self-advantage according to circumstances – in such immense waste of primary and youthful life, those only come forward to maturity from the strict ordeal by which Nature tests their adaptation to her standard of perfection and fitness to continue their kind by reproduction.

'From the unremitting operation of this law acting in concert with the tendency which the progeny have to take the more particular qualities of the parents, together with the connected sexual system in vegetables, and instinct limitation to its own kind in animals, a considerable uniformity of figure, colour, and character, is induced, constituting species; the breed gradually acquiring the best possible adaptation of those of its condition which it is susceptible of, and when alteration of circumstance occurs, thus changing in character to suit those as far as its nature is susceptible of change.'

No wonder Darwin did not want to take on this argument. Matthew gives a wide ranging principle and not Darwin's every slight variation if profitable. Suppose the profitable variation is no longer profitable in the next set of circumstances. Both Darwin and Matthew were naturally speculating; it would seem to me that Matthew's avoidance of slight variations, if profitable, was a breeder's awareness that slight and profitable variations would never produce change from one species to another.

At least, agreement was reached on one aspect of natural selection:

Darwin: 'It may be said that natural selection is daily and hourly scrutinizing . . .'

Matthew: 'Natural selection is in constant action.'

Darwin then races though other names who had commented on varieties becoming species – Von Buch, Rafinesque, Haldman, d'Halloy. *The Vestiges of Creation,* because there was no hint of Natural Selection, is given quite a good write-up. Indeed, Darwin had criticized Thomas Huxley for the 'needless savagery' of his critique: 'In my opinion it has done excellent service in this country in calling attention to the subject, in removing prejudice, and in thus preparing the ground for the reception of analogous views.' In other words it helped to take the heat out of the furore when the *Origin* was published. The author was Robert Chambers who feared for his family's publishing business, such was the prejudice against evolutionary ideas even in the 1840s.

It has been said that the reason for the *Historical Sketch* was to counter Richard Owen's claim to have published the theory of Natural Selection before Darwin. But Darwin dismisses the claim by pointing out that Dr Wells and Patrick Matthew had preceded even him.

Geoffroy St Hilaire who had countered Cuvier's anti-transmutation in Paris all through the 1820s, always in support of Lamarck, is dispensed with in one paragraph.

A paragraph is devoted to Herbert Spencer. In *Darwin Revalued,* Sir Arthur Keith writes, 'What was the reason for Darwin's stand-off manner towards his great contemporary? One would expect that Darwin, who found evolutionary-minded men of great rarity, would extend a welcoming hand to one who was clearly a supporter of the theory of evolution. Yet his letter to Spencer was very different from those he addressed to Hooker.' Keith asks his question after noting that in November 1858 Darwin received a copy from Herbert Spencer, of his *Essays, Scientific, Political and Speculative* (1858). Keith goes on to say that

Darwin's letter was rather stiff. Of course it had to be because Spencer was on the Darwin trail. But Keith, like so many Darwin fans, was never able to come to terms with the complex character Darwin was and how resolutely he behaved in his attempt to prove to the world that he owed nothing to his predecessors. In the *Sketch* no mention is made of Spencer's 1858 publication. And he is not indexed in the *Origin* although a Lord Spencer is.

No mention of Edward Blyth occurs in the *Sketch*. Blyth had certainly no influence on Darwin in so far as the transmutation of species is concerned but for much information on a multitude of natural phenomena, and particularly varieties, he was deeply in debt. In the *Origin* there are a few references to Blyth but in *The Descent of Man* there are over 40 references to the publications of Blyth. Darwin made reference in his publications to most if not all of Blyth's field observations. The one reference which Darwin never mentioned is Blyth's 1835–37 essays on varieties published in *The Magazine of Natural History*. More of this is discussed elsewhere. Blyth earlier on had come in for Darwin's derogatory treatment when he described him to Hooker as, '. . . a very clever, odd, wild fellow who will never do what he could do from not sticking to any one subject.' These remarks would not stimulate one to seek out the essays of 1835–37.

Another individual who does not appear in the *Sketch* is Mr Barrande. When Charles Lyell wrote Darwin in 1855 urging him to elect Joachim Barrande to the Royal Society Foreign list, the message was sent on to Huxley because he was going to the Crystal Palace on the day of the Society meeting. Now Barrande was not an unknown character to Darwin; indeed, he was very well acquainted with his work and there is reference to it in the *Origin*. Darwin is discussing here the remarks of de Verneuil and d'Archiac who were of the opinion that changes in species, '. . . were dependent on general laws which govern the whole animal kingdom.' 'Mr Barrande has made forcible remarks to precisely the same effect,' notes Darwin. Further on in the same chapter Darwin notes, 'In regard to the invertebrata, Barrande, and a higher authority could not be named, asserts that he is every day taught that Palaeozoic animals, though belonging to the same orders, families, or genera with those living at the present day, were not at this early epoch limited in such distinct groups as they are now.' So why should Darwin give the cold shoulder to Barrande when they had so much in common? It was precisely because they had so much in common before the *Origin* was published that the cold–shoulder technique had to come into play. Barrande was not elected and never was. Herbert Spencer was not a breeder and so did not argue the importance of Natural Selection but proclaimed the survival of the fittest. Spencer's 1858 *Essays* were so much in favour of evolution that Darwin had no option but to omit them from the *Sketch*.

The next naturalist to appear in the Sketch is C. V. Naudin. He is described as 'a distinguished botanist' who in 1852 stated, '. . . in an admirable paper on the *Origin of Species* his belief [is] that species are formed in an analogous manner as varieties under cultivation . . . but he does not show how selection acts under nature.' It would have been pure speculation if he had attempted that task. What Darwin does not reveal was the letter he received from Joseph Hooker in 1852 enclosing an extract from the very paper noted above: 'We don't believe that nature has proceeded to form its species, in another manner than we ourselves proceed in creating varieties; let us say better: it is her very procedure that we have transported into practice.' In his reply to Hooker Darwin dismissed the article because there was nothing in it about the struggle for existence! In 1852 Naudin's argument was too close to his own and so Hooker had to be deflected from the significance of the statement until the *Origin* had been published which at that time appeared to be a long time away. 'The struggle for existence' came to Darwin from Lyell who lifted it from Lamarck. Other individuals mentioned in the *Sketch* are not indexed in any edition of the *Origin* – Schaaffhausen, Lecoq, Von Baer and Naudin.

People who had no influence, on the other hand, would be praised to the heavens. 'Linnaeus and Cuvier were my gods,' he would declare, in spite of the fact that everyone knew that Cuvier was opposed to species mutation, and catastrophes played no part in the *Origin*. At other times, although in constant disagreement with Charles Lyell, he would declare that some times he felt that all his work came from Lyell's brain! The same Lyell was very slow to accept Natural Selection but more and more, to Darwin's annoyance, became a supporter of Lamarck.

Then in the *Autobiography* (1876) comments are made which are scarcely credible. For example, what happened one day in Edinburgh when out on a walk with Grant who, '. . . burst forth in high admiration of Lamarck and his views on evolution. I listened in silent astonishment, as far as I can judge, without an effect on my mind.' Darwin expects us to believe that. It is known that the young Darwin received a good grounding in Lamarckism while he was in Edinburgh during a period of two years. As we have noted elsewhere he was made to read Lamarck's study of invertebrates before he demonstrated to the Plinian Society his discovery of cilia on an invertebrate. (Desmond and Moore, 1991.)

8

Matthew the Obscure

'You have no idea of the intrigues that go on in this blessed world of science. . . . For instance, I know that the paper I have just sent in is very original and of some importance, and I am equally sure that if it is referred to the judgement of my 'particular friend' Professor Owen that it will not be published. He won't be able to say a word against it, but he will pooh-pooh it to a dead certainty.'

A letter from Huxley to a friend
The Encyclopaedia of Evolution (1990)

Thomas H. Huxley himself was not without sin. Along with Charles Lyell and Darwin he slandered Lamarck and reduced that worthy evolutionist to a 'trumpeter of Erasmus Darwin'. For a dressing down of Huxley for distorting Lamarckian concepts, one should consult the essay of Cannon (1955–56). Darwin's ignorance about who Patrick Matthew was and his anger at being anticipated led him to rubbish Matthew by reducing him to 'an obscure writer on forest trees'. Darwin was very skilful in rubbishing people who came near to what he called 'my theory'. Why did he have to use this adjective? Why have an adjective at all? Well, 'obscure' caught the imagination of science writers in the second half of this century. Here is how the intrigues go.

Matthew the obscure seems to start in earnest with Eiseley (1958). In his interesting and quite informative book Darwin's century, Matthew is classified as a 'minor evolutionist' along with William Wells and Robert Chambers. Eiseley was obsessed with 'obscure' and the more he used this adjective the more light is lost and obscurity takes over. This is Eiseley's opening statement: 'Matthew's system perished, not only because it had been published by an obscure man but because uniformitarian geology at the hands of Lyell was about to weaken and overthrow the

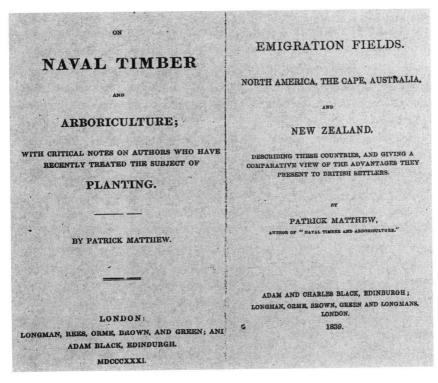

ON

NAVAL TIMBER

AND

ARBORICULTURE;

WITH CRITICAL NOTES ON AUTHORS WHO HAVE
RECENTLY TREATED THE SUBJECT OF

PLANTING.

BY PATRICK MATTHEW.

LONDON:
LONGMAN, REES, ORME, BROWN, AND GREEN; AND
ADAM BLACK, EDINBURGH.

MDCCCXXXI.

EMIGRATION FIELDS.

NORTH AMERICA, THE CAPE, AUSTRALIA,

AND

NEW ZEALAND,

DESCRIBING THESE COUNTRIES, AND GIVING A
COMPARATIVE VIEW OF THE ADVANTAGES THEY
PRESENT TO BRITISH SETTLERS.

BY

PATRICK MATTHEW,
AUTHOR OF "NAVAL TIMBER AND ARBORICULTURE."

ADAM AND CHARLES BLACK, EDINBURGH;
LONGMAN, ORME, BROWN, GREEN AND LONGMANS,
LONDON.

1839.

Photocopy of the publishers' notices of the works of Patrick Matthew

catastrophist philosophy.' This may sound strange to us today when every schoolboy has heard how the last great catastrophe, about 70 million years ago, destroyed the dinosaurs and most other creatures and plants.

Matthew had no reason to doubt Cuvier's demonstration of a series of catastrophes. His concept fits in to what is now New Catastrophism. The fact that catastrophes are linked to cyclic cosmic events still leaves the problem about the new series of species that appeared after the upheavals. It is now known that very small mammals and other creatures survived that massive upheaval of 70 million years ago. Matthew did not accept Cuvier's miraculous birth of new species. Great attention has been paid in recent years to the catastrophe which exterminated the dinosaurs and other animals and plants. Many explanations have been suggested and recently more attention has been paid to cosmic events. Cuvier did not specify what he actually meant by a catastrophe except that there was evidence of mass extermination by some gigantic upheaval. There was a catastrophe after the melting of the last ice age, which exterminated the mammals in north America, which cannot be related to cosmic events. It is possible that the melting ice caused vast inundations, so drowning all living creatures. The flooding of the land would have occurred long before the forests grew up and human hunters entered the area.

Eiseley proceeds to let us know that he had no more information about Matthew than Darwin had. 'It is regrettable that no published information exists beyond what we can gain from his book, as to the intellectual life history of this crotchety but perceptive man.' This was all wrong as well. Like Mendel's paper of 1865 or the Darwin–Wallace communications to the Linnean Society in 1858 no one paid any attention to the *Appendix* because what the author had to say was ahead of the times. Thomas Huxley did not bother to go to that meeting at the Linnean Society. Those present at the meeting, Darwin let it be known years later, had nothing to say. Had the review of the *Origin* by Huxley in *The Times* not raised a storm of protest in society, the *Origin* also may have been ignored. Even so the main message of the *Origin*, Natural Selection, only met with lukewarm reception and was not really secure until 1930.

Unlike poor Mendel's paper Matthew's book was favourably reviewed in the top journals of the day. Only two reviewers commented on the appendix; Loudon who did not understand it and the reviewer in the *United Services Journal* who would have nothing to do with its political aspect. Matthew's book was ignored because it was too far ahead of its times and not because he was a catastrophist. Darwin never mentions catastrophism among his derogatory remarks. The usual criticism in the nineteenth century was that the *Appendix* was brief and a mere recapitulation of Erasmus Darwin!

Had Eiseley appreciated that Matthew had picked up his evolutionary ideas not only from Cuvier but also and more importantly from Lamarck, he would have realized there was no contradiction between accepting catastrophes and change of species over immense time. At different depths in the earth's crust there were different fossils; were they created miraculously or was there an unbroken series of species changing over the millions of years between each upheaval? That was the centre of debate right up to 1859.

Eiseley berates Matthew because he was a catastrophist. American authors write in terms of Matthew the Catastrophist and Darwin the Uniformitarian. If Darwin paid little attention to catastrophes that does not make Matthew hopelessly lost in a world of Uniformitarianism. This point is discussed in more detail in the next section dealing with the *Historical Sketch*.

After an analysis of Matthew's *Appendix* Eiseley then takes the attitude of the full-time state-paid academic: 'It is a great tragedy that he did not bring his views into the open because the amount of ground he was able to cover in a few paragraphs suggests that he might have been able to sustain a longer treatise.' It's that brevity again! Matthew, although a rich man, was a man working for a living and was not concerned, as an academician would be, with the minutiae of the subject. Although Darwin had to admit that Matthew's views were mighty close to his own Eiseley dismisses Matthew as he does Dr William Wells: 'Their words were obscure flashes in the dark . . . It was time for something weightier to appear . . . *The Vestiges of the Natural History of Creation*.' Well, his students must have been confused by now. That the *Vestiges* aroused great interest in evolution is well known but the Creator was still controlling the universe and there was not one word about Natural Selection.

Some alternatives to Matthew the obscure are that he was an enigma or an anomaly. But, according to one author, not only was Matthew himself obscure but the book was published in an obscure place! De Beer (1961) informs us that the '. . . predecessors [i.e. Wells and Matthew] who actually published the principle of natural selection in obscure places remained completely unnoticed . . .' Matthew's publishers were Longman's in London and Adam and Charles Black in Edinburgh. If De Beer had read the 1832 review by Loudon he would not have made this ridiculous statement: '. . . these works show that neither Wells nor Matthew had any appreciation of the magnitude on which they had stumbled or any competence to work it out.' Such is the arrogance of the full-time academic. How can one 'stumble' on Natural Selection? Jay Gould (1983) rounds it all off by finding that the context in which the *Appendix* was published was obscure.

Jay Gould (1983) would also agree with Darwin's assessment that the burial of such insight in the appendix to a work on naval timber not only guaranteed its obscurity but also indicates that Matthew really did not fully grasp the revolutionary extent of what he proposed. This is another ploy used by, what Richard Dawkins calls, Real-Life Darwinists to round off their petty criticism. Here is Matthew expounding a universal law encompassing all plant and animal life including man; the law of Natural Selection! This man, we are advised, did not understand what he had expounded. Part of the problem is that Matthew's second book had not been read by the Real-Life Darwinists. *Emigration Fields*, published in 1839, involves the universal law to justify cold-blooded colonization; the survival of the fittest in its proper context. We will deal further with this aspect in the section devoted to *The Descent of Man*.

Gould (1983), with an imaginative sweep, discovered what Matthew had done with his Natural Selection and no more obscure place could be found: '. . . he buried it in his forest trees and saw no forest.' And yet, the same author in an article (1987) defending the honour of Richard Owen, had this to say: '. . . but scholars do make a tacit pledge when they enter this exacting profession – to honour the struggles of those who have gone before and to treat arguments with respect and integrity.' Although in the same article the great man chides Hoyle for not reading Richard Owen's report on the archaeopteryx, he himself is guilty of the same offence for he had spent but a few minutes on a small part of Matthew's thesis.

Although Jay Gould's jibe about Matthew burying his thesis in his forest trees is nonsense, had he made a closer reading of *Naval Timber and Arboriculture* it would have revealed that Matthew may have preferred to have himself buried among the forest trees rather than in Errol Churchyard. This passage indicates that, in spite of J. Gould, Matthew certainly saw not only the forest but was deeply impressed with its awesome majesty as well:

'We have little belonging to earth more sublime, or which bears home to man a deeper sense of his bodily insignificance, and puny transient being, than an ancient majestic forest, whose luxuriant foliage on high, seems of itself almost a firmament of verdure, supported on lofty moss-covered columns, and unnumbered branched arches – a scene equally sublime, whether we view it under the coloured and flickering light and shadows of the summer eve and morning, resounding to the song of the wild life which harbours there – or under the scattered beams streaming downward at high noontide when all is still – or in winter storms, when the

wild jarring commotion, the frightful rending and lashing of the
straining branches, like the arms of primeval giants, contending
in their might, bear accompaniment to the loud roar and bellow
of the tempest, forming a drone and chaunter to which demons
might dance.'

Another argument put forward, and started by Darwin, is that the
Appendix is brief and merely enunciates the theory of Natural Selection.
Another criticism is that Matthew did not follow up his theory. As was
stated above, *Emigration Fields* was an exposition of Natural Selection
transferred to the human situation of the 1830s. It was a political policy
so that the fittest (i.e. the Caucasians) would survive through colonization. The savages were to make way for the fitter Caucasians and would
be eliminated. Darwin holds out a similar fate for savages in *The Descent
of Man*.

Had Jay Gould (1983) read the whole of the *Appendix* carefully he
would have found that Matthew was a brother-in-arms. No one more
than Jay Gould and Niles Eldredge attacked the modern synthesis of
Julian Huxley. It was fossil and genetic evidence which Jay Gould claimed
pointed to varying rates of species change. It has been well established
that during the Miocene age, which lasted 14 million years, there was a
fantastic increase of horse species and varieties. There was at the same
time progressive changes in the environment where soft foliage gave way
to hard grass lands.

Those authors introduced the 'punctuated equilibrium' model of
evolution which regarded the history of the earth having long periods
of stability interrupted by catastrophes and periods of rapid change. This
was Matthew's view which horrified Kentwood Wells (1973) because it
differed so much from Darwin's steady state and gradual change. Thomas
Huxley was the first to criticize Darwin about his concentration on
gradual changes with no allowance for rapid changes. Julian Huxley
(1942), contrary to his grandfather's opinion, remained with Darwinian
slow and gradual change but claimed that the synthesis allowed for periods
of rapid change: 'The net result will be that, for all practical purposes,
most of the variability of a species at any given moment will be continuous,
however accurate are the measurements made; and that most evolutionary
change will be gradual, to be detected by a progressive shifting of a mean
value from generation to generation.'

The critic who appears to have read more of Matthew's writings than other critics, yet produced the greatest misapprehension, is Kentwood Wells (1973). From the outset one can sense that Matthew is in for some severe criticism. From the very first sentence the stage is set: 'Of all the men who have been put forward as forerunners of Darwin, perhaps the most obscure is Patrick Matthew (1790–1874).' Obscure again! One could believe this statement if one were ignorant of the fact that Matthew had one of the largest orchards in Scotland and was elected the representative of East Fife and Perth for the Great Chartist Convention in London in 1839. Kentwood Wells knew that.

Of course, Kentwood Wells argues, Matthew only became a forerunner after the *Origin* had been published. This logic would make Mendel a forerunner of genetics after the publications of Correns and his other two contemporaries. Then he points out that Darwin was not quite accurate in writing to de Quatrefages that 'no single person ever noticed the scattered passages in his book'. Darwin was spreading this falsehood far and wide. Kentwood Wells takes up the point: 'Matthew's ideas were largely, but not completely, ignored. In the *Gardeners' Magazine* for 1832, a reviewer wrote . . .' Now the reviewer, as has been mentioned elsewhere, was John Loudon – the founder and editor of this and several other journals. What is more important is that Loudon was the most distinguished arboriculturalist in the country at that time. His arboretum at Derby became the blueprint for Central Park in New York. Kentwood Wells noticed an important sentence prior to the announcement about the *Appendix*: 'An appendix of 29 pages concludes the book and receives some parenthetical evolutions of certain extraneous points which the author struck upon in prosecuting the thesis of the book.' Matthew's *Appendix* would have been a bigger book had he not been diverted to political activity by the French Revolution of 1830. At least Loudon realized that the *Arboriculture* and the *Appendix* were linked.

One has some sympathy for Kentwood Wells because he became hopelessly mixed up because of his unfamiliarity with Matthew's affairs and background in the early nineteenth century. He says, 'Matthew has left us few clues from which to deduce the intellectual origins of his theory.' The fact is that Matthew had relatives in France and visited the country several times. He had also been a student at Edinburgh University for two years; his father died and he was obliged to return home to look after the estate. So Matthew would get to know what was being discussed in Paris and later in Edinburgh in the 1820s. We have made reference to this elsewhere. Despite an entrenched religious bigotry Edinburgh was a ferment of social and political ideas in the 1820s; several of the university staff were given chairs of various sciences in London (Desmond 1989). Matthew was also a fruit farmer and hence familiar with hybridization. Why he chose to write about forest trees rather than fruit trees was because his political ideas forced him to protest about the poor state of the national forests. Had his involvement with Chartism not become dominant in his life he would have enlarged the *Appendix* to a large volume. At least Kentwood Wells got this right: 'His two books were practical works intended for practical men.' Both books had political motives – one to secure the efficiency of the navy and the other (*Emigration Fields*, 1839) an attempt to solve mass unemployment; the population of Britain between 1801 and 1840 had risen by 60%.

It is when Kentwood Wells comes to discuss Matthew's approach to geology that he really gets mixed up. The mix-up is partly due to the fact that Kentwood Wells seems unaware that geologists believe in catastrophes today and that this belief is quite compatible with Uniformitarianism. He is not aware that Charles Lyell lifted a lot of ideas from James Hutton in Edinburgh; even an emigré Scot – John Hunter – wrote out Uniformitarianism in 1792 but his brother-in-law buried the essay. Richard Owen eventually found it and recognized its significance and managed to have it published. So when Matthew had something to say about geology he was not a babe in arms. Cuvier had shown the evidence of a series of catastrophes. That is what Matthew accepted; the Scottish geologists had accepted this since Hutton introduced the subject. Today there is evidence that catastrophes occur every 70 million years and some smaller ones every 26 million years. It is generally believed today that after each catastrophe the animals and plants which survive continue evolving. That was Matthew's opinion and Lamarck's teaching.

In order to demonstrate how ridiculous and how inferior Matthew's view of earth history was compared to Darwin's, Kentwood Wells contracts their views: 'For Darwin, change was a gradual and continuous process, operating in an almost infinite time scale.' But For Matthew, the picture was totally different: 'Change had been sudden and discontinuous, a series of geological catastrophes which destroyed most life on earth. The surviving remnants . . . adapted themselves to the new circumstances . . . new set of species . . . evolved . . . to replace those which had been destroyed . . . periods of rapid evolutionary changes were followed by "millions of ages of stability . . ."' No better exposition of punctuated equilibrium could be made – *pace* Jay Gould! As has been pointed out before, Darwin in his *Historical Sketch* made the same charge about Matthew. Darwin's statement implied that Matthew's views were nonsense. What Darwin and later on others down to Kentwood Wells had failed to appreciate was that Uniformitarianism, although manifestly true as far as it went with Charles Lyell, lacked the full picture – lacked catastrophes!

Cuvier did not accept that species had mutated and as proof that species did not mutate he produced, to his everlasting shame, the mummies of animals brought from the tombs of Egypt. He had not gone on that fantastic, ill-fated voyage down the Mediterranean to Egypt with Napoleon. However, the mummies of the various animals on display were exactly the same as their present day representatives.

Charles Lyell, when revising the 12th edition of his *Principles* in 1875, made the point of quoting what Cuvier, Lacépède and Lamarck had written in their report on the mummies. 'We can scarcely restrain the transports of our imagination, on beholding thus preserved, with their minutest bones, with the smallest portions of their skin, and in every particular most perfectly recognizable, many an animal . . .'

Although Cuvier was dishonest in claiming that the age of the mummies (4,000 years) disproved mutation of species, Lamarck did not agree. Lyell stresses this difference: 'It was by this constant reference to time as an essential element even in the definition of a species, that the teaching of Lamarck differed from Linnaeus, Blumenbach and Cuvier.' Lyell continued with his revision of the 12th edition: 'I have reprinted in this chapter word for word, my abstract of Lamarck's doctrine of transmutation as drawn up by me in 1832 in the first edition of the *Principles of Geology* Vol. 11, Chapter 1. I have thought it right to do this in justice to Lamarck, in order to show how nearly the opinions taught by him at the commencement of the century resembled those now in vogue amongst a large body of naturalists respecting the indefinite variability of species and the progressive development in past time of the organic world.'

So Matthew accepted that some species had lasted 40 centuries with little or no change – for his day and age Matthew was right: the animals that survive the catastrophe partly by luck and partly by Natural Selection those (circumstance-suited) continue the new life; the new life was then steady for an indefinite period. The only evidence at that time was Cuvier's 40 centuries.

Kentwood Wells rubs it in: 'Matthew's system is a paradox . . .' Matthew had no idea what a species was and so Kentwood Wells tells us: 'A species, then, is a group of organisms who resemble one another.' What a nonsense this is. Here is Matthew taking a 'Darwinian line' against Wallace's supposed new law (1855): '. . . the progeny of the same parents, under great influence of circumstance, might, in several generations, even become distinct species, incapable of co-reproduction.'

With the typical arrogance of the shallow academic, Kentwood Wells really falls in a mud bath of confusion when he comes to geology. Having gone out of his way to misinform about Matthew's concept of species he continues on the same tack with geology: 'Thus, we have his picture of one set of species replacing another, with like individuals "herding" together. If this is applied to the survivors of the last catastrophe, which apparently occurred something over 4,000 years ago, we are left with a picture very similar to the traditional one of the 1820s. For what we essentially have, in non-theological terms, are the survivors of Noah's Flood, herding together by twos or by hundreds, subjected to the action of natural selection and adapting themselves to the new world after the Deluge.' One has to reply to this absurd nonsense: Cuvier was prepared to argue that the last catastrophe could have occurred 4,000 years ago in order to defend desperately his anti-mutation stand by producing 4,000-year-old mummies. Nor could Kentwood Wells have understood what Darwin wrote in his *Historical Sketch*: 'The differences of Mr Matthew's views from mine are not of much importance . . . He clearly saw the full force of the principle of natural selection.' To this Kentwood Wells would argue that Darwin did not understand Matthew!

Kentwood Wells, like so many uncritical academics, really believed that Darwin was influenced by Malthus; we have made reference elsewhere to the fact that his close companion for 30 years wrote to Darwin in 1863 to ask him if he had read Malthus.

Mayr (1982), on the other hand, who has spent more time searching through Darwin's documents, is of the opinion that the influence of Malthus was minimal. Malthus is mentioned briefly in one sentence in Notebook D. Malthus is mentioned twice in the paper he read to the Linnean society in 1858 and in the *Origin* of 1859. Indeed, I can not find any other reference to Malthus except that curious letter to Wallace.

Recovering from a bout of malaria Wallace tells us he remembered Malthus. After that Darwin had to remember as well.

Never at a loss to point out deficiencies which Kentwood Wells imagines are in Matthew's writings, he plays what he believes is a trump card: 'Matthew never mentioned any direct link between man and animals, and there is no evidence that he even considered the question.' Neither did Darwin in the *Origin* and that is why he had to write *The Descent of Man*. But Matthew would have been aware, what every educated Scot would know, that Lord Monboddo had seen the orangutan and concluded man had a simian origin. When Darwin got around to publishing *The Descent of Man* a long review of it appeared in the *Scotsman* newspaper. The reviewer was Patrick Matthew. It was a favourable review but not a critical one; he could have stressed the fact that Darwin had changed his mind about the supreme importance of Natural Selection. This review is further discussed in another section. It is clear that the favourable review did nothing to endear him to Darwin as one can judge from the curt reply acknowledging Matthew's letter and the enclosed copy of the review. Had Kentwood Wells read that review he would have realized that Matthew had thought hard about man's relation to other animal species.

Kentwood Wells's confusion arises partly from his assumption that conditions in Scotland, where Matthew wrote his books, and England, where Darwin wrote his books, were similar. The eighteenth-century intellectual ferment in Scotland produced geologists who had no concern for Holy Writ which was completely sacrosanct at Oxbridge until 1830 when the Reverend Sedgwick dismissed Noah's Flood. James Hutton had a brilliant mind but was quite incapable of writing his material; Professor Playfair did it for him. *The Theory of the Earth* was published in 1795 and bore no relation to the biblical account. There was a long debate amongst the Edinburgh geologists who were divided into Neptunists and Vulcanists. These two schools based their beliefs on the natural evidence as they saw it; there was no reference to Holy Writ. So Matthew's background would be irreligious. With his university education and contacts with atheistic Paris he came to be acquainted with the modern views of geology, evolution and the political vision of pre-Napoleonic revolution.

Most critics of Matthew usually dismiss him as obscure but Kentwood Wells goes even further. He seems to have built up so much antipathy toward Matthew that his criticism is a prolonged invective. 'Matthew was not a scientist . . . His discussions of natural selection were not attempts to "cover ground" in advancing a particular scientific theory, but were simply reflections of his own assumptions about the natural world. Where Matthew saw a series of stable worlds interrupted by violent upheavals, Darwin saw a continuous process of change in an ever-fluctuating world.' Where Matthew states that the species are 'steady' for long periods between catastrophes, Darwin puts it this way: '. . . I do believe that natural selection always acts slowly, often only at long intervals of time, and generally on only a very few of the inhabitants of the same region at the same time.' Both authors were obliged to be vague because they knew they were speculating.

It would appear from Kentwood Wells's criticism of Matthew's vision of a steady organic world interrupted by violent upheavals, that he has not been influenced by the writings of G. G. Simpson – a fellow American! No one, at least after Matthew and Blyth, has exploded single-line evolution more than Simpson. If ever anyone in recent times was involved in spreading the gospel of diverging ramifications it was Simpson in his classical magnum opus – *Horses*. Anti-mutationists, like Cuvier and Richard Owen, considered these interruptions as evidence against the mutation of species. Darwin took the view that there were gaps in the fossil record. Another aspect of evolution which Simpson stressed was that the periods of stability, what Matthew referred to as 'steady', were followed by what appeared to be periods of rapid speciation. How these periods of rapid change were achieved modern palaeontologists have no idea beyond 'a power of change'. Diverging ramifications had come to stay and Matthew included the evolution of man in terms of diverging ramifications.

Matthew makes the point in his review of *The Descent of Man* that there cannot be straight line evolution of man from ape; there had to be diverging ramifications. Until recent times human evolution was considered as a ladder of evolving ape-like creatures. But this concept was exploded in 1975 when Richard Leakey discovered some of the diverging ramifications – *Australopithecus boisei*, *Homo habilis*, *Homo erectus* and others unidentified. More have been found recently. All or some of these ramifications had apparently co-existed at the same time. According to Matthew the best 'circumstance-suited' variety would survive to procreate. In this way Matthew viewed populations becoming circumstance-suited.

One wonders if Kentwood Wells was aware of all the evidence that catastrophes had occurred and well established in the nineteenth century. One wonders also if he had caught up with continental drift and how, after years of persecution, the theory of Alfred Wegener had been vindicated. In Darwin's day the big discussion centred on whether new species were created miraculously, as Cuvier and Owen professed, or there had been a continuous flow of species changing over time as Lamarck maintained. This problem would not have existed were it not for the fact that Cuvier had demonstrated the series of upheavals and the new species which came after them. Kentwood Wells does not appreciate that with the overthrow of Catastrophism catastrophes tended to fade from some English naturalists' minds and so the bare problem of the origin of species was being debated between 1832 and 1859 almost out of context.

As some light relief from all this supposed obscure Matthew we can let in a few words of Mayr (1983): 'The person who has the soundest claim for priority in establishing a theory of evolution by natural selection is Patrick Matthew . . . a wealthy landowner in Scotland, well educated, very well read . . .' No hint of an obscure man in this statement; it almost sounds as if there is some mis-identification.

Although Darwin recognized the role of Natural Selection leading to extinction of species according to Kentwood Wells, Matthew did not: 'Matthew's mechanism of extinction was geological catastrophe.' That is the mechanism accepted today as the major cause. Naturalists at the time Matthew was writing were aware that the dodo had become extinct in Mauritius and in England the bear, the beaver and the wolf and many birds such as the capercaillie had become extinct. The cause of these extinctions was man's ruthless suppression. But these extinctions were nothing compared to those caused by catastrophes which are now believed to be caused by extra-terrestrial objects colliding with our planet. Both Matthew and Darwin recognized selection favouring some individuals and then the fittest variety bringing about the extinction of the less favoured ones. There is today some suspicion that the Neanderthals were exterminated by Cro-Magnon populations.

In trying to draw a distinction on perfection of adaptation between Matthew and Darwin, Kentwood Wells introduces a yawning gap because he made the irreligious Matthew into a Providentialist!

Now there is providence. Kentwood Wells confuses this with

Providence as a synonym for the First Great Cause as Edward Blyth would say. The discussion is about Note B in *Emigration Fields* under the title 'Radical Charity'. Because Matthew started one sentence with a capital P for Providence the confusion begins, although a few sentences further on Matthew writes about 'the laws of providence'. Matthew should have made it clear that providence in Scotland indicated thrift or frugal management in friendly societies – provident societies and later co-operative societies. All the same one would have thought that a proper reading of the whole Note B would have made it clear that Matthew was distinguishing between charity and providence. Matthew can be at times as confusing as any imperialist of his time; they all lived in a mass of contradictions. By this I mean industrial tycoons like the Scot, Andrew Carnegie, who employed thugs to beat up any workers trying to form a union or protesting about the miserable conditions they had to work under and then bestowed all his money to the betterment of his fellow Scots – particularly his setting up of libraries. Although not an industrial tycoon Matthew could also show two sides to his social ideas: in Note D (*Naval Timber and Arboriculture*) is this statement: 'The rougher excitement of hatred, ambition, pride, patriotism, and the more selfish passions, is necessary to the full and strong development of our active power. That Britain is leaving the impress of her energy and morality on a considerable portion of the world, is owing to her having first borne fire and sword over the countries . . .' Then in Note B (*Emigration Fields*) is this statement: 'The rich man's charity is an unnatural offence, a human interposition counteracting the laws of providence.'

Note B sets out Matthew's abhorrence of charity: 'Common charity (alms giving) is much of an aristocratical thing, and has been the means of rivetting the chains of indirect slavery . . . The providently charitable will endeavour to reform the laws which express the industry of the country, and which prevent the diffusion of useful information, and thus enable his fellow men to employ themselves in such a manner as render them independent of all charity. . . the rich man, however, likes to do good in a lordly manner; . . . he is much more disposed to build churches than to build schools . . .' 'Providence, the reverse of this, works by wholesome general laws – and does not give charity – does not give for the asking, but for the doing – does not interpose by miracles to obstruct the working of these general laws . . .' 'The working man hates charity . . .'

It must be clear that Matthew was no Providentialist. Yet Kentwood Wells insists: 'Although he never wrote in strict natural theological terms, Matthew's providential outlook is evident throughout his writings.' In fairness to Kentwood Wells, Matthew should have made it clear what his 'Scoticism' meant.

Kentwood Wells piles on so many misinterpretations of Matthew's views that he reached a stage when he nearly wonders whether perhaps he has got it all wrong. He asks but is unable to provide an answer: 'Why was Matthew, in contrast to virtually all his contemporaries, not an advocate of special creation of species?' And he continues still unaware that he has got it all wrong: 'Given his providential outlook, his catastrophism, and his acceptance of the traditional definition of species, one wonders why Matthew was led to embrace evolution and natural selection at all.'

What Kentwood Wells fails to appreciate is that Darwin's steady state organic world was a reflection of Charles Lyell's steady state inorganic world devoid of catastrophes. It took a long time for Charles Lyell to accept the concept of evolution and when he did he received the sneers of his erstwhile ally: 'Lyell has swallowed the whole theory, at which I am not surprised – for without it, the elements of geology, as he expounded them, were illogical.' (*Life and letters of Reverend Adam Sedgwick*, 1890.) Lyell's hesitation to go along fully with Natural Selection was because he could not see species developing in his day; in the inorganic steady state Lyell could demonstrate that what was going on today was what was going on in ages past.

But Lyell had not swallowed the whole theory as set out by Darwin. He veered more and more, to the annoyance of Darwin, towards Lamarckian evolution. He spent his last years trying to assuage his injustice of 1832 in the first edition of Volume 2 of his *Principles*. As he veered towards Lamarckian ideas he kept finding difficulty in distinguishing between Darwin's and Lamarck's view of evolution. The reason is Darwin was veering towards Lamarck!

There is one other person in the 'obscure' industry to consider. Brackman, in 1980, published *A Delicate Arrangement* in which he mentions, in passing, the 'obscure' book of Patrick Matthew – not the person but the book! Brackman's book is partly a brief biography of Alfred Wallace but also deals exhaustively with one of the shady episodes which ardent Darwin fans either are quite unaware of or wish to eschew. The main part of the book deals with the dishonourable way Charles Lyell and Joseph Hooker arranged a joint meeting at the Linnean Society in order to preserve Darwin's priority and, at the same time, thwart Wallace's priority. In dismissing Brackman's claim for Wallace's priority or Darwin's for that matter, it should be pointed out that the published work of Cuvier, Lamarck, Patrick Matthew and Edward Blyth is not even referred to let alone discussed. For this reason Brackman was unaware how closely the essays of Darwin and Wallace resembled those essays Blyth and Matthew had published more than twenty years previously.

Darwin referred to 'this delicate situation' as a 'miserable affair', although he denied he had any hand in it. The delicate arrangement was also a strange affair and the strangest member of the affair was Sir Charles Lyell. No one in England, besides Richard Owen and Robert Grant and his set, knew more than he about French science and particularly the French contribution to evolution and the mutation of species; the cold materialism of Lamarck left him horrified at such a thought that man was no more than a class of mammal! Lamarck was rejected mainly on religious grounds. The scientific rejection was based on Uniformitarian principles: only causes now in operation could be used to explain the history of the earth and life. When this principle was applied to species there was no evidence. Lyell's overthrow of Cuvier's Catastrophism made him the greatest authority on geology in England. The vast majority of the members of the Geology Society was in agreement with Lyell's attitude to the immutability of species. The effect in England of Uniformitarianism, the denunciation of Lamarckism and the baleful influence of Cuvier was to hold up any progress in upsetting the Linnean contention that species were fixed.

Hooker had been taken into Darwin's confidence about Natural Selection in 1844. Hooker's position in his early days was too insecure to allow him to accept Darwin's views openly or enthusiastically. Darwin gave him an essay to study and comment on in 1847 but Hooker did not feel competent to give a considered opinion. And then Darwin went off for seven years to classify cirripeds!

It is probable that Lyell started to take a serious interest in the organic world after 1844. The years passed and a decade of *The Vestiges of the Natural History of Creation* had prepared the intelligent sections of the middle classes to consider evolution as a possibility, albeit still with a Creator in charge. The élite at Oxbridge were dead against such a concept.

So in 1855 while glancing through *The Magazine of Natural History*, Lyell came across Wallace's essay. He immediately recognized that there was more than a hint of evolution in what Wallace had written. Lyell then rushed off to Darwin to discuss the essay and the intention of making Darwin start writing his book. Certainly there was no reference to the miraculous birth of species which most naturalists accepted at that time including Lyell himself. Furthermore, Wallace had now committed himself to the concept of the mutation of species. When even this was not considered new, according to Darwin, he must have included Robert Grant and his London set who were pupils of Lamarck and long established mutationists. Darwin was not disturbed by Wallace's so-called 'Sarawak' law because it was not an argument in favour of descent from a common ancestor. Although Darwin confidently dismissed Wallace's essay he himself had not published one word on evolution, mutation of species or Natural Selection by 1855.

We do not know how *au fait* Lyell was with the past literature on the subject Wallace had introduced; Lyell opened his own scientific journal after reading Wallace's paper. What we do know is that Lyell, in volume 2 of his *Principles*, had witten out in 1832 the principles of Lamarckism. Over the next eight years it would seem he forgot all about this as will become evident later. Darwin, on the other hand, assures us that he read widely the horticultural and agricultural journals and so his reaction to the essay was less enthusiastic. Why was he not so enthusiastic as Lyell? It was because Darwin knew that what Wallace had claimed as something new was not new! Desmond and Moore (1991), I think, have got it wrong in asserting that Darwin did not understand Wallace's 'coded' language; whatever that means. Indeed, these authors point out that Darwin on his own copy of the journal wrote, '. . . nothing new . . . uses my simile of tree.'

Darwin was quite right – there was nothing new. Except for the simile of the tree of life what other evidence did Darwin have that there was nothing new in the essay? Why Darwin did not tell Lyell why Wallace's essay contained nothing new is very odd. In 1844 Darwin had written to Hooker (11 January 1844): 'In my most sanguine moments, all I expect is that I shall be able to show even to sound Naturalists, that there are two sides to the question of the immutability of species – that facts can be viewed and grouped under the notion of allied species having descended from common stocks.' This was not quite what Wallace had in his essay. In his letter to Jenyns (October 1845) Darwin again raised the point that '. . . allied species are co-descendents from common stocks.' Having discussed 'allied species' ten years previously Darwin was quite right not to be impressed with Wallace's so-called novel statements and write on his copy of the journal 'nothing new'. The rest of that letter to Hooker is his usual diatribe against Lamarck. Thus by 1844 Darwin was thinking in terms of 'allied species'. This aspect had been rejected by Matthew in 1831.

What became known as the 'Sarawak' law was discussed many years before; Matthew had criticised and rejected it in the *Appendix*. Although Darwin always denied having seen the *Appendix*, Matthew had presented the argument as if it had been discussed before. Why did he take until 1857 before he wrote congratulating Wallace? Was Darwin aware that Matthew had discussed descent from 'closely-allied species'? The title of Wallace's essay did not imply that new species were created miraculously! Up till that time only Lamarck and his pupils in England were so orientated. But no mention of this from Darwin.

Wallace's 'gnarled oak' (1855) was probably derived from Blyth. Darwin's 'tree' of 1837 was probably derived from Blyth's 'reiterate diversity' or Matthew's 'diverging ramifications' or Lamarck's 'collaterals'. Furthermore, there was not a hint of Natural Selection in Wallace's essay. So – it would seem – Darwin felt secure that his theory had not been anticipated which would explain his reluctance to get down to work on his book. Brackman (1980) keeps repeating that the 1855 essay disturbed Darwin. There is no evidence. It was at this stage that Darwin let Lyell into his 'secret' of Natural Selection. It is now 1856, the cirriped business was finished and Darwin made a start on his book.

By the time Wallace's 1858 essay arrived at Darwin's house little progress had been made with the book. Darwin had a difficult time from 1856 with domestic problems. After reading the 1858 essay Darwin must have felt the game was up. The information in this essay was the information he had for his book. Both had taken much from Blyth's essays of 1835–37. Although Darlington (1959) realized how much relevant material Darwin took from Blyth, he did not realize Wallace had done the same. No wonder Darwin wrote to Lyell, 25 June 1858: 'There is nothing in Wallace's sketch which is not written out much fuller in my sketch, copied out in 1844, and read by Hooker some dozen years ago.' Some authors have pointed out that this was not quite true. Any discussion of divergence was nowhere to be found in either the 1842 or 1844 sketch. However, in fairness to Darwin, he had drawn a tree of life in his notebook of 1837. Was the absence of any reference to divergence the reason why Darwin did not submit his 1844 essay for the joint meeting at the Linnean Society?

Darwin extended his thoughts about his tree of life in the *Origin*. The tree of life concept derives from the Orient. The father is the trunk and the branches are his progeny. The Crusaders adopted the image and so introduced it to the West in the form of the 'family tree'. Darwin's extensive reading familiarized him with the 'tree of life' concept which was and still is a frequent theme in Persian carpet design.

The fact that divergence was missing in the two sketches but a convincing exposition under 'Divergence of Character' in the *Origin*, led some authors to suspect that Darwin lifted divergence from Wallace. All that may be said is that the 'gnarled oak' of Wallace's 1855 essay may have jolted his memory of Blyth's 'reiterate diversity'. When authors accuse Darwin of deriving divergence from the Ternate (1858) essay they are quite wrong. The 'gnarled oak' and 'vascular system' pictures of the branching of organic life are in the 1855 essay published in *The Magazine of Natural History*. Darwin wrote on his copy of the journal that his 1837 tree of life was similar to that used by Wallace. There are only two brief references to divergence in the Ternate essay. So many American authors have an *idée fixe* on the Ternate essay that perhaps one should note at this point what the essay is all about. It can be divided into two parts. The larger part devoted to Blyth's data and the other part the usual distorted criticism of Lamarck's inheritance of acquired characteristics.

There was still no hint in the 1858 essay of Natural Selection, however, so a book stressing mainly that aspect would secure priority. But where to publish? Darwin kept writing to Hooker about this. He did not want a journal because that would mean a peer review. What he was determined to do was to write without references. Why? Darwin has come in for some criticism over the years about this strange approach to what was supposed to be a scientific book. With Lyell's help the publisher of *The Origin of the Species*, John Murray, was forced to publish Darwin's manuscript as an abstract. In the introduction is this statement: 'This Abstract, which I now publish, must necessarily be imperfect. I cannot here give references and authorities for my many statements; and I must trust to the reader reposing some confidence in my accuracy . . . I must regret that want of space prevents my having the satisfaction of acknowledging the generous assistance which I have received from very many naturalists . . .' Darwin had another twelve years and five more editions of the *Origin* to correct this but avoided giving any further references.

Wallace had not given his sources either in his essay so struggle for existence and the rest would appear his own invention. What was so disturbing about the 1858 essay, so far as Darwin was concerned, was that struggle for existence as regulated by Natural Selection was his theory. At least Wallace had not introduced Natural Selection and, indeed, was to oppose it for many years. That and the fact that Wallace did not understand the laws controlling domestic and wild varieties and species would downgrade Wallace. When Darwin got around to writing to Wallace about the 1858 essay he made sure this point of difference would be stressed.

In the first instance Darwin appealed to Lyell and Hooker for help when he forwarded Wallace's essay to Lyell. Lyell who must have been only too aware of Lamarck's priority in evolution and the mutation of species now behaved as if he was quite unaware. He was now determined to secure priority for Darwin and to thwart Wallace. So he and Hooker set in motion what Darwin referred to as the 'delicate situation' – why? What induced these two highly respected scientists to such dishonest and precipitate action? The story is told in great detail with a great deal of inaccuracies by Brackman (1980). Lyell's behaviour, after the delicate arrangement, is even more inexplicable. At the next British Association meeting in Aberdeen, some months later in 1858, he reported that Darwin was engaged in writing a book about the origin of species, '. . . for which no other hypothesis has been able, or has even attempted to account.' (Darwin, F., 1892.) All this from a distinguished scientist who later on, in 1875, stated in his *Principles of Geology* that he was writing 'word for word' what he had written in the first edition of 1832 how Lamarck had stated it all at the beginning of the century and that many naturalists were now confirming!

Francis Darwin (1892) recorded the joint meeting at the Linnean Society: 'The joint paper of Mr Wallace and my father was read at the Linnean Society on the evening of July 1st.' Further on Francis noted, 'There was no semblance of a discussion.' It should be noted that the only paper presented was that of Wallace. Darwin could only produce two letters which were amended at the proof stage. Darwin wrote to

Hooker from the Isle of Wight (21 July 1858): 'I received only yesterday the proof sheets which I now return . . . I have begun a better abstract for the Linnean Society. My excuse is that it never was intended for publication. I have made only a few corrections in style . . . I suppose some one will correct the revise. (Shall I?) . . .'

In August 1858 Darwin was still on the Isle of Wight and, having received the MS, wrote to Hooker: 'I am much obliged for the correction of style . . .'

The 'better abstract for the Linnean Society' mentioned in the July letter became *The Origin of the Species*!

One has to turn to the Journal of the Geological Society of Dublin Vol. III, 137 (1860) to get Professor Haughton's report about the 'joint paper' because he attended the meeting. Darwin's letters were dismissed as an application of Malthus's doctrine: 'To this there can be no objection, except that of want of novelty.' In his concern about unlimited variation in Wallace's paper the Reverend Haughton failed to notice that Darwin had inserted a few words about Natural Selection in item 3 of the letter to Asa Gray. How could the Reverend Haughton have missed, in Darwin's first extract, the first sentence of the last paragraph: 'Besides this natural means of selection . . . the struggle of the males for the females'? In all editions of the *Origin* Darwin dropped 'the means' and only used Natural Selection. One can not help recalling Matthew's 'natural process of selection' which, of course, Darwin always denied having seen. Brackman (1980), in his haste to laud Wallace's priority, failed to notice what Darwin had put into his extracts. It should be realized that Darwin had the advantage of correcting and amending the proofs of his two extracts. Wallace's paper was published as the Linnean Society received it and the original manuscript apparently has disappeared. There is no mention of Natural Selection in Wallace's essay. As regards diversity, Darwin mentioned it in item 6, as he was later to do in the *Origin*, when discussing the significance of the number of plants able to exist on a yard of turf. Because the Reverend Haughton made no mention of diversity – was it old hat? If the Reverend Haughton failed to recognize the significance of diversity other authors have seized on this first reference to diversity by Darwin as proof he lifted it from Wallace. If Darwin lifted diversity from anyone it was from Blyth or even Lamarck. The example of diversity being manifest in 'a yard of turf' sounds too much like Darwin's observations to be mistaken for Wallace's approach.

The problem is that Darwin amended the extracts at the proof stage. No one knows whether what appeared in print was exactly what was read out at the meeting which might explain why the Reverend Haughton missed so much. If, on the other hand, what was finally printed closely approximates to what was read out at the meeting, then the Reverend Haughton was very unfair in his criticism of Darwin's extracts. The Reverend was not only unfair but ignorant. In his criticism of Wallace's essay he also demonstrated his ignorance of botanical affairs. This would tilt the blame for the confusion towards the Reverend Haughton. It is extraordinary that the Reverend Haughton did not protest that in neither Darwin's extracts nor Wallace's paper were any religious undertones and no reference to a Creator. This was something new in philosophical discussions of biological subjects and obviously not appreciated by the Reverend. If one looks carefully through the transactions of the Linnean Society over fifty years prior to this meeting one can realize that there never was a discussion on the origin of species. On species, yes, but not their origin.

It was Wallace's paper that sorely disturbed the Reverend Haughton: 'The possibility of departing indefinitely from the original type is here assumed and must be an hypothesis contrary to our experience, and at variance with all we know of other departments of nature.' It would seem that the Reverend Haughton had never read Blyth's essays in which varieties could become 'very unlike the original type'.

The 'delicate arrangement' got very little publicity, was soon forgotten and many teachers of biology have never even heard about this episode. So − when at the end of November 1859 the first edition of the *Origin* was published − it was Darwin and he alone who came to be acclaimed as the founder of evolution by Natural Selection.

The years pass by, the 'delicate arrangement' (Leonard Huxley's word) had come and gone, three editions of the *Origin* had been published and then, in 1863, Lyell's conscience stirred him to write Darwin to say that he now realized that he had done Lamarck an injustice. From then on he could see no difference between Darwinism and Lamarckism. Here was a scientist who had denounced Lamarck for thirty years and now for the remaining thirteen years of his life would be spent eulogizing him!

Darwin, naturally, did not like that letter and wrote Lyell to express his alarm at what Lyell was now thinking. The letter of 13 March 1863

can be read in full in *Life of Charles Darwin* by F. Darwin (1892). One
need only pick out the relevant points: '. . . lastly, you refer repeatedly
to my view as a modification of Lamarck's doctrine of development and
progression . . . I can see nothing else in common between the *Origin*
and Lamarck. I believe this way of putting the case is very injurious to
its acceptance . . . what I consider, after two deliberate readings, as a
wretched book, and one from which (I well remember my surprise) I
gained nothing.' Darwin had previously told Lyell that he had gained
nothing from Lamarck's book. Any one reading the *Origin* will realize
that Darwin gained quite a few ideas from Lamarck.

Lyell continued his veering towards Lamarck in each new edition of
his *Principles*. The tenth edition appeared in 1867 and 1868 and indicated
how far Lyell had departed from his earlier attitude to evolution and
mutation of species. Is it just coincidence that about this time Darwin,
too, ceased slandering Lamarck? Francis Darwin (1892) includes Wallace's
comment on the tenth edition in April 1869 (*Quarterly Review*): 'The
history of science hardly presents so striking an instance of youthfulness
of mind in advanced life as is shown by this abandonment of opinions
so long held and so powerfully advocated. If for no other reason than
that Sir Charles Lyell in his tenth edition has adopted it, the theory of
Mr Darwin deserves an attentive and respectful consideration from every
earnest seeker after truth.' Wallace might have added that the real reason
why Lyell was changing from his earlier beliefs was because he was
veering towards Lamarckism. Between 1868 and 1875 Lyell accepted
Lamarckism as he had fully written it out in 1832.

Whether by design Francis Darwin (1902) includes no more information about the further editions of Lyell's *Principles*. But unwittingly he
includes a great deal about Darwin's constant worry over his own
Lamarckisms, pertaining to use and disuse and the direct action of the
environment for which he ridiculed Lamarck! We come now to 1875
and Lyell has revised the 12th edition of his *Principles*. This was to be
the last edition because he died a few months later. In turning to the
1875 edition we find this:

'In former editions of this work from 1832–1853, I did not venture
to differ from the opinion of Linnaeus that each species had
remained from its origin such as we see it, being variable, but
only within fixed limits. I have reprinted in this chapter, word

for word, my abstract of Lamarck's doctrine of transmutation as drawn up by me in 1832 in the first edition of *The Principles of Geology*, Volume 11, Chapter 1. I have thought it right to do this in justice to Lamarck. In order to show how nearly the opinions taught by him at the commencement of this century resembled those now in vogue amongst a large body of naturalists respecting the indefinite variability of species, and the progressive development in past time of the organic world. But, speaking generally, it may be said that all the most influential teachers of geology, palaeontology, zoology and botany continued till the middle of this century either to assume the independent creation and immutability of species, or carefully to avoid expressing any opinion on this important subject. In England the calm was broken by the appearance in 1844 of a book entitled *The Vestiges of the Natural History of Creation*.'

The only supporter of Lamarckism during all those years of Lyell's anti-Lamarkism was Robert Grant. He had died in 1874 so Lyell was on his own in 1875 when he made his last desperate attempt to rehabilitate Lamarck. What was Huxley's attitude to Lyell at this time? Judging by his previous attitude to Lamarck, inspired indeed by Lyell himself, there would be no support. In his *Life and Letters* Vol. 11, page 138, Huxley recounts the period 1851–1858: 'Within the ranks of biologists at that time, I met nobody, except Dr Grant, of University College, who had a word to say for Evolution – and his advocacy was not calculated to advance the cause.' That Dr Grant was an outspoken supporter of Lamarck would, in Huxley's agnostic state of mind, damn him as a ridiculous maverick and later on when Huxley espoused Darwinism that estimate would be reinforced.

What Lyell's reaction was towards Matthew's letter to the *Gardeners' Chronicle* way back in 1860 is nowhere to be found. It is possible that he never heard about it. But Matthew's letter initiated a second delicate arrangement which was as equally dishonest as the first. That letter was approved by Joseph Hooker before Darwin sent it to the journal. It was sufficiently apparently honest but damning to sink Matthew almost without trace. It was a rage reaction so different from Darwin's meek acceptance of Wallace's essay. Although Darwin wrote to Hooker to thank him for the 'delicate situation' he felt ashamed of the whole affair.

'You must let me once again tell you how deeply I feel your generous kindness and Lyell's on this occasion but in truth it shames me.' He never confessed shame about that dishonest letter he sent to the *Gardeners' Chronicle*; in fact, he repeated it all twelve years later in the *Historical Sketch* in 1872.

Brackman (1980) seemed to be mainly concerned with the way Wallace was cheated of priority. But, more importantly, the result of that episode set the way evolution and its so-called founder Darwin would be taught in English-speaking countries right up to the present time. We may take a recent example: '. . . nobody thought of it until Darwin and Wallace in the mid-nineteenth century . . . How could such a simple idea go so long undiscovered? . . . Why did it have to wait for two Victorian naturalists?' (Dawkins 1988.)

If we compare what Dawkins has to say with what Lyell stated with some emotion in the twelfth edition of his *Principles of Geology* of 1875, how are we to explain the discrepancy? Like Darwin himself most real-life Darwinists are careless and, indeed, ignorant in many instances about history. And Dawkins is very angry when ignorant people do not like Darwinism. In his earlier life Darwin was not over-generous in his credits. In the last decade of his life, however, Darwin became more considerate towards Lamarck and here in an example from the introduction to *The Descent of Man* (1874): '. . . the conclusion that man is the co-descendant with other species of ancient, lower, and extinct forms is not in any degree new. Lamarck long ago came to the conclusion, which has lately been maintained by several naturalists and philosophers.' Darwin might have pointed out that Lord Monboddo also, in the eighteenth century, had come to the conclusion that man was of simian origin.

Brackman (1980) seemed to think that priority in enunciating the theory of evolution turned on who introduced divergence first – Wallace in his 1855 and 1858 essays or Darwin after May 1858. Diversity in a simple form had a long history. Buffon introduced diversity on many occasions in his *Histoire Naturelle*! Here is Erasmus Darwin in *Zoonomia*: 'The third great want amongst animals is that of security, which seems to have diversified the forms of the bodies and the colouring of them.' (Erasmus Darwin 1801.) It has been noted elsewhere that Cuvier set the serious investigation of divergence when he introduced the four main branches. Lamarck added the collaterals because he now recognized the genetic link or heredity between evolving species which Cuvier always denied. Then Matthew came in (1831) with 'diverging ramifications' and Blyth with 'reiterate diversity' (1835–37).

In Wallace's 1855 essay the 'gnarled oak' and 'vascular system' of a body gave a pictorial view of diversity. In the 1858 essay diversity is mentioned briefly twice: 'Exhibiting several diverging modifications of form' and '. . . progression and continued divergence deduced from the general laws which regulate the existence of animals in a state of nature.' This was no more than Blyth stated. Divergence became important after Lamarck linked the species genetically and evolving through immense time. There is nothing of this or Natural Selection in Wallace's essays.

We can end by asking this question: who is right? Darwin: 'There is no obvious reason why the principles which have acted so efficiently under domestication should not have acted under nature.'

Or Wallace (1858): 'It will be observed that the argument rests entirely on the assumption that varieties occurring in a state of nature are in all respects analogous to or even identical with those of domestic animals, and are governed by the same laws as regards their permanence or further variation. But it is the object of the present paper to show that this assumption is altogether false.'

In his panic following the receipt of Wallace's 1858 essay, Darwin wrote to Charles Lyell (25 June 1858): 'We differ only, [in] that I was led to my views from what artificial selection has done for domestic animals.' Darwin meekly accepted Wallace's 1858 essay devoid of the term 'natural selection', with no mention of descent from a common ancestor, with nothing new together with the unbelievable nonsense Wallace proposed about domestic and wild varieties. Wallace was not a breeder and had no knowledge of breeding whereas Darwin had spent a considerable time with breeders and, indeed, was presently breeding domestic pigeons.

Darwin wrote to Wallace to tell him about 'the delicate situation'. It was not till 23 January 1859 that Darwin was able to inform Hooker that all was well with Wallace. 'He must be an amiable man,' Darwin commented with relief! On 25 January 1859 Darwin wrote to Wallace a long letter in which the following remarks can be abstracted: '. . . I had absolutely nothing whatever to do in leading Lyell and Hooker to what they thought a fair course of action, yet naturally could not but feel anxious to hear what your impression would be.' If one now refers to the prefatory letter to the Linnean Society by Lyell and Hooker one finds this statement: 'So highly did Mr Darwin appreciate the value of the views there in set forth, that he proposed, in a letter to Sir Charles Lyell, to obtain Mr Wallace's consent to allow the Essay to be published as soon as possible.' Wallace at this time was in Indonesia and letters took about three months to reach that area. Darwin received Wallace's essay on 18 June 1858 and immediately wrote to Lyell and forwarded the essay. On 1 July 1858 Darwin's letters and Wallace's essay were read to the Linnean Society long before any consent from Wallace was obtained!

That it was Hooker who was the main perpetrator of the 'delicate arrangement' is seen in Darwin's letter of 13 July 1858: 'I am more than satisfied at what took place at the Linnean Society. I had thought that your letter and mine to Asa Gray were to be only an appendix to Wallace's paper.' That Darwin was aware that Lyell was fully implicated as well can be seen in a letter to him on 18 July 1858: 'I have never half thanked you for all the extraordinary trouble and kindness you showed to me about Wallace's affair. Hooker told me what was done at the Linnean Society, and I am far more than satisfied, and I do not think that Wallace can think my conduct unfair in allowing you and Hooker to do whatever you thought fair.' It would seem that Darwin supporters over the years are quite happy with the way that bizarre episode was conducted. The object of the episode was to proclaim Darwin's priority – a priority which in five years' time Lyell would start to dispute in favour of Lamarck and continue to uphold until his death in 1875.

So, the ease with which Lyell and Hooker misled the Linnean Society and the safe bedding of Wallace's essay in its *Transactions* within twelve days of arriving at Down House – is it any wonder Darwin was, '. . . far more than satisfied . . .' with the result? But does this episode leave these three pillars of British science standing on the high moral ground? A recent author (Postgate, 1995) has argued that a moral outlook pervades the lives of scientists but that science is morally neutral and does not impose moral values.

A little further on in the letter to Wallace Darwin brings up the point of difference he had mentioned in a letter to Lyell (25 June 1858): 'When ever published, I will, of course, send you a copy, and then you will see what I mean about the part which I believe selection has played with domestic productions. It is a very different part, as you suppose, from that played by "Natural Selection".' So why was Wallace so meekly accepted as the co-founder of evolution and Patrick Matthew cast to oblivion?

Darwin was really beside himself when writing that letter to Lyell and ended in a grovelling mood: 'My good dear friend, forgive me, I will never trouble you or Hooker on the subject again.' When it came to forcing Murray to publish the *Origin* a year later, Darwin had to plead, once again, for Lyell's help. And he got it! The publisher, Murray, wrote to Darwin about the strange 'natural selection' in the title. Only then and for the first time Darwin blurted out that it was a term used in breeding circles.

9

Edward Blyth and his
Classification of Varieties

'. . . A very clever, odd wild fellow who will never do what he
could do from not sticking to any one subject.'

(Darwin to J. Hooker)

It is just as well that Edward Blyth had such an observant butterfly
eye otherwise Charles Darwin would have had to carry out much
more searching of the literature. In the *Origin* Blyth is mentioned twice
and on one occasion Darwin made this comment: '. . . whose opinion,
from his large and varied stores of knowledge, I should value more than
almost any one, thinks that all breeds of poultry have proceeded from
the common wild fowl.' Once the *Origin* was in print Darwin could
afford to present Blyth in a much better light than the comment made
to Hooker. When it comes to 1868 and the publication of *Variation of
Animals and Plants under Domestication* there are about 40 references to
the observations of Blyth. Darwin thanks him for these observations:
'Mr Blyth has freely communicated to me his stores of knowledge on
this and all other related subjects.' In 1871 *The Descent of Man* was
published and in this volume there are about 40 references to Blyth.

As I have found and as Eiseley (1959) was the first to point out there
is no reference in any of Darwin's publications to the important essays
which Blyth wrote before he left England for India in 1842. The essays
are concerned with the classification of varieties but in addition there is
extensive discussion of problems which were to appear in the *Origin*,
and in the essays of Wallace. The essays were published in *The Magazine
of Natural History* in 1835–37. Although Darwin's references to Blyth's
observations involving this magazine are mentioned on numerous occasions there is no mention of these essays we are particularly interested

Portrait of Edward Blyth

in. Why? Eiseley (1959) was of the opinion that Blyth had, '. . . shaped a key that dropped half-used from his hands when he set forth on his own ill-fated voyage. That key . . . was no less than natural selection.' There are some problems with this conclusion. Blyth's voyage was still a few years away and it was not ill-fated; he made a fantastic amount of observations which he regularly sent back to Darwin and he was made Curator of the Museum in Calcutta. He continued every year to pour out monographs, reports and short observations. Even when he returned to England in 1862 he continued to write extensively.

The key that dropped 'half-used' was the obverse of Natural Selection. Blyth was naïvely devout and, like Charles Lyell, refused to consider descent by modification: 'May not, then, a large proportion of what are considered species have descended from a common parentage? I would briefly despatch this interrogatory . . . It is, moreover, foreign to the professed object of this paper.' (1837.) That is clear enough and there is no evidence that Blyth ever changed his mind. He stood, like most of his contemporaries, for the fixity of species by the hand of the Creator and all the observations he ever made were directed to that belief. One should remember that the young Blyth had carefully read the second volume of Lyell's *Principles*. Lamarckian principles were laid bare in that volume, including descent from a common ancestor, but also Lyell's mistranslations and horror of Lamarck's stark materialism that was not in accord with Christian doctrine. The young devout Blyth was impressed by that latter aspect of Lyell's attitude and set out to show that species did every thing possible to retain their fixity: the weak went to the wall, the grouse without its proper colours of concealment taken by a fox, and an animal off guard taken by the swoop of the falcon. Any mutation was detrimental to the stability of the species.

'There are many phenomena which tend in no small degree to favour the supposition . . . [which] I have termed the localizing principle.' It was a well observed fact that there was this aspect in the life history of species. Patrick Matthew had reduced the localizing principle to a few words: 'There is a law universal in Nature, tending to render every reproductive being the best possibly suited to its condition . . . this law sustains the lion in its strength and the fox in its wiles . . .' Blyth provided a mass of evidence supporting this side of the coin of life; Matthew referred to a 'steady state'. The amazing point of this tale is not just that Darwin never acknowledged these essays but neither did Edward Blyth refer to them ever again! The other fact is that Blyth never wrote another essay in quite the same style; the rest of his written work was strictly concerned with observation of nature without any philosophical or religious overtones.

Although we do not agree with Eiseley (1958) that Blyth was almost on the road to Natural Selection his scientific observations were well recognized by Darwin and could be turned to the theme of Natural Selection. Why should Darwin devote the first two chapters of the *Origin* to a discussion of varieties and, as we have noted elsewhere, lift an idea from Blyth for the first sentence of the *Origin* if he had not studied these essays?

Eiseley (1958) makes a reasonable case for the 'Natural process of Selection' of Patrick Matthew being turned into the 'natural means of selection' by Darwin in the 1842 essay. Eiseley (1959) did not find any previous statement in the scientific literature of the time with reference to the term Natural Selection. No one else has offered evidence that Matthew acquired the term from somebody else. Eiseley goes further in suggesting Darwin was aware of Matthew's book in the essay of 1844. Darwin, of course, excused himself for not having found Matthew's work in *Naval Timber*. That was only half the title and the lesser important part.

Matthew made his protest against Darwin's untrue assertion that no one had noticed his book. It is remarkable that Matthew, like Blyth, seems to bear no bitterness towards Darwin in spite of the way he was treated. Even after writing a favourable review of *The Descent of Man* Darwin did not let up on his obvious frustration with Matthew.

There is another aspect to the 1835–37 essays. It has to do with Alfred Wallace who is acknowledged as the co-founder of Natural Selection with Darwin. I find this extraordinary because in neither the 1855 or 1858 essays is there the remotest reference to Natural Selection; the term is not even mentioned. Indeed, as we have shown elsewhere it was only in 1889 in his book 'Darwinism' that Wallace seems happy with 'natural selection'. We have referred to the fact that the 'law' which Wallace concluded the 1855 essay was a problem discussed in Matthew's *Appendix*. Wallace's law was concerned with descent from 'nearly allied species'.

Blyth (1836) also refers to nearly allied species: '. . . different species, nearly allied by either of these physiological relations, exhibit no mutual, no relative adaptation towards each other's habits and structure . . .'

Wallace (1855) used the term 'closely allied' species. Darwin in the *Origin* in the chapter on Variation under Nature also used 'closely-allied': '. . . every reason to believe that many of these doubtful and closely-allied forms . . .'

From the way Matthew introduced the problem it would appear that naturalists had been debating descent from 'nearly allied' species; it would seem for some time previous to 1831. I presume Matthew picked this problem up in Paris because I cannot find it discussed in the English literature. Wallace introduced his 'law' as something new! Matthew even threw out the possibility of 'nearly allied' species in favour of a common ancestor which would be a 'Darwinian' view. The perplexing problem now is why did Darwin write to Wallace agreeing with the conclusion in the 1855 essay?

Could Darwin, at that period, be arguing for descent from a common ancestor? If he was why did he not, as Matthew had done thirty years before, reject this so-called new law of Wallace. The 'Sarawak' law, as it was referred to, involved a hint of evolutionary theory and yet Darwin was not stimulated to get on with his book. As far as Matthew was concerned in rejecting the 'nearly allied' theory was his belief, derived from Lamarck, that descent by modification was from a common ancestor. Even Blyth made this point in his essays and rejected it because he was not a mutationist. When Wallace's essay was published in 1855 it was Charles Lyell who spotted it and brought it to Darwin's attention. Lyell recognized the evolutionary theme of the essay and pleaded with Darwin to get on with his book. Some time later in 1857 Darwin replied to a letter, about the essay, from Wallace. In that letter he agreed with 'the law' Wallace had proposed. This could not have been a hurried decision. So when did Darwin get around to descent from a common ancestor?

Blyth was still in India when Wallace's 1855 essay was published. However, the magazine which contained the essay reached India because Blyth, ever watchful for the interests of Darwin, wrote recommending the 1855 essay. Because descent from a common ancestor would not have Blyth's support he would not have noticed any problem in that essay with Wallace's conclusion about descent from 'nearly allied species'.

Beddall (1972) considered that Blyth's letter must have alerted Darwin to the fact that Blyth, '. . . had fully grasped the significance of Wallace's paper.' I have not come across any philosophical comments about the origin of varieties and species from the pen of Blyth since his essays on the subject in the mid-1830s when he was anti-evolutionist . Now in 1855 he is prepared to write to Darwin and state that, 'Wallace has, I think, put the matter well.' If Blyth could say that now had he become a mutationist or evolutionist? Blyth ends the letter, 'Has it at all unsettled your ideas regarding the persistence of species?' Persistence of species! Had Darwin not told him, as he had confided to Hooker in 1844, that he now believed that species mutated? One can only assume that at some stage earlier in their relationship Blyth had the impression that Darwin was not a mutationist as, indeed, he was not prior to 1844. (F. Darwin 1902.) Beddall (1972) does not appear to have noticed that Darwin was not impressed with Wallace's 1855 essay. He subscribed to that journal and on his own copy wrote 'nothing very new'. Darwin was right but why he agreed with the conclusion of the essay is quite a mystery.

Stranger still, why did Darwin get so agitated with the 1858 essay when he rejected the main thrust of its opening remarks? This paragraph in particular: 'It will be observed that this argument rests entirely on the assumption, that varieties occurring in a state of nature are in all respects analogous to or even identical with those of domestic animals, and are governed by the same laws as regards their permanence or further variation. But it is the object of the present paper to show that this assumption is altogether false, that there is a general principle in nature which will cause many varieties to survive the parent species.'

Even today, as it was accepted by Matthew and Naudin (1852), it is accepted that the varieties which man created involve a process similar to what nature does more slowly. Dr Wells way back in 1813 had written in those precise terms and on this alone was awarded first place in the theory of Natural Selection by the partly relieved Darwin.' So poor old Patrick Matthew is not the first and cannot, ought not, any longer to put in his title pages, 'Discoverer of the Principle of Natural Selection'. This was in a letter to Hooker in 1865. Nature not only produces varieties slowly but species as well. Breeders have not matched nature.

Matthew was adamant about the difference between the wild and domestic varieties: '. . . those only come forward to maturity from that strict ordeal by which Nature tests their adaptation to her standard of perfection and fitness to continue their kind by reproduction.' Blyth also was in no doubt about it: 'The same law, therefore, which was intended by Providence to keep up the typical qualities of a species, can be easily converted by man into a means of raising different varieties; but it is also clear that, if man did not keep up these breeds by regulating the sexual intercourse, they would all naturally soon revert to the original type.' We will note that 'revert to the original type' comes into Wallace's essay!

As has been discussed elsewhere it was well known for many years before Matthew and Blyth that breeding constantly with the same relatives produced what seemed to be chaos. One had no idea what sort of variety would turn up. Darwin brought this into the *Origin*. With a statistical analysis of the results of this kind of breeding Mendel showed there were definite ratios. That was the main factor that was new. So far as breeding in the wild, Blyth and Matthew indicated that a different situation obtained. It was now the best-adapted variety that would survive and reproduce.

Before we come to discuss the Blyth–Wallace relationship I wish to make it clear that when authors are widely read and there is a vast amount of general knowledge available, one author may include in his essay a point that some other author has commented upon. For example:

From the *Appendix*, Note F:

'. . . as far back as can be traced, there does not appear, with the exception of man, to have been any particular engrossing race . . . but it is man alone from whom any imminent danger to the existence of his brethren is to be dreaded.'

From the Blyth essay of 1837: 'It has already been intimated that man is the sole species that habitually destroys for other purposes than those of food.'

One would be hard put to try to make a case here of Blyth lifting from Matthew. When it comes to the Blyth–Wallace relationship it is altogether different.

If we now turn to the main statement in Wallace's 1858 essay we find that it is virtually a repeat of what Blyth had written in some detail in the essays of the 1830s. The list of similarities is considerable:

1. 'The life of wild animals is a struggle for existence.' This phrase is in Blyth's essays, in Volume 2 of Lyell's *Principles*, in Lamarck's essays and, of course, in the *Appendix*.
2. The differences between domestic and wild animals: in respect of food supply, concealment, carnivores are less numerous than herbivores, survival of varieties and species related to their superior adaptation. These and others are all well documented by Blyth.

(Eiseley, 1959, points out that Darwin lifted most of Blyth's true varieties – tailless cats, rumpless fowls, Ancons sheep.)

3. Wallace announces, as if it was something new, that the animal population of a country is stationary. Darwin made use of this as well.

4. Comparative abundance or scarcity of individuals of several species is entirely due to their organization. Well, we have indicated that Matthew's *Appendix* knew all about that and so did Blyth.

5. Blyth's constant use of 'original type'. Note the title of the 1858 essay: 'On the tendency of varieties to depart indefinitely from the original type.'

Wallace continues with an extraordinary statement: 'We see, then, that no inferences as to varieties in a state of nature can be deduced from the observation of those occurring among domestic animals.'

Why this last statement has not been challenged by authors besides Darwin is very odd. It was already well known what would usually happen to a domestic variety when it was left in the wild without man's protection. In rare instances the domestic variety might survive in the wild. Darwin, Lyell and Hooker must have been aware of this. It was all a question of heredity – understood but not fully understood.

We come now to the final paragraph of Wallace's essay:

> We believe we have shown that there is a tendency in nature to the continued progression of certain classes of varieties further and further from the original type – a progression to which it appears no reason to assign any definite limits – and that the same principle which produces this result in a state of nature will also explain why domestic varieties have a tendency to revert to the original type. This progression, by minute steps, in various directions, but always checked and balanced by the necessary conditions, subject to which alone existence can be preserved, may, it is believed, be followed out so as to agree with all the phenomena presented by organized beings, their extinction and succession in past ages, and all the extraordinary modifications of form, instinct, and habits which they exhibit.

Note 'revert to original type' Wallace even used Blyth's classification of varieties but did not acknowledge Blyth. As one reads through Wallace's essay one finds 'revert to the original type', balance of nature, instinct and habits and all other data listed above and it seems déjà vu! Nowhere does Wallace inform the reader what the 'principle' he mentions is all about. The principle which Matthew and then Darwin were concerned with was Natural Selection. If one reads the last paragraph of Wallace's essay several times can one really divine Wallace's principle was Natural Selection? He was more concerned with 'survival of the fittest' which is not the same principle. If it is why is Herbert Spencer not installed in the pantheon of Natural Selection? By 1881, however, Wallace was converted to Natural Selection.

Why did Darwin submit to this short essay and why have many generations of naturalists not wondered why an essay devoid of any actual reference to Natural Selection should share equal place with the *Origin*? Darwin, from the very first day (18 June 1858) he received Wallace's essay, disagreed with its absurd conclusion. In forwarding the essay to Lyell this was pointed out. Later on Wallace was informed of this as well (25 January 1859). Yet it was Darwin himself who created the impression that Wallace shared his views about evolution and Natural Selection. Even when Wallace argued for years against the use of the term 'Natural Selection' there were those who continued to believe Wallace was originally a natural selectionist; even today Dawkins (1988) believes this. Authors took, at face value, Darwin's letter to Wallace on 18 May 1860: 'Here is a curious thing, a Mr Pat Matthew, a Scotchman, published in 1830 a work on *Naval Timber and Arboriculture* and in appendix to this, he gives most clearly but very briefly in half-dozen paragraphs our view of natural selection. It is most complete case of anticipation.' There it is: '. . . our view of natural selection.' In his *Darwinism*, some 40 years later, Wallace (*Darwinism*, 1901), now accepting Natural Selection, omitted, from his list of predecessors of Darwin, Patrick Matthew but included naturalists who had never envisaged or mentioned Natural Selection! Other authors down to modern times have stressed the 'very briefly' part but omitted 'most complete case of anticipation'! Such sometimes is the history of science.

The Magazine of Natural History where Blyth's essays were published was well read by every naturalist of the period. Darwin must have suspected where Wallace derived his ideas for his essay. Why did Darwin fall for all the nonsense of how Malthus had stimulated Wallace to write his essay? If one reads Malthus and Blyth's essays one cannot doubt who really inspired Wallace and it was not Malthus. It seems that Darwin realized he could echo Wallace about Malthus in order to divert attention from Blyth's 1835–37 essays. It has been indicated elsewhere that even devoted admirers of Darwin, like Ernst Mayr, could find no evidence that Malthus meant anything of importance to him.

Blyth was still in India. Lyell and Hooker were appealed to by Darwin for advice about Wallace's essay. These two were among the most distinguished scientists in England and so they quite easily arranged, what has been described as 'the delicate arrangement', with the Linnean Society that joint papers should be read. An article in *The Encyclopaedia of Evolution* (1990) presents it: 'Although Wallace's was the only real paper submitted, the fragmentary Darwin letters were published in first position by Hooker and Lyell.' Lyell and Hooker let the Linnean Society know that Darwin and Wallace had agreed to a joint publication; Wallace, at that time, was on the other side of the world!

And why was Wallace so self-effacing on his return to England? And why was Darwin, at least in the beginning, so friendly towards Wallace? Compare his attitude towards Wallace with his rage reaction against Patrick Matthew which he kept going for the rest of his life. The last long friendly letter Darwin received from Matthew in 1871 was curtly replied to in six lines.

There is a further twist to the story: Blyth and Wallace, as good friends, go to visit Darwin in 1868!

The article in *The Encyclopaedia of Evolution* ends: 'And, however, one interprets the machinations of Darwin's friends, the "delicate arrangement" – glorified in dozens of books as a classic example of unselfish collaboration – was certainly not one of the brighter episodes in the history of science.' Real-life Darwinists, like Richard Dawkins, will not relish that comment. Darwin and his friends managed to stave off Wallace and shortly afterwards had to stave off Patrick Matthew – almost for good.

Now a word on divergence because there seems to be some disquiet that Darwin lifted this subject from Wallace. Here is the statement Wallace made in his 1855 essay: 'But if two or more species have been independently formed on the plan of a common antitype, then the series of affinities will be compound, and can only be represented by a forked or many-branched line.' Further on, Wallace writes: '. . . in the actual state of nature it is almost impossible, the species being so numerous and the modifications of form and structure so varied, arising probably from the immense number of species which have served as antitypes for the existing species, and thus produced a complicated branching of the lines of affinity, as intricate as the twigs of a gnarled oak or the vascular system of the human body.'

Darwin had a tree of life illustrated in the first edition of the *Origin;* not a 'gnarled oak' perhaps but a tree with branches. It is still believed by some authors that diverging speciation, in the form of a branching tree, started with Darwin's *Origin!* At the most the branching tree was in his ken by 1837.

Here is what Matthew had to say in 1831: 'In endeavouring to trace, in the former way, the principle of these changings of fashion which have taken place in the domiciles of life, the following questions occur. Do they arise from admixture of species nearly allied producing intermediate species? Are they the diverging ramifications of the living principle under modification of circumstance? Or have they resulted from the combined agency of both? . . . It is improbable that much of this diversification is owing to commixture of species nearly allied, all change by this appears very limited, and confined within the bounds of what is called species; the progeny of the same parents, under great difference of circumstance, might, in several generations, even become distinct species, incapable of co-reproduction.'

And now Blyth: 'But it would be endless to follow Merula into all its diversified ramifications . . . Thus, the starling type is comprehended in the omnivorous or corvine plan structure, and in its turn, comprises others of less importance, upon all of which may be organized in an indefinite number of species, diversely modified to suit a variety of localities . . .' If one reads the chapter in the *Origin* entitled 'Natural Selection' subheaded 'Divergence of character' one can recognize a basic similarity. Blyth has more: 'The true physiological system is evidently one of irregular and indefinite radiation, and of reiterate divergence and ramification from a varying number of successively subordinate plants . . .' One wonders why Blyth, with all his diverging ramifications and reiterate divergence, continued to resist descent from a common ancestor. Matthew was confident to the point of arrogance that his diverging ramifications involved descent from a common ancestor. After all this was Lamarck's teaching in Paris.

In the 1858 essay of Wallace divergence is only mentioned twice, but briefly, although 'indefinite radiation' is in the title. We must point out again that 'indefinite radiation' is Blyth's idea of divergence; this has been referred to in another chapter. If Wallace ever thought that Darwin had lifted divergence from him he never betrayed his suspicion. We can pass over the years to 1889 to *Darwinism*, first edition, and read what Wallace had to say about divergence. If Wallace was the source of diversity it will be rather difficult to explain why Darwin's subtitle in the *Origin* is copied exactly under the same chapter headed 'Natural Selection'; the subheading is 'Divergence of Character'. What Darwin wrote in the *Origin* is dished up in *Darwinism*.

We have discussed divergence elsewhere and noted that Cuvier was the first to put divergence on the scientific stage. Since Darwin drew so heavily on Blyth's copious output of biological observations, why did he not introduce diverging ramifications? Divergence of character, as Darwin expressed it in the *Origin*, did not give the dynamic picture of the extreme pulsating diversity of life. All six editions of the *Origin* had virtually the same text; his idea of divergence remained unchanged. I would submit that Matthew produced a more dynamic picture after a catastrophe: '. . . destroying all living things, must have reduced existence so much, that an unoccupied field would be formed for new diverging ramifications of life . . .' Even the branches were diverging!

How is it that Darwin and his set so rapidly accepted Wallace as a co-founder of evolution? Darwin protested to Hooker, as we have noted elsewhere, that Wallace's 1858 essay was very similar to his own 1844 essay. That would be enough to satisfy the ever dutiful Hooker, and Lyell had already been convinced by Wallace's 1855 essay. Wallace's 1858 essay is mainly built on facts taken from Blyth's essays of the 1830s. Darwin's essay of 1844, and its complete reconstruction in the *Origin*, also shows many signs of Blyth's essays as has been pointed out before. Darwin in two letters made the important point about the 1858 essay that Wallace did not understand the similar process controlling domestic and wild varieties. In addition to that, the 1858 essay has not one word about Natural Selection, very little on divergence and no mention of descent from a common ancestor. In spite of all that the essay was accepted as the basis of evolution. Is it possible that Darwin accepted Wallace's essay in order to divert attention from his own dependence on Blyth's 1830 essays?

10

Neo this and that

Scholars do make a tacit pledge when they enter this exacting profession – to honour the struggles of those who have gone before and to treat arguments with respect and integrity.

(*The Fraud that Never Was* S. J. Gould.)

Patrick Matthew did not alter one word of the appendix to *Naval Timber and Arboriculture*. He made no alteration to his follow–up book *Emigration Fields*. There were no second editions to either book. So is there any need for Neo-Matthewism? What is without dispute is that Natural Selection first appeared in print from the hand of Patrick Matthew. Since 1831 the theory of Natural Selection has had its ups and downs but since about 1931 – a hundred years later – the theory has had a fairly secure place in evolutionary studies and the theory is entirely accredited to Charles Darwin.

Darwin had maintained back in 1860 that Matthew had 'merely enunciated' the theory and that no one had ever seen the *Appendix*. Darwin had no evidence for this but then he made many statements for which he had no evidence. But Darwin was believed and one finds only a decade ago Jay Gould (1983) repeating the falsehood with glee and claiming that it is not enough to enunciate a theory. How many theories have been 'merely enunciated'? It is odd, therefore, to read in the *Historical Sketch*: 'The difference of Mr Matthew's views from mine are not of much importance . . .' So Matthew did not merely enunciate the theory! One must be very cautious in accepting anything Darwin says without checking. And again in Eiseley's confused review of Matthew there is this comment, '. . . the amount of ground he was able to cover in a few paragraphs suggests that he might have been able to sustain a longer treatise.' Matthew, as we will show, covered most of the important points available in his day. Matthew was not concerned with writing an encyclo-paedia of other naturalists' work – like Darwin.

A few words may be added about Matthew's views on extinction and the evolution of species. Matthew was a product of Parisian biological thought in the 1820s. He had attended the University of Edinburgh for two years and had made several visits to France where he had relatives. It is quite clear that he was intimately immersed in the work of Cuvier and particularly Lamarck. Because he was an irreligious man, like many of the Edinburgh intellectuals of the period, he could not accept Cuvier's miraculous creation but he accepted that catastrophes had occurred at several periods in the history of the earth. Matthew accepted Lamarck's gradual, slow change over the ages and when species changed Matthew considered it was by 'a power of change'. Cuvier made no comment on the rate of change in evolving species; there were no data at that time.

That, then, is the background to Matthew's *Appendix*. If we return to the *Historical Sketch* we will complete Darwin's sentence which ap-peared in the foregoing remarks; 'he seems to consider that the world was nearly depopulated at successive periods, and then restocked.' Was this a difference? The statement is Cuvier's teaching of geology and palaeontology. Cuvier later on conceded that some creatures could possibly survive the catastrophe – oases of survival. But he mixed this concession with his belief in the new miraculous birth of species after each catastrophe. Would it be unfair to say that Darwin did not go along with this concept of the history of the world? Darwin was cemented to Lyell's view of the geological past which was devoid of upheavals. In introducing Uniformitarianism Lyell dispensed with catastrophes and so did Darwin. Matthew's *Naval Timber and Arboriculture* with its appendix was published before Lyell's *Principles* and so catastrophes formed an essential element of the history of the inorganic world. In the 1826 essay in the Edinburgh journal and attributed to Robert Grant or Professor Jameson or both were involved – there is reference to upheavals in past history of the inorganic world. Grant, being a pupil of Cuvier, as well as Lamarck, would certainly be aware of the importance of catastrophes. Oxbridge at this time was firmly committed to Mosaic and Ptolemaic cosmology.

Extinction was discussed briefly by Darwin in the chapter on Natural Selection and the subject was taken up again in the chapter on geology. In neither chapter did Darwin even mention mass extinctions as Cuvier

had described them. He seemed more concerned with lesser extinctions
as in this passage: 'We need not marvel at extinction; if we must marvel,
let it be at our presumption in imagining for a moment that we understand
the many complex contingencies, on which the existence of each species
depends. If we forget for an instant, that each species tends to increase
inordinately and that some check is always in action . . .' And so on.
The age of Cuvier's mass extinctions as a result of catastrophes had been
pushed aside by Uniformitarianism and Darwin was greatly influenced
by Charles Lyell. The odd occasion when Darwin actually introduced
'catastrophes' he dismissed them contemptuously. 'The firm conviction
of the necessity of a vegetation possessing a character of tropical luxuriance
to support large animals, and the impossibility of reconciling this with
the proximity of perpetual conjelation, was one chief cause of the several
theories of sudden revolutions of climate and of overwhelming catastrophes which were invented to account for their entombment.' (Darwin,
1845.) Cuvier did not 'invent' catastrophes. The ice ages had not been
fully described by 1839 when the first edition of the *Researches* was
published. By 1845 Darwin should have modified what he had written
in 1839. It shows, however, how cemented he was to Lyell's geology.
Lyell did not accept that ice ages had occurred. Presumably because ice
ages were not happening at the present time they could not have happened
in the past. This was the reason why Lyell rejected mutation of species
and catastrophes. Therein lies the limitation of the concept of Uniformitarianism. By 1863, however, Lyell seems to have accepted glacial ages
(Lyell, 1863.)

Darwin introduces extinction again in the discussion on classification
as if Cuvier had never uttered a word about mass extinctions: 'Extinction
. . . has played a part in defining and widening the intervals between
the several groups in each class. We may thus account even for the
distinctness of whole classes from each other . . .' This was all implicit
in Cuvier's catastrophes. And then with a long statement which Matthew
would dispose off with 'diverging ramifications', Darwin states, 'Finally,
we have seen natural selection, which results from the struggle for
existence, and which almost inevitably induces extinction and divergence
of character in the many descendants from one dominant parent species.'

Mass extinctions, or catastrophes as Cuvier referred to them, are now
considered to be of major importance. A recent study suggests that there
have been mass extinctions at regular intervals of about 70,000,000 years

caused by asteroids colliding with this planet (Russell, 1982). The asteroid collisions are thought to be due to that postulated star Nemesis (Clube, V., and Napier, B., 1982). The hunt is on to find it. The mass extinction after the last ice age was probably not caused by extra-terrestrial bodies.

If we take just Darwin's statement we can quite confidently fit it into the modern theory of punctuated equilibrium of Eldredge and Gould (1985); much, no doubt to Jay Gould's horror! Matthew was quite clear that there were catastrophic episodes and what he called 'steady' states in between. This is the view of Eldredge and Gould. It is a wonder this concept has not been advocated before these two distinguished scientists came to consider it. During the 'steady' state Matthew made it clear that Natural Selection was in constant action. When Matthew visualizes the aftermath of a catastrophe he could be pronouncing what enlightened naturalists think today: '. . . destroying all living things, must have reduced existence so much, that an unoccupied field would be formed for new diverging ramifications of life . . .' Where Matthew obtained this concept is uncertain. He certainly did not derive it from Cuvier but probably Lamarck; these authors did not have ramifications in their view of organic life. If, however, we have underestimated just what Lamarck meant by 'collaterals' then the 'diverging ramifications' of Matthew were a correct interpretation.

Draper (1871) in his lecture on evolution made quite reasonable objections to the use of the term 'Natural Selection'. 'It is to be regretted that this phrase 'natural selection' has been introduced. It is very unscientific, very inferior to the old expression adaptation. But nature never selects, knows nothing about duties, nothing about fitness or unfitness. Nature simply obeys laws. Natural Selection is thus supposed to perpetuate an organism after adaptation to the environment has taken place. The change implied by adaptation must precede it. It should be regarded rather as a metaphysical expression than a scientific statement of an actual physical event. Darwinism, therefore, does not touch the great question as to the manner in which variation of organisms arises. It only teaches how such variations are perpetuated.'

It was the result of trying to fathom how varieties were perpetuated in the wild that some people came to realize that the process might be similar to that employed by hybridists in artificially selecting varieties in attempting to produce new varieties. It was not just by accident that a hybridist – Patrick Matthew – coined the phrase 'natural process of selection'. Despite its limitations it is here to stay until a better phrase is introduced.

It must be said, however, that Matthew does include adaptation in his text as, for example, 'The self-regulating adaptive disposition of organized life . . .' Sometimes Matthew substitutes 'accommodates' as, for example, '. . . a very slight change of circumstance by culture inducing a corresponding change of character – may have gradually accommodated themselves to the variations of the elements containing them, and, without new creation, have presented the diverging changeable phenomena of past and present organized existence.'

This view, no doubt, required a 'certain grasp of mind', as Matthew usually put it, and it would seem this view of a steady state interrupted by periods of upheaval is not to be found in Darwin's view of evolution and, apparently, not considered until recently. Punctuated Equilibrium came into conflict with the Synthetic Theory which was the new interpretation of Darwin's slow, gradual change. The Synthetic Theory (1942), its supporters claimed, always took into account slow and rapid changes. Whenever any criticism of Darwinism is voiced in comes Richard Dawkins; in his *Blind Watchmaker* (1988) there is a whole chapter devoted to rubbishing 'punc eek' as a theory opposed to Darwinism. None of us know at what rate species have evolved; guesses are made from time to time which are only the various interpretations of new evidence like the Miocene fossils provided. In spite of all the scientific disciplines which have addressed the evolution of species we are in no better position than Darwin was.

If Huxley was Darwin's bulldog in the nineteenth century then Richard Dawkins is Darwin's gadfly in this century and here is his message: 'What needs to be said now, loud and clear, is the truth: that the theory of punctuated equilibrium lies firmly within the Neo-Darwinian Principle.' Indeed, within the old-style Matthewism. No mention of Patrick Matthew whom Dawkins regards as an enigma! How can Dawkins claim that punctuated equilibrium lies within Neo-Darwinism when Darwin had no use for catastrophes? Darwin's attempt, in the *Historical Sketch*, to make Matthew look ridiculous was why he made the remark, '. . . he seems to consider that the world was nearly depopulated at successive periods, and then restocked.' Catastrophes were no longer fashionable in England. Punctuated equilibrium is not just about different speeds of speciation but about catastrophes and mass extinctions as well.

On the geological and palaeontological evidence by 1830 Matthew was able to set the nature of the history of the world – both organic and inorganic – into a reasonable perspective. Upheavals of massive dimensions had occurred throughout earth's history and species in mass amounts had been rendered extinct but there was evidence, provided by Lamarck's study of molluscs, that there was a continuity of life all though the ages. Matthew was perceptive enough to see this but his vision in no way dismisses Matthewism, indeed, it strengthens it although Matthew supported Darwin's publication – the *Origin*. In his letter, of 1860, all Matthew wanted to point out was the fact that he had written out Natural Selection many years before. In another chapter it has been indicated that one author ridiculed Matthew's view of the history of animal life – steady state in between catastrophes – because it differed so much from Darwin's gradualism. Although in England in the 1840s and 1850s the subject of catastrophes had been almost forgotten after the triumph of Uniformitarianism, on the continent more evidence of catastrophes continued to be found. By the time the sixth edition was published in 1872 Darwin should have been aware of this evidence.

So Eldredge and Gould should now place Matthew's name in front of punctuated equilibrium – Matthew's Punctuated Equilibrium; an aspect of Matthewism. An article on Punc eek in the *Encyclopaedia of Evolution* (1990) includes this brief note, in spite of what Dawkins has said: '. . . in the brief interval since it was proposed, the theory of Punctuated Equilibrium seems to be holding its own.' And rightly so if it does not conform to what Dawkins thinks it should be.

It should be remembered that so far as the pace of speciation was concerned Lamarck saw only a steady state. Lamarck's evolution was by the inheritance of minute variations over immense time. Darwin was to take on this concept and pass it off as his own invention. It is strange that Lamarck did not incorporate Cuvier's catastrophes into his philosophy. Catastrophes occupied the dominant position in the organic world of French and English naturalists during the first three decades of the nineteenth century. Lamarck's belief that species changed over time rather obscured his view of the reality of the extinction of species by catastrophes. That species changed through time inspite of catastrophes was only part of the picture. It is remarkable that Patrick Matthew, a contemporary of Cuvier and Lamarck, should be the first to realize that the steady state was interrupted by a series of catastrophes. And to that he added Natural Selection and diverging ramifications.

The steady state interrupted by catastrophes was Matthew's analysis of the evidence at the time. What is now referred to as Punctuated Equilibrium is the basis of Matthewism; it has nothing to do with Darwinism. The word 'catastrophe' is not indexed in the *Origin;* nor does it come into the two pages Darwin devoted to extinction in the chapter 'Natural Selection'. Extinction is introduced to this chapter because, '. . . it must here be alluded to from being intimately connected with natural selection.' Note here that Darwin is not linking extinction with catastrophes. In the 'Geological Succession' there is a section on extinction which is linked to Natural Selection. 'On the theory of natural selection the extinction of old forms are intimately connected together.' Again not a word about catastrophes. If Dawkins cares to read the *Origin* more carefully than he seems to have done he will confirm what I have stated. Punctuated Equilibrium is Matthewism which is Cuvier–Lamarckism.

By 1863 three editions of *The Origin of the Species* had been published. Up to this period Darwin was under the influence of Lyell and so there is nothing positive about mass extinctions or catastrophes. Darwin followed Lyell quite closely, in the *Origin*, with what Lyell formerly had believed: 'Among the many causes of extinction enumerated by me, were the power of hostile species, diminution of food, mutations in climate, the conversion of land into sea, and of sea into land, etc.' (Lyell, 1863.)

In 1863 Lyell had a complete change of mind. It was now Lamarck who should have priority: 'While, in 1832, I argued against Lamarck's doctrine of the gradual transmutation of one species into another, I agreed with him in believing that the system would afford, when fully understood, a complete key to the interpretation of all the vicissitudes of the living creation in past ages. I contended against the doctrine, then very popular, against the sudden destruction of vast multitudes of species, and the abrupt ushering into the world of new batches of plants and animals.' (Lyell 1863.)

Although Lyell had changed his mind there are no alterations to the text of the *Origin* in the last three editions. Catastrophes and mass extinctions are not Darwinian concepts.

Neo-Darwinism

Richard Dawkins complains, 'There are people in this world who desperately want not to have to believe in Darwinism,' and he lists a number of irrelevant people. He could have added that a number of people, including himself, do not want to know about Matthewism. But, '. . . others confuse Darwinism with Social Darwinism which has a racist and other disagreeable overtones.' It is quite misleading for Dawkins to say that Darwinism can be confused with Social Darwinism. Matthew, Darwin and Spencer all used survival of the fittest as an extension of Natural Selection to justify the extermination of savages or the poorer classes, in the case of Spencer. Darwin's views and Spencer's in this respect delighted the Victorian industrial tycoons who used gangs of bully boys to intimidate the workers. At this stage one should glance through the relevant chapter in Darwin's *Descent of Man* to realize where the 'disagreeable overtones' originate. Dawkins is an apologist for Darwin: one must not read the sixth edition of the *Origin* because it contains a number of mistakes, like Pangenesis, which poor Darwin was talked into writing. Rubbish! Darwin was very proud of Pangenesis. Darwin wrote to Lyell in August 1867: 'I have been particularly pleased you have noticed Pangenesis. I do not know whether you ever had the feeling of having thought so much over a subject that you had lost all power of judging it. This is my case with Pangenesis (which is 26 or 27 years old), but I am inclined to think that if it be admitted as a probable hypothesis it will be a somewhat important step in biology.' But Wallace was in the act as well! Darwin wrote to Hooker in February 1868: 'I heard yesterday from Wallace, who says (excuse horrid vanity), "I can hardly tell you how much I admire the chapter on Pangenesis . . . I shall never be able to give up until a better one supplies its place, and that I think hardly possible." Now his foregoing words express my sentiments exactly and fully . . .' (Darwin, F. 1902.) So we can see that Darwin apologists who try to make out that Pangenesis was produced because of criticisms of the *Origin* are quite wrong. Darwin had been thinking about Pangenesis long before the *Origin* was published. Again one should point out that many Darwin enthusiasts cum apologists are careless about history.

Even a distinguished science journalist appealed in a national newspaper that any prospective reader of the *Origin* should not read the sixth edition because it has too many 'mistakes'! Huxley pointed out to Darwin that

Buffon had made this 'mistake' a hundred years before. The apologists do not seem to realise that Pangenesis first appeared four years before the sixth edition of the *Origin* in *Variation of Animals and plants under conditions of Domestication* (1868); the whole edition of 1,500 copies sold out rapidly. It would seem that Dawkins and other Darwin enthusiasts do not realize that in the sixth edition of the *Origin* Darwin explained the reason for the new edition: 'The most important alterations are connected with the expansion of knowledge between 1860 and 1872.' So why did Darwin not deal with the catastrophes which were being discovered on the continent long after the death of Cuvier? The Darwin enthusiasts seem as careless of history as Darwin was himself. Furthermore, in the first edition of *The Descent of Man* (1871) Darwin had changed his mind about the supreme importance of Natural Selection; in the second edition of 1874 he had not changed his mind about this. No mention is ever made of the mistake in every edition of the *Origin* where the Creator was dragged into the last paragraph! So, is there to be a ban on those other writings of Darwin? Every effort is being made to sweep Darwin's so-called 'mistakes' under the carpet and so forgotten.

So what is Neo-Darwinism? It was a term coined by George Romanes who became a fervent admirer of Darwin. The term appeared in 1905 in order to rid Natural Selection of Pangenesis. Mendel's ratios had been discovered in a German review in 1900. Darwinism was in danger of being rendered obsolete. It would be fair now to have Neo-Lamarckism defined without the inheritance of acquired characteristics. Some people at the time thought Darwinism was dead but Romanes correctly envisaged that Mendelism and Darwinism were compatible as indeed they turned out to be. So we will jump the years and accept the Modern Synthesis of Julian Huxley and consider the review of Neo-Darwinism by H.H. Smith (1974). 'The study of evolution receives a different emphasis according to the discipline from which it is approached.' That being said what is new? Smith summarizes Neo-Darwinism in six points:

1. 'Gene mutation is the main cause of heritable variability.' Nothing new in this. Genes were substituted for sports in 1909.
2. 'Variability, once established in a population, may be maintained.' Nothing new in that.
3. 'Natural selection is the main directive force in evolution.' Matthew stuck with this as a universal law of Nature but Darwin had his

doubts in the last essays he wrote. If we give Darwin the benefit of the doubt then there is nothing new here.

4. 'There are gradual accumulative trends resulting from the action of selection on variability.'

   In the *Origin* Darwin made this point: '. . . we may, I think, assume that the modified descendants of any one species will succeed by so much the better as they become more diversified in structure and are thus enabled to encroach on places occupied by other beings.' This was the argument that Matthew (1839) used to justify the better structured Caucasians taking over the lands of the less structured savages. Blyth in his 1835–37 essays recounts how a population of Ancons sheep developed from 'one ewe' which produced a male lamb with badly structured legs which, so far as the farmer was concerned, was a favourable mutation because the sheep were unable to jump fences! So nothing new here. Such sheep would not survive in the wild.

5. Increasing divergencies, and gaps which accentuate them, result from organisms (genotypes) developing in different environments – that is under different selection pressures.

   The diverging ramifications of Matthew and Blyth would encompass this statement. Diverging ramifications meant more, especially to modern naturalists, than mere divergencies. Remember: it is no longer a branched tree but a branched bush!

6. 'Isolating mechanisms arise, which hinder the flow of genes among groups, and species originate. When some condition inhibits or prevents mixing of the gene pool of populations within the reproductive range, the stage of incipient speciation is reached.'

Matthew had nothing to say on this subject unless there is a hint of geographic isolation in, 'Change of place within certain limits of latitude, seems to have a tendency to improve the species equally in animals as in plants' (*Emigration Fields*, 1839).

Blyth just hints at geographic isolation. By the next decade, however, the subject is in the 1842 and 1844 notebooks of Darwin.

Advances in the understanding of factors affecting mutation rate came in this twentieth century. Matthew and Blyth knew nothing of this.

Smith (1974) continues: 'In spite of the undirected force *mutation,* and the unsystematic force *chance*, the process of evolution according to classical, Neo-Darwinian theory does have direction through time by the continuing action of *natural selection*. The direction is generally toward *adaptation*.'

Matthew had this to say (Note F *Appendix*): ' . . . Those only come forward to maturity from the strict ordeal by which Nature tests their adaptation to her standard of perfection and fitness to continue their kind by reproduction.'

Not much there that is new.

Smith continues, 'In recent times man has speeded up the evolution of plants: either indirectly or directly but unintentionally, or directly and intentionally, for example, through altering ecological conditions – clearing forests and cultivating fields indirectly favoured the occurrence of polyploids introgressive hybridization, and weedy plants that invade the borders of tilled fields . . . through accidental transportation of plants or seeds into new areas he has directly and unintentionally influenced evolution . . . Man has been directly and intentionally influencing the rate and the direction of evolution of plants.'

Had Darwin written *Naval Timber and Arboriculture* he would have heartily agreed with this statement. Matthew complained bitterly about the poor state of the forests and the inadequate quality of the trees that were being planted. He was convinced that excess fertilizer was being applied to the cultivated fields; guano had recently been discovered and imported into Britain. He had this to say: 'Man's interference, by preventing this natural process of selection among plants, independent of the wider range of circumstance to which he introduces them, has increased the difference in varieties particularly in the more domesticated kinds.'

So far as Matthewism is concerned nothing very new in all this; polyploids and introgressive hybridization were unknown in his day.

Matthew's use of adaptation would not be the same as a biologist would understand it today. In fact, the modern biologist finds the term meaningless. Matthew probably understood adaptation as Cuvier had introduced it. Cuvier, as is well known, founded a method for reconstructing the form of fossil animals. Certain morphological characters were always associated with a particular form of life. In his second letter to the *Gardeners' Chronicle*, which countered Darwin's untrue assertion that no naturalist had ever seen *Naval Timber and Arboriculture*, Matthew mentions Cuvier who could construct an animal from one bone.

Species survive as long as circumstances allow them. Matthew always thought in terms of circumstance-suited. But however well suited species may be they are condemned to extinction after a period of time only to be followed by another species to take their place.

In conclusion, Neo-Darwinism is: 'Basically, evolution is genetic change in populations through time.' Both Matthew and Blyth would nod in agreement with that.

One caveat to molecular biologists – Dawkins is displeased with this group! 'Cladists are obsessed with branches.' It is a pity that Dawkins has not given up the 'tree of life'. That was Darwin's outmoded view; he imagined he had introduced something new. Dawkins should realize the tree is now a branched bush; as Matthew and Blyth would express it, a 'diverging ramified' bush. Dawkins does not appear to accept that the sequence of evolutionary branching is very important in biological classification. Look back to Lamarck's struggle with the Monotremes. Dawkins should remember, however, that Darwin was a modest ramifier. Diverging Ramifications! Much more elegant than mere branches and closer to reality.

Molecular biology is a sign of the times. The centre of gravity of evolutionary studies has gradually moved from the earth sciences to microbiology. In considering the host of molecules which are and have been studied, then one can appreciate that DNA given time can create anything. The wonder is that only Patrick Matthew has conceived that there might be a Proteus-like principle, '. . . capable of gradual circumstance-suited modifications and aggregations.' (Note F *Appendix*.) Without that speculation he also saw clearly that life was a series of 'diverging ramifications'.

In spite of the objections of Dawkins the molecular biologists have done and are doing very relevant work. Experiments in the Hawaiian Islands not only confirm but prove that a common ancestor can found colonies from which other species arise. These experiments have used the chromosome pattern of drosophila to prove the point. By analysing the chromosome patterns of each species it was possible to distinguish older ancestral species from newly derived species. It has been shown that single egg-bearing, gravid females dispersed from one older island to another younger island or vice versa, can found a colony which then diverges into new species. It is considered that this speciation of drosophila in the Hawaiian Islands has been going on for six million years. Although these interesting experiments prove that a common ancestor can found colonies that diverge in time this is really proof of observations and speculations about descent from a common ancestor derived from Lamarck and introduced to England via Robert Grant, Patrick Matthew and Lyell and from them to Wallace and Darwin.

Neo-Lamarkism

Draper (1871) gave a lecture on evolution which has had little publicity. 'Lamarck recognized the struggle of each against all. He saw plainly the influence of heredity, and understood the relation of the environment and adaptation. He defined in the clearest manner the doctrine of transmutation and the theory of descent. According to him, if time enough be allowed, any modification may take place.'

Today we would combine with time DNA's ability to create any living creature or plant. Patrick Matthew envisaged a Proteus principle of life; DNA would fit this speculation.

If Lamarck had recognized all that Draper listed how is it today all that Lamarck is known for is the inheritance of acquired characteristics? The reason is the distortions perpetrated by the nineteenth-century gang of four – Charles Lyell, Charles Darwin, Thomas H. Huxley and Alfred R. Wallace. Never in the history of science have four men deliberately distorted the work of one naturalist, such as the four; Lamarck, being dead, could not defend himself. Such was the esteem in which Lyell was held among English naturalists in overthrowing Cuvier's Catastrophism that his unjust criticism of Lamarck stuck and has remained stuck although we have indicated elsewhere that Lyell tried to repair the damage he had single-handedly created.

Charles Lyell has a lot to answer for. Not only did he distort Lamarck's teaching but he turned on the distinguished mineralogist Abraham Werner as well (Ospovat, 1976). His distortions took some time to be corrected as in the mean time academics copied the distortions down to recent times. So far as Lamarck was concerned, the oddly devout Lyell was horrified by Lamarck's materialism and atheistic views. That aspect came through loud and clear. The other aspect hardly had a supporter except in Scotland, Robert Grant. Lyell, unwittingly, provided an English audience with the details of Lamarckism but it, for the most part, fell on deaf ears or eyes that would not see. As we have described elsewhere, the London radicals under Robert Grant kept promoting the teaching of Lamarck.

Neo-Lamarckism is dead and now New Lamarckism is on the science stage. Is the inheritance of acquired characteristics dead? The hunt is on for possible mechanisms by which inherited characteristics may be inherited. But this subject is not what Lamarck was mainly interested in; the subject had been launched by Buffon and Lamarck was his pupil so the master's ideas were carried on in an academic way. Various naturalists have tried to prove the inheritance of acquired characteristics, like the Baldwin effect, but nothing has come of them. But Lamarck would not be all that interested in this kind of research. Lamarck would settle for what Cannon (1955–56) explained as being what Lamarck had actually written.

But Cuvier had a hand in slandering Lamarck, as Draper (1877) records: 'So far from meeting with acceptance, the ideas of Lamarck brought upon him ridicule and obloquy. The great influence of Cuvier, who had made himself a champion of the doctrine of permanence of species, caused Lamarck's views to be silently ignored or, if by chance they were referred to, denounced.' And this is where Charles Lyell comes in so far as England is concerned. In France Geoffroy St Hilaire stood up to Cuvier and kept the Lamarckian flag flying. In Scotland, at Edinburgh University, Robert Grant, who befriended the young Darwin when he was there as a medical student, continued to support Lamarck for the next few decades.

What Darwin said in private is not always what he said in public. He let it be known that Lamarckism was all nonsense. Later in life, as his young friend Romanes noticed, he came closer and closer to Lamarck. In *The Descent of Man*, in response to some criticism, he wrote, '. . . I distinctly stated that great weight must be attributed to the inherited effects of use and disuse, with respect both to the mind and body. I also attributed some amount of modification to the direct and prolonged action of changed conditions of life.' This is true as anyone can check in the *Origin* in the Laws of Variation. This was in response to criticism that Darwin had attributed all changes of corporeal structure and mental power exclusively to Natural Selection.

There is one other anti-Lamarckian who can be added to the gang of four because he has done nothing to clarify the Lamarckian prejudice and even added to the slander. In fact he has made such a mess of Lamarck it will require some disentangling; he has written an invective of Lamarck in *The Blind Watchmaker* (Dawkins, 1988).

The scene is set in chapter 11 and the title is 'Doomed Rivals'! 'The obvious way to decide between rival theories is to examine the evidence.' This would seem to presage a good examination of the evidence. But this is not to be: 'Lamarckian types of theory, for instance, are traditionally rejected – and rightly so – because no good evidence for them has ever been found . . .' The evidence is that Dawkins is only apparently aware of the hoary old tale of the inheritance of acquired characteristics. Lamarck did discuss use and disuse and as we have seen above Darwin wanted to be in on this as well but put it about that Lamarckism was all nonsense.

In the introduction to the English translation of Lamarck's *Philosophie Zoologique* (1809), Elliot (1914) makes this statement: '. . . that the reputation of Lamarck is to stand or fall by that one theory is a suggestion which can scarcely be made by any one who closely studies the present translation.' In the *Historical Sketch* (1872) Darwin makes the claim that before 1859 most naturalists believed in the fixity of species. He could have made it clear that during all those previous years of the century it was Lamarck, St Hilaire and their Scottish and English followers who kept the concept of the mutability of species alive. The conservative forces in England resisted the concept. It would appear that Dawkins and other academics are blissfully unaware of the debt biology owes to Lamarck. For all his great contributions to palaeontology Cuvier had a baleful influence on biology throughout the nineteenth century and he consistently maintained the fixity of species for religious reasons and based on dishonest scientific evidence.

Dawkins seems to have forgotten that Darwin had recourse to 'Lamarckisms' in the *Origin* and in the first edition at that. This is the edition that Dawkins regards as the pure and undefiled Darwinism! This in spite of the fact that Darwin confessed in *The Descent of Man* (1874) that he had attributed too much, in the earlier editions of the *Origin*, to Natural Selection.

Dawkins makes this point: 'This is not a history book, and I shall not attempt a scholarly dissection of exactly what Lamarck himself said.' This was a very infelicitous statement and unworthy of a university teacher discussing a major world scientific figure. Another academic (Cannon, 1955–56) wrote an article entitled 'What Lamarck really said'; Dawkins does not seem to have consulted this article. Dawkins is quite right, of course, because here is what he had to say: 'If you put the inheritance of acquired characteristics together with the principle of use and disuse, you have what looks like a good recipe for evolutionary improvement.' There then follows several pages up the wrong track which treat the subject as a joke and end with great satisfaction: 'Our refutation of Lamarckism, then, is a bit devastating.' And that is it! To reduce Lamarckism to the inheritance of acquired characteristics is as absurd as reducing Darwinism to Pangenesis. To present the evidence for Lamarckism in terms of speculations initiated by Buffon was, to say the least, misleading. But even if he had wished to present those speculations correctly as Cannon (1955–56) has done, he would still not have presented the evidence which convinced Lamarck of evolution and is the quintessential Lamarckism. He could have copied out the evidence which Charles Lyell presented in the twelfth edition of his *Principles*. Indeed, he could have just repeated what Darwin had to say in his *Historical Sketch* in the sixth edition of the *Origin*; there is no mention of speculations in that short eulogy. For the sake of those who have not read the statement in the *Historical Sketch* it can be repeated now: 'In these works [those mentioned in my text] he upholds the doctrine that all species, including man, are descended from other species. He first did the eminent service of arousing attention to the probability of all change in the organic world, being the result of law, and not of miraculous interposition.' Dawkins, who prides himself on being a real-life Darwinist, appears to be unaware of what Darwin wrote in the *Historical Sketch*. This is not surprising since Dawkins warns against reading the sixth edition of the *Origin*.

The essential scientific evidence which Dawkins should have presented and which has nothing to do with Erasmus Darwin is in *Histoire Naturelle des Animaux sans Vertèbres* in which order was brought into the subkingdom of Invertebrata; this term was introduced by Lamarck. The classification of vague forms called Vermes by Cuvier was broken up and other aspects of Cuvierian classification rearranged; some parts had to be changed later on. Lamarck had first to establish evolution and mutation of species as a fact and he succeeded in doing so with a detailed study of invertebrates. The study involved a demonstration to Lamarck that some living molluscs had analogues among the fossil molluscs; therefore, over time, life can slowly change and so evolve. That is a simple and truthful statement which any lay man could understand. Only after establishing evolution as a fact did Lamarck turn to the problem of how species changed. Change over immense time was the best suggestion he made and it would seem we are no further advanced today.

Cuvier found no such vertebrate fossil analogues; subsequently they have been found, and so no mutation of species. The tragedy is that Cuvier demonstrated that species changed over the millenia but each new species, he stubbornly continued to assert, was created miraculously. Now when we come to Lamarck's other tome *Philosophie Zoologique* we meet up with many speculations, in only one chapter of a book extending to over 400 pages, about how species might have changed. There was not sufficient hard evidence at that time to propose clear scientific reasons as to how species changed. So Lamarck speculated about how organ change might have occurred and this involved use and disuse. For this Lamarck was and is still much criticized. It is this minor section of Lamarckism which Dawkins claims as Lamarckism. Darwin also discussed this problem in the *Origin* and was clearly influenced by Lamarck.

What Darwin referred to as 'inherited effects of use and disuse' is referred to by other people, including Dawkins, as inheritance of acquired characteristics. In the preface to *The Descent of Man* (1874) Darwin stated in response to previous criticism: 'I distinctly stated that great weight must be attributed to the inherited effects of use and disuse, with respect to the mind and body. I also attribute some amount of modification to the direct and prolonged action of changed conditions of life.' Darwin was right in 1874 to defend what he had written in 1859. Turning to the second edition of the *Origin* and the chapter on Laws of Variation there is this heading, 'Effects of use and disuse', which is followed by remarks on the effects of the conditions of life. One can look in vain for any reference to Lamarck who was much concerned with these topics. The reader will have noticed that in the *Origin* the heading 'Effects of use and disuse' is not preceded by 'hereditary'. The inclusion of hereditary in the 1874 statement was not accidental. The sentence is quite unambiguous. Taken with the second sentence, quoted above, one can recognise Lamarck's doctrine. No one more than Darwin, in his private letters, ridiculed Lamarck about this very subject. In the *Blind Watchmaker* (1986) Dawkins states '. . . the inheritance of acquired characteristics, seems to be false in all life-forms that we have studied.'

If we now refer to the section noted above, we find Darwin arguing thus: 'The state of the eyes is probably due to gradual reduction from disuse, but aided perhaps by natural selection.' When the blind Lamarck proposed disuse as the cause of the blindness of these animals Cuvier made the crude and hurtful remark – was Lamarck's blindness due to disuse?

And further: 'As it is difficult to imagine that eyes, though useless, could be in any way injurious to animals living in darkness, I attribute their loss wholly to disuse.' And another example: '. . . I believe that the nearly wingless condition of several birds, which now inhabit or have lately inhabited several oceanic islands, tenanted by no beast of prey, has been caused by disuse.'

The reader should clearly understand that Darwin here is discussing inherited effects. Darwin's statement is a far cry from the arrogant argument Dawkins makes out for Natural Selection as the alternative explanation. Darwin's argument in this section seems to involve arbitrary assessments of the cause of various effects – sometimes Lamarckian sometimes Natural Selection and sometimes a bit of each. Although Darwin in 1874 claimed 'I distinctly stated', when one checks the statement in the *Origin* it would appear that Darwin was not quite so 'distinct'. 'On the whole, I think we may conclude that habit, use and disuse, have, in some cases, played a considerable part in the modification of the constitution, and of the structure of various organs; but that the effects of use and disuse have often been largely combined with, and sometime overmastered by the natural selection of innate variations.' Patrick Matthew was adamant that Natural Selection was in constant action even in the 'steady state' between catastrophes; Darwin in other sections of the *Origin* has Natural Selection in constant action. The hereditary element and the natural process of selection should always proceed simultaneously. This rather woolly statement in this section of the *Origin* downgrades the importance of Natural Selection. Little wonder that Lyell, Hooker and others were lukewarm about the importance of Natural Selection when the *Origin* was published. By attributing all change to Natural Selection is sheer speculation and in no way explains the actual mechanism of change which is still a mystery although hereditary involvement is obvious now. It was because Lamarck stressed that animals and plants can change over immense time that made Lyell point out that in this he differed profoundly from Cuvier. The Lamarckism which Dawkins claimed to have refuted, in a devastating manner, is part of *The Origin of the Species*. Dawkins's hostility to what he calls Lamarckism has bereft him of any acknowledgement of the revolutionary basis for evolutionary studies that Lamarck bequeathed us and has apparently wiped out any sympathy for the aged and blind philosopher bravely withstanding the cruel taunts of the Baron Cuvier.

Darwin constantly explained how individuals were preserved: 'Owing to this struggle for life, any variation, however slight, and from what ever cause proceeding, if it be in any degree profitable to an individual of any species . . . will tend to the preservation of that individual . . .' (Struggle for Existence, *The Origin of the Species*) This is quite plausible speculation but it was no more than Lamarck envisaged with his struggle for existence. Because he had no idea, like Darwin, how species can evolve into a different species he referred to the whole process as 'change over time'. This was fact.

One cannot claim that Lamarck covered correctly all the diverse problems he became immersed in; he made several mistakes mainly due to speculations But he was a very distinguished biologist and of this there is no doubt. His 'struggle for existence', picked up by Lyell, found a secure place in evolution in English speaking countries and, sad to say, became linked with Malthus. One other major contribution Lamarck made, besides the evolving of species, was to stimulate the study of biology; that was another word he introduced. Lamarck, like most of the earlier evolutionists, was not a breeder and so selection never entered his essays, but he saw species evolving and so was a strong advocate of evolution. Lyell picked up this term when he was in Paris and introduced it to an English audience as 'evolution'. We have already drawn attention to Lyell's twelfth edition of his *Principles of Geology* in which he made a last desperate effort, a few months before he died in 1875, to salvage the injustice he had done to Lamarck in 1832. But his pleading for a rehabilitation of Lamarck, as indeed Darwin did in his *Historical Sketch*, has gone on being ignored in English speaking countries. And so we leave the distorted tale that Dawkins obviously passionately believes in. Perhaps he should study the scholarly essay by Cannon (1955–56).

The Descent of Man (1871) and *Variation of Animals and Plants under Conditions of Domestication* (1868) are loaded with what might be called Lamarckisms. I suppose no Darwin apologist wishes to promote these essays. In contradistinction to Dawkins rubbishing Lamarck, the early English and Scottish Lamarckians honoured the man as a great biologist. Support for Lamarckian concepts took root in Edinburgh long before London. In fact it was Robert Grant, a Scot from Edinburgh, when appointed to the Chair of Zoology at University College who led the

Lamarckian radicals in London. On the continent Lamarck was honoured as well. Here is Schmidt of Strasburg (1881): 'We come now to a courageous writer, whose principle work is *La Philosophie Zoologique.* This is J. B. Lamarck, who first formulated the doctrine of Descent, and in 1804 actually propounded the propositions which Darwin has constructed afresh and more completely . . . From comparisons of the facts of hybridization and the formations of varieties, he inferred, "that all organizations are true productions of Nature, gradually evolved in the course of a long succession of ages . . . individuals which originally belonged to another species ultimately find themselves converted into a new one. The limited period of our existence has accustomed us to a standard of time so short as to give rise to the vulgar and false hypothesis of stability and immutability." Lamarck touches on the struggle each against all but does not discover Natural Selection.'

Lamarck's vision of species evolving into new kinds of species is quite clear to us now. During the overlordship of the Jurassic and Cretaceous dinosaurs some reptiles evolved into warm-blooded mammals – small shrew-like creatures which were mainly insect eaters and nocturnal. Little change in these tiny mammals occurred during the reign of the dinosaurs which confirms Lamarck's and then Matthew's belief in a 'steady state'. These mammals appear to have developed from a common ancestor and are grouped in the order Insectivores. Some of the early mammals have changed little in the last 150 million years; golden moles, for example, have changed little in 25 million years but have radiated out into a variety of habitats (Gorman & Stone, 1990). Why the steady state of mammals existed during the reign of the dinosaurs is not understood but at the end of the Cretaceous Period mammalian expansion rapidly occurred following what is regarded as a catastrophe causing extinction of a massive amount of life and leaving the mammals as the dominant group. So what were regarded by most naturalists in the early nineteenth century as 'new miraculously-created' species were not new at all as Lamarck maintained. Matthew certainly had no recourse to a Creator in passing on the concepts of Cuvier and Lamarck. Why some species over the last millions of years have mutated and others have hardly changed at all is still the supreme mystery.

In discussing the eyes of moles Darwin throws in Natural Selection to explain the transformation: 'The eyes of moles and of burrowing rodents are rudimentary in size, and in some cases are quite covered up in skin and fur. This state of the eyes is probably due to gradual reduction from disuse, but aided perhaps by natural selection.' This kind of statement explained nothing. Darwin's concentration on the eyes of moles without any comment on the other organs indicates that the concepts of 'conditions of life' (Lamarck) and 'conditions of existence' (Cuvier) had not been adequately absorbed; a fact Darwin confessed late in life. Millions of years ago moles started to seek a new niche for food and protection and went underground. In order to live such a life moles had to change most of the body – the hands became diggers, the skin covering became moisture-resistant fur, the eyes became covered with fur for protection and a sleek body to enable them to scamper along the subterranean tunnels and they had to develop other sensory organs for life in the underground darkness. The eyes of European moles are fully formed and open which allows them to gather bedding on the ground and detect day-length which determines their breeding cycle (Gorman and Stone, 1990). So to conclude that the eyes changed because of gradual disuse is to miss the point. The moles, millions of years ago, assumed the necessary adaptations for an able-bodied life under and above ground. The adaptations reached a stage at which the moles were in a 'steady state' which has lasted now for millions of years with little change. The golden moles of the Namibian Desert had quite different conditions to adapt to so are blind and, having reached a 'circumstance-suited' stage as Patrick Matthew would say, have changed little in 25 million years and still remain very successful animals.

It is clear that Patrick Matthew, although not mentioning the name of Lamarck, made an effort to expound his ideas along with some of Cuvier's. As an active, philosophical breeder he was able to add Natural Selection to the French contributions to biology. It is perhaps in this context one should more clearly understand why Matthew in 1860 stated that he did not realize that he had introduced something new. At the time he was writing his *Appendix* no other naturalist, engaged in a philosophical discussion of species, was a breeder. It was because he was a breeder he could think in terms of selection but that concept was attached to a Lamarckian–Cuvierian view of the organic world. It took thirty years for Darwin, also influenced by the breeders, to recognize distinctly the basic significance of Natural Selection. In his last years he lost faith in the supreme importance of Natural Selection. Matthew altered nothing.

What did Lamarck mean by 'evolved in the course of a long succession of ages'? Further on in that passage he writes, 'individuals which originally belonged to another species ultimately find themselves converted into a new one.' The operative words are 'a new one'. Now Mayr (1969) suggests that the reason Darwin did not use the term 'evolution' in the *Origin*, at least not until the fifth edition, was because of its connotation. Mayr (1969) suggests that the term 'evolution' is derived from the concept of unfolding, and this connotation continued well into the post-Darwinian period. But evolution had many connotations and what Mayr suggests is the theatrical use of the term. A critic might write 'The plot evolves in many subtle ways . . .' but there is nothing new at the end. As Lamarck used the term it is perfectly clear – something new evolves at the end. That would be the French meaning of the term. An article in the *Encyclopaedia of Evolution* (Milner, 1990) attributes the coining of 'evolution' to Herbert Spencer (1820–1893). Herbert Spencer was six years old when the '1826 Edinburgh essay' appeared which introduced the term 'evolved'. Lamarck was the first to use this term and it would appear that Charles Lyell transported it to England when Herbert Spencer would have been twelve years old!

In the 1826 essay in Edinburgh, attributed either to Robert Grant or Professor Jameson – the editor of the journal – the word 'evolve' was introduced. In situations where he might have used this term Matthew expresses his meaning in plain words: '. . . the progeny of the same parents, under great difference of circumstance, might in several generations, even become distinct species, incapable of co-reproduction.' Had he used 'evolve' he could have cut out a number of words! If Lyell in the second volume of his *Principles* introduced 'evolution' surely it would have been in the French meaning of the word.

Edward Blyth did not use the term 'evolve' although he had read Lyell's Volume 2. Wallace in neither essay (1855 and 1858) used the term. But these two authors used the term 'type'.

Blyth used the term 'type'. Matthew never used this term but in his review of *The Descent of Man* (1871) he used 'proto-type'! According to Mayr (1969), 'The assumptions of population thinking are diametrically opposed to those of the typologist.' But Wallace wrote in terms of a typologist and a populationist! Matthew did not use 'type' in his essay although he was acquainted with Cuvierian ideas. Darwin went back to Cuvier and claimed that 'conditions of existence' was embraced by the principle of Natural Selection. And on the Unity of Type, Darwin explained, 'in my theory, unity of type is explained by unity of descent.' According to Mayr (1969) typology and a misconstrued idea of evolution had to be got rid of before the modern view clarifying evolutionary concepts could be entertained. It would seem a lot of semantic nonsense had to be swept aside.

Neo-Darwinism includes statements by De Beer (1960): 'Darwin was, therefore, a pioneer in claiming that the senses and mental activities can play a part in selection.'

In the *Appendix* (1831), Matthew wrote: 'This circumstance-adaptive law, operating upon the slight but natural disposition to sport in the progeny (seedling variety), does not preclude the supposed influence which volition or sensation may have over the configuration of the body . . . and to investigate how much variation is modified by the mind or nervous sensation of the parents . . . and how far on the will, irritability and muscular exertion, is open to examination and experiment.'

And Lamarck had covered all this as well! Lamark's *Philosophie Zoologique* is in three parts: Zoology, Physiology and Psychology.

11

Natural Selection and its
Justification of Colonialism

Colonization is comparatively a simple matter, when few Aborigines are in the way, or when they are to be swept down
without compunction, as the incumbering trees of the forest.

(*Emigration Fields*, 1839)

Darwin complained, in his angry criticism, that Matthew's Natural
Selection was to be found in only 'scattered passages' but he made
no comment on the 'scattered passages' devoted to the social and political
consequences of regarding Natural Selection as 'a Universal Law'. There
is some little evidence that Darwin bothered to read the Arboricultural
part of Matthew's book of 1831 *Naval Timber and Arboriculture*. There is
a short reference to the forest trees in *Variations in Plants and Animals
under Domestication* (1868). Had he read more he would have come across
this passage: 'Man's interference, by preventing this natural process among
plants, independent of the wider range of circumstances to which he
introduces them, has increased the difference in varieties, particularly in
the more domesticated kinds; even in man himself, the greater uniformity, and more general vigour among savage tribes, is referable to nearly
similar selecting law – the weaker individual sinking under the ill
treatment of the stronger, or under the common hardship.' That was a
hint of what was to appear in the *Appendix*.

Prior to the section which has just been quoted Matthew had introduced what was to become Darwin's favourite definition of Natural
Selection – to whit, any favourable change in a plant or animal favoured
survival. Here is Matthew's version: 'The use of the infinite seedling
variety in the families of plants, even in a state of nature, differing in
luxuriance of growth and local adaptation, seems to be to give one (the

strongest best circumstance-suited) superiority over the others of its kind around, that it may, by overtopping and smothering them, procure room for full extension, and thus affording, at the same time, a continual selection of the strongest, best circumstance-suited, for reproduction.'

Forty years later *The Descent of Man* was reviewed in the *Scotsman* newspaper by Patrick Matthew. Included in this review were several passages from the book. It would appear that Matthew had not changed his mind about the fate of barbarous savages as we can see from this passage, no doubt specially selected and presented without comment. 'At some future period not very distant as measured by centuries, the civilized races of man will almost certainly exterminate and replace throughout the world the savage races. At the same time the anthropomorphic apes, as Professor Schaeffhausen has remarked, will no doubt be exterminated. The break will then be rendered wider, for it will intervene between man in a more civilized state, as we may hope, than the Caucasian, and some ape as a low baboon, instead of as present between the negro or Australian and the gorilla.' A chilling prospect and an odd message from one who was to be laid to rest in Westminster Abbey. Thomas H. Huxley was also of the opinion that the savages were irreclaimable.

Although Darwin tells us that he had a horror of slavery, this horrific forecast, stated above, is an extrapolation from what had happened in the new world during the previous 350 years. The invading Europeans had slaughtered many of the Indian tribes and many others were forced into slavery. In the United States of America in spite of 'It is self-evident that all men are born equal . . .' most of the Indian tribes were herded into areas and allowed to degenerate by means of alcohol. The American settlers from Europe found a way of quickly containing the Red Indian tribes: they slaughtered their food supply. Five million bison, hundreds of horses and many Indians were slaughtered over a period of a few years.

Darwin saw what was going on in his lifetime and concluded the annihilation of savage tribes would continue at the same rate until there was to be no animal between the Caucasian and the lowest baboon. As it turned out, the predictions of Matthew and Darwin and later Huxley were too extreme. The negro, the Aborigines and the gorilla are still with us.

The present state of the gorillas, however, gives cause for concern. As for the Aboriginals their past way of life has been so disturbed by the invasions of the Europeans, there is now evidence of a severe decline in their state of health. Abandonment to poor agricultural areas and encouragment to consume alcohol together with a poor diet has had its effects. Some effort is now being made to redress the deplorable state of a people whose ancestors cared for the ecology of Australia for thousands of years.

Writing in 1872 Frederick Engels commented, 'Darwin did not know what a bitter satire he wrote on mankind when he showed that free competition, the struggle for existence, which the economists celebrate as the highest historical achievement, is the normal state of the animal kingdom.' And that goes for Matthew too.

Of course colonialism had been going on in the East ever since Gama found the sea passage to India. Even by 1787 India was being reduced to more and more poverty by the East India Company. William Fullerton MP made this statement in Parliament: 'In former time Bengal countries were the granary of nations, and the repository of commerce, wealth and manufacture in the East. But such has been the restless energy of our misgovernment that within the short space of twenty years many parts of these countries have been reduced to the appearance of a desert. The fields are no longer cultivated; extensive tracts are already overgrown with thickets; the husbandman is plundered; the manufacturer oppressed; famine has been repeatedly endured; and depopulation has ensued.'

Burke added his denunciation: 'Were we to be driven out of India this day nothing would remain to tell it had been possessed, during this inglorious period of our dominion, by anything better than the orangutang or the tiger.'

If one was unaware, and many British are, that this was the history of colonization one would be in for a rude shock on reading *Emigration Fields* published by Patrick Matthew in 1839. This book appeared some sixty years after Burke's statement and it is clear that one is in for more of the same but now shored up and justified by a philosophical concept; the Universal Law of Natural Selection.

In the 1830s there was restriction of trade including the hated Corn Laws. Matthew, as an heir to Adam Smith's free trade policy, was up in arms against this Tory policy. Matthew was concerned about the contradiction between restricted trade at a time when productive capacity had expanded as a result of all the new inventions. Added to the problems caused by restricted trade there was widespread unemployment and homelessness. So:

'Prevented by our trade-restrictive system from obtaining a market in foreign nations for the immense surplus fabrics which this vast increase of power is capable of producing, there is only one other available resource – to transplant our surplus working-population to new lands.'

That was the motive for colonization and here is the justification for it; one will note, as always, that Matthew never estranges his politics from his biological concepts: 'Change of place, within certain limits of latitude, seems to have a tendency to improve the species equally in animals as in plants, and agricultural and trading occupations are far more congenial to health and increase, than manufacturing occupations. It cannot therefore be doubted that the increase of the British race (evidently a superior race), and their extension over the world, and even the vigour of the race itself, will be more promoted by this colonizing system, than by the utmost freedom of trade without the colonizing system, and the turning of our entire energies to manufacturing indus-try.' The 'change of place' theme is described in some detail in section C of the *Appendix*.

Ever since Captain Cook's exploration of the Pacific Ocean a few settlers had landed in New Zealand. By the 1830s colonialist eyes were concentrating on New Zealand as not only suitable for coloniz-ation but settlers were preparing to invade. It was now that Patrick Matthew, thwarted by the Chartist Movement's inability to solve unemployment in Britain, turned his attention to New Zealand and this interest was to continue for the rest of his life. So it was that in 1839 he produced, in *Emigration Fields*, his plans for the complete takeover of these islands. Matthew concentrated on New Zealand because he thought those islands had a future. Before dealing with New Zealand he made a brief survey of North America including Canada, the Cape and Australia.

There is nothing really new in his plans or justifications. The usual excuses are that the present occupants are savages and so settlers need protection and that means government intervention. With all the colo-nist's hypocrisy that the takeover of the country must be accompanied by just and humane laws Matthew proceeds with the outlines of his plans. He introduces the old ploy of encouraging the settlers to marry the Aborigines so as to damp down revolt. This ploy is ancient: it was employed by Alexander the Great when he encouraged his soldiers to marry the Persian women. It was always to be understood, however, who were the conquerors and who the conquered. The predicted effect of inter-marrying of conqueror and conquered did not quite work anywhere it had been tried:

> The amalgamation of the two races (British and New Zealand), the one the foremost in civilized life, and the other in savage life, or natural stamina, like engrafting the finest fruits upon the purest crab, may be expected to produce a people superior in physical and moral energy to all others.

One may notice again Matthew's consistent linking of the biological to the human social problems:

> Independently even of the pacification and civilization of the native tribes, the protection of British subjects, who, to the amount (it is said) of 2,000, are already located in the country, is sufficient reason for the interference of Britain . . . From the state of barbarism, and the difficulty of communication in so rugged and extensive a country, it is impossible that any general or presiding native government could exist.

Matthew was then concerned that the British Government was not taking sufficient interest in the colonization of New Zealand perhaps because of the ferocity of the Aborigines. But also, 'A fear has been expressed, that these tribes, under colonization, might dwindle and become extinct, as has sometimes occurred.' One has only to recall what European colonization perpetrated in the New World to agree. Matthew continues, 'It, however, appears that the New Zealand tribes are fast decreasing in numbers under the present intercourse with Europeans; that many places, a few years ago comparatively populous, are now absolutely desolate . . . without being counterbalanced by the great advantages which a more intimate connection with Britain, a strong general government, and the firm administration of just and benignant laws, would afford.'

Matthew was all for just and humane laws and his colonization ambitions were not entirely barefaced imperialism. At least that was part of his attitude. He deplored what the white man had done in South Africa. He did not seem to quite understand the inner contradictions in any conquest of a backward country. His universal law with its attendant survival of the fittest forced him to consider a tree (best-circumstance-suited, of course) smothering all neighbours in order to gain dominance was exactly analogous to a dominant human race (the Angles, of course) smothering its neighbours in order to survive and procreate.

Having demonstrated the need and the motive for colonization Matthew then settles down to the means whereby the project can be accomplished.

'Colonization is comparatively a simple matter, when few Aborigines are in the way, or when they are to be swept down without compunction, as the incumbering trees of the forest, or reduced to slavery, and made subservient to the progress of the settlement.' But is this possible in a country like New Zealand, Matthew wonders. There would have to be strict justice and humanity but 'a strong moral and physical force will require to be employed'. And who is to do this deed? The British government or the settlers? It did not take Matthew long to come to a decision:

> How much better it would be to do the thing in a bold straightforward manner. The following proclamation might suffice: 'Be it known to all men – Whereas the group of islands, sometimes called New Zealand . . . taken possession of by the British Crown by Captain Cook . . . whereas the inhabitants of these islands are in a state of murderous anarchy and cannibalism, shocking to humanity, and totally incapable of establishing social order among themselves, of reducing the numerous banditti or pirates who shelter in these parts . . . and whereas a nation such as Great Britain, which, from a superior social organization and the advancement of the arts of life, has attained a very dense population, beyond the means of competent subsistence within its own confined territory, has a natural right to extend itself over the waste or comparatively desolate regions of the earth.'

Such, then, is imperialism in all its naked greed and the justification of satisfying that greed. Thirty years later *The Origin of the Species* and *The Descent of Man* were instilling into the British people what became known as Social Darwinism. Imperialism had got a bad reputation and has now to take on another face – that it was civilizing, humane and spreading the gospel of Christianity.

I have said Social Darwinism but there was also Social Spencerism. Herbert Spencer (1820–1903) devised a program for the elimination of the poor and unfit classes. Matthew and later Darwin were quite happy to eliminate the 'savages'; it was all a question of the survival of the fittest. Wallace became attracted to this concept and urged Darwin to give up 'natural selection' in favour of 'survival of the fittest'. British military success and naval supremacy as a direct result of the Industrial Revolution inspired in the middle classes that might was right. Pope's vision had come into its own: 'whatever is, is right'.

Matthew would draw the line of invading other people's territory where the inhabitants were gainfully employed. Pastoral societies should not be disturbed and he was dismayed that this was happening in South Africa. The problem for Matthew was the solution of mass unemployment at home with all the misery, starvation and homelessness which ensues. His humanity extended only to his own people:

> A nation . . . has a right [in other words, under the above circumstances] to extend itself over the uncultivated regions of the earth . . . and, to displace the miserable hordes of wandering savages . . . It is sickening to listen to the affectations of pseudo-philantropists, who make such a lament over the loss of a tribe of starved savages . . . while they are silent respecting the hundreds of thousands of fine men and women (a far superior race) in London and other places in Britain who are equally lost to re-productive existence . . .

And *Emigration Fields* is loaded with this sentiment.

But Matthew is not finished yet. He sets off at a tangent to denounce the smoking habit which, he claims, is being encouraged by the missionaries: 'Sucking tobacco smoke has become so general . . . as must have a powerful effect upon the destinies of the species. In the north and east of Europe, it has increased to such a degree, as to act as a considerable population check; and I would desire to introduce it to the notice of our Malthusian philosophers . . . The disposition or desire to suck is no doubt instinctive – a baby reminiscence – and increased in the north of Europe, by the practice of suckling their male children too long . . . Although tobacco smoking has not so immediately obvious an effect upon the system, as drinking intoxicating liquors, yet . . . it has a more powerful impression to disorder the brain mechanism . . .' Matthew may have got the wrong organ but his prediction that something grave would happen came clear in the 1950s when there was evidence for lung cancer as a result of smoking cigarettes. Matthew should have written to Darwin about the dangers of smoking: Darwin was a chain smoker of cigarettes.

In 1864 two sons of Patrick Matthew landed in New Zealand. They carried on the tradition of fruit growing as they had done at Gourdie Hill. Saplings were sent from their father's extensive orchard. The two sons laid out the first commercial fruit orchard in the Antipodes. By this time the British government had taken over and firm administration was in place. Matthew had observed that a change of place was beneficial to animals and plants; a proof exists in New Zealand today – one only has to observe these manly monsters dressed in black shirts and pants on the rugby field.

Matthew gave notice of what was to come in the opening statement of the *Appendix*:

> A nation which, by the establishment of social order, and the advanced arts of life, increases its population beyond the means of a full subsistence, within its territory, has the right to extend itself over the uncultivated regions of the earth; and, should this not be otherwise accomplishable, to displace the miserable hordes of wandering savages, who can neither bring out the powers of productiveness of the country they roam over, nor submit to the social order amongst civilized men.

This was the thesis he was to work at over the next decade little knowing that at some date in the future his sons would settle in that land which in the mean time would see its Aborigines pushed to the wall in accordance with the universal law.

If just humane laws are introduced into a conquered country Matthew's 'circumstance-suited' aspect of his Universal Law may come into operation:

> . . . it may be expected should the system be continued, that the circumstance-suited race will again increase, and by superior producing powers, the result of superior climate-adaptation, gradually

undermine the invaders, and become the dominating population. In cases where two races exist in a country, under anything approaching to equal law, it is not the most moral or most civilized which increases the fastest, or which ultimately prevail. This is being exemplified in Ireland, and in Great Britain, hence the Milesian race is fast gaining ground, and also in Hungary, where the Slavonic race is gradually overwhelming the Magyar, by superior powers of increase. In both cases the conquered are conquering, although lower in the scale of civilization.

This, we can see, is the real context for the concept of 'the survival of the fittest'.

Neither Matthew nor Darwin predicted that the descendants of the brutal slave trade, which Europe had only officially abandoned six years before, would now reach the heights in sports of all kinds and are in ever increasing demand by the fashion houses. Nor could they imagine that within another hundred years the colonial systems would be abandoned and handed over, as Marx predicted, to the very capitalists which Imperialism had engendered as a means of subjugating a nation.

Matthew's distaste for the savages of the world was as extreme as any other Victorian colonialist:

The Aborigines of these regions are a race of savages, perhaps the farthest removed from civilized man of any existence. Those inhabiting Tasmania, who are even a degree inferior to those of Australia, having been found extremely mischievous and irreclaimable, were recently rooted out and removed to a small island in Bass Straits, under superintendence, where they are fast dying of ennui . . . Perhaps the aridity of Australia and the absence of edible plants and fruits, and the scarcity of fish on the coast, with the want of tame animals, accounts sufficiently for the inferior nature of the indigenes.

Note the unusual word these days, 'irreclaimable'. It has been alluded to above that Huxley used the same word. Perhaps he had glanced through *Emigration Fields*!

It then occurred to Matthew that the lack of intelligence of these savages may have had something to do with their method of fighting. Matthew had obviously heard tales about the method of clubbing one another on the head and only those with thick skulls survived. This would be one way Natural Selection would achieve thick-skulled Aborigines. This, curiously, is held by some physical anthropologists today. While it may have been a factor in local micro-evolutionary processes there is not sufficient evidence to support it as a general hypothesis. A recent modern view is as follows: Aborigines are a relatively diverse cultural group and possess numerous ways of settling disputes other than taking turns to hit one another over the head. The particular practice described by Matthew has not been widely described and appears to have been restricted to the south-east of the continent where it is just one of a number of methods of fighting. It is also highly unlikely that a single method of dispute settlement would have been sufficiently widespread over the continent both geographically and chronologically to effect a general change in morphology.

There is other evidence in Australia that different forms of warlike conflict occurred in very ancient times. Analysis of rock paintings in north-west Australia indicate that some form of organized fighting with weapons occurred. According to the Australian Museum in Sydney these rock paintings could be 10,000 years old. This conclusion upsets previous beliefs that organized warfare started in quite complex societies about 5,000 years ago. Rock paintings in Europe estimated at about 25,000 years old indicate that the hunt was the most important occupation of small groups of hunter-gatherers.

The method of fighting, described by Matthew, must have been '. . . a selecting influence – the thin-skulled falling prematurely, and the thick-skulled remaining as breeders, to render them a thick-skulled race, which they literally are, their skulls being nearly double the thickness of the European skull . . . this must act to lower the mental capacity of the race.' The main reason for introducing Matthew's rather ridiculous correlation between a method of fighting and thick skulls is that Natural Selection is still very much in his thinking. One wonders whether Darwin was thinking about this correlation when he wrote in the *Historical Sketch* that Matthew 'saw the full force of Natural Selection'!

Matthew's theory, for all its Natural Selection, does not stand up to today's findings: as for the matter of a thick skull equating with reduced mental capacity it should be realized that skull thickness is usually associated with overall robustness. Size-related robust skulls tend to be big and have proportionally larger brain cases in modern humans. Brain size does not, however, correlate with intelligence in modern populations. The attempt to assess the mental capacities of modern *Homo sapiens* based on skull characteristics is now entirely discredited.

The origin of the robust cranial morphology is to be found in the earliest populations to arrive in Australia which could be 100,000 years ago. Early fossil evidence indicates morphological variability. Later populations appear to have an overall reduction in size and variability. There is no agreement as to what this means. Matthew's idea that the Aborigines were denied a good food supply is not supported by recent fossil evidence (Thorne and Raymond, 1989).

Matthew, Darwin and most Victorians had contempt for what they called 'savages'! 'On the whole they appear to me to stand some few degrees higher in the scale of civilization than the Fuegians.' (Darwin, 1845.) This was Darwin's commentary after a few days in Australia. The Fuegians, Darwin reckoned, were the lowest of the low. When one reads in the *Journal of Researches* (1845) what Darwin had to say about the Fuegians one can feel that he was very unfair to the Aborigines. In this century many anthropologists have taken a more humane and scientific view of the Aborigines. As an example one can quote from the writings of a distinguished author from the early twentieth century. Sir Arthur Keith (1866–1955) was a Scot who was born in Matthew's lifetime and was to become a most distinguished anthropologist. Many skulls of primitive man were dug up after Matthew's demise and these are discussed in an authoritative way in *The Antiquity of Man* (1929 edition). Dealing with fossil finds in Australia Keith commented:

> In this continent has come down to us, much changed by specialization of a superlative nature, mammals which are really living fossils, representatives of a very ancient stage in mammalian evolution. In the same way this continent has preserved for us a very ancient type of man. It is true the jaws of this ancient type have grown smaller in his descendants, but they have kept his essential characteristics. More than any other man, the aborigine of Australia and Tasmania seems to have conserved the qualities of the stock which gave rise to all modern breeds. We may look upon him as the best living representative of Pleistocene man.

It is now known that modern man extends back into the Pliocene age which started about eleven million years ago. Modern man's lineage now extends to about five million years but future finds may extend this even further back.

Although this discussion about colonialism has been confined to the attitude that scientific minds had approached the subject, they were not the only section of Victorian Society with similar views and contempt for impoverished peoples. At about the time when Patrick Matthew was finishing off his *Naval Timber* book in 1830 Disraeli was making an Eastern tour. Now Disraeli is the politician that Tories revere as the preacher of one nation in spite of his harsh and inhuman views. During his eastern tour he visited Albania where he had an audience with the Grand Vizier. Afterwards he wrote home: 'The delight of being made much of by a man who was daily decapitating half the province.' (Blake, 1966.) His harsh views had not changed in his old age when he was quite pleased to allow the Turks to massacre the Greeks and before them the Serbs. Disraeli did not like rebels in or outside the Empire.

If we come to the height of the Victorian period it is Rudyard Kipling who portrays the British distaste and, indeed, acute embarrassment for the miserable plight of the negroes who were released from bare-faced slavery only about fifty years before. Here Kipling expressed the abject poverty and complete degradation of one part of humanity:

> Now remember when you're 'acking round a Gilded Burma god,
> That 'is eyes is very often precious stones
> An' if you treat a nigger to a dose o' clearin' rod
> 'E's like to show you everything 'e owns.

To be sure there were missionaries galore eager to convert the heathen in those stolen lands. Matthew's only comment was that they were spreading tobacco among the savages.

But twenty years on from all his bluster about the wiping out of savages Matthew was a changed man or so it seems. In December 1862 while in London on what he termed 'mercantile concerns' he wrote to Darwin. In this letter he mentions that one of his main concerns was methods of 'enriching the vegetable mould'. This was the last subject that Darwin committed to a book (1881); he had studied the way worms tilled the top ten inches of soil and produced the vegetable mould. Matthew explained that his main interests lay in the social and political spheres. Then, rather pathetically, he states, 'I am not satisfied with my existence here to devour and trample upon my fellow creature. I cannot pluck a flower without regarding myself a destroyer.'

Darwin did not reply to this letter for a year and even then got Emma, his wife, to sign the letter. Darwin was indisposed again!

Matthew continued with his political and social interests up until 1871; his letters indicate what these interests were. 1871 was the year *The Descent of Man* was published and Matthew wrote a long review which was published in the *Scotsman* newspaper. There are no signs of the depressed mood he was in during 1862. Indeed, he appears to be in the same old state of mind and fully supported Darwin in the extermination of the savages. He pointed out a weakness in Darwin's exposition. There could not be a straight line from ape to man; there had to be varieties and this, indeed, is how the evolution of man has come about.

12

Patrick Matthew's Review
of *The Descent of Man*

At some future period not very distant as measured by centuries, the civilized races of man will almost certainly exterminate and replace throughout the world the savage races.

(*The Descent of Man*)

Puzzled by a sentence in the last letter Patrick Matthew sent to Darwin in 1871, I began an investigation. The sentence runs: 'I enclose an Article from the Scotsman Newspaper which will shew I am not yet quite effete.' Darwin replied on 15 March 1871: 'You show no signs of your fourscore years in your letter or in the newspaper article, which seem written with your pristine vigour.'

In searching through the archives of the *Scotsman* newspaper for March, 1871, I found that the newspaper article was a review, by Patrick Matthew, of *The Descent of Man*!

Patrick Matthew usually sent his letters to the *Dundee Advertiser*. Did the editor of the *Scotsman* newspaper, Edinburgh, invite Matthew to write this review or did Matthew just send it in? Matthew was now 81 years of age and died in 1874 in his 83rd year. There was no obituary in the *Scotsman* but a few words announcing his death were sent by his family.

The review is long and contains excerpts from the book. It is not a critical review; Matthew made no adverse comment although he could have done. Other admirers of Darwin were dismayed to read '. . . in the earlier editions of my *Origin of Species* I perhaps attributed too much to the action of natural selection or the survival of the fittest. I have altered the fifth edition of the *Origin* so as to confine my remarks to adaptive changes of structure.' Matthew never changed what he had written in 1831.

Lord Monboddo (1714–1799) had seen the orangutan and let it be known that man was of simian origin. So Darwin's essay on man's origin was rather old hat. Perhaps Darwin's confession needed no further comment: 'This work contains hardly any original facts in regard to man . . .' He could have entered the same confession about the *Origin*.

One should really read Matthew's *Emigration Fields* and then read *The Descent of Man*. Both refer to the extermination of the 'savages'. It was perhaps for this reason that Matthew included the most chilling paragraph in the whole book:

> At some future period not very distant as measured by centuries, the civilized races of man will almost certainly exterminate and replace throughout the world the savage races. At the same time the anthropomorphous apes, as Professor Schaeffhausen has remarked, will no doubt be exterminated. The break will then be rendered wider, for it will intervene between man in a more civilized state, as we may hope, than the Caucasian, and some ape as low as a baboon, instead of as at present between the negro or Australian and the gorilla.

Matthew in *Emigration Fields* maintained that the Caucasians had a right to exterminate and colonize the lands occupied by useless savages. Such was the ethics of the Victorian naturalists. They were not the only ones. Herbert Spencer would have eliminated the poorer classes on the basis that they were unfit. Racism is the belief that less developed human groups are so inferior to the Caucasians that they can be eliminated. Of course survival of the fittest became so mixed up and any meaning could be attached to the slogan that it was bound to wither away.

It is surprising that Matthew did not include a rather curious statement by Darwin which, I suppose, was an effort to stress the importance of competition even among men: 'There should be open competition for all men and the most able should not be prevented by laws or customs from succeeding best.' This statement is rather milder than Matthew's exuberance: 'There is a law universal in nature, tending to render every reproductive being the best possibly suited to its conditions that its kind, or that organized matter, is susceptible of . . . The law of entail, necessary to hereditary nobility, is an outrage on this law of nature, which she will not pass unavenged.'

Matthew made the point that it was all very well to talk about the road from ape to man but there must have been varieties; hominids in modern language. Darwin did not mention this important aspect of the evolution of man although he stated, 'The sole object of this work is to consider firstly, whether man, like every other species, is descended from some pre-existing form . . .' By introducing varieties Matthew was clearly pointing out that there must have been competition among them until Neanderthals and Cromagnons emerged from the struggle.

Edward Blyth is accorded 42 references in the *Descent* which made him the largest contributor, by a very wide margin. There is no reference to the 1835–37 essays. Here is Blyth: 'Why, for example, should the pipits (Anthus) shed their plumage twice a year, and the larks (Alauda) but once?' (1836.)

Here is Darwin: '. . . some coloured pipits (Anthus) shed their plumage twice in the year, and the larks (Alauda) but once.' Darwin gives the Blyth reference; Ibis, 1867!

Matthew included this section from *The Descent of Man*: 'Breaks occur in all parts of the series, some being wide, sharp and defined, others less so in various degrees; so between the Orang and Lemuridae – between the elephant and in a more striking manner between the Ornithorynchus, or echidna and other mammals.' There is no reference to this statement.

Here is Blyth 1836: 'The Ornithorynchus, among mammifers, approximates very remarkably towards birds . . .'

Matthew sent the review to Darwin along with a long letter. Darwin sent a curt reply but with no comment about the review. By the time the second edition appeared in 1874 Matthew had died.

There were other aspects which Matthew should have commented on: 'Whether the foregoing modifications would have become hereditary, if the same habits were followed during many generations, is not known, but it is probable.' Probable? Pure Lamarckism!

In another section: 'If, however, we look to the races of man as distributed over the world, we must infer that their characteristic differences cannot be accounted for by the direct action of different conditions of life even after exposure to them for an enormous period of time.' But surely the period of time was insufficient. This is similar to Cuvier presenting the mummified animals from the tombs of Egypt as evidence against mutation.

The *Descent* contains a mass of contradictions. Darwin quotes the report by Pritchard in 1844 about the Quechua Indians living at a very high altitude: '. . . have acquired chests and lungs of extraordinary dimensions,' then concludes, 'From these observations, there can, I think, be no doubt that residence during many generations at a great elevation tends, both directly and indirectly, to induce inherited modifications in the proportions of the body.' Inheritance of acquired characteristics! Poor Lamarck! A university professor of zoology once told me, apropos of IAC, 'we are not stupid!' IAC was well down in Lamarck's list of laws and it was all Buffon's idea.

In his introduction to the book Darwin states that he was encouraged to go ahead and publish the notes he had collected over the years because more and more naturalists were in agreement that, 'species are the modified descendants of other species'.

Matthew should have drawn attention to the conclusions of the introduction: 'In conclusion that man is the descendant with other species of ancient, lower and extinct forms is not in any degree new. Lamarck long ago (i.e. 70 years ago) came to the same conclusion, which has lately been maintained by several eminent naturalists and philosophers.' We have indicated elsewhere that Charles Lyell was vainly, in 1875, trying to rehabilitate Lamarck. Even Darwin's belated effort did nothing to restore Lamarck to scientific respectability in English speaking countries.

Then because he had been criticized for attributing, in the *Origin*, all changes of corporeal structure and mental power exclusively to the Natural Selection of such variations he made this statement:

'I distinctly stated that great weight must be attributed to the inherited effects of use and disuse, with respect both to the mind and body. I also attributed some amount of modification to the direct and prolonged action of changed conditions of life.' But that amounted to convergence which was a Lamarckian idea which Darwin had always referred to as 'nonsense'. G. J. Romanes, the Canadian psychologist who became a great admirer and friend of the ageing Darwin, reminisced, 'The longer he lived, and the more he pondered these points, the less exclusive was the role which he attributed to natural selection.' Modern Darwin apologists are making every effort to shield Darwin from his 'mistakes'! But Darwin, in spite of his encyclopaedic fund of other people's researches and the vast number of the works of Edward Blyth that he carefully read and stored away all through the years, and eventually referenced, never allowed himself to make the 'mistake' of recognizing those seminal essays of 1835–37. Darwin never attempted to get Blyth elected a fellow of the Royal Society – and if there was such an honour as a posthumously recognized fellow he should be made one.

The Descent of Man and Selection in relation to sex by Charles Darwin, MA, FRS, London: John Murray, 1871.

Of late years a sect of philosophers has arisen who maintain the doctrine of the evolution of the animals, which at present inhabit the earth, from mothers of simpler form, which in their turn, are the off-spring of former still more simple. In this way the origin of man himself is carried back to ancestors of a type so low as to have neither brain nor heart distinctly developed. The object of the work before us is to point out the grounds on which this hypothesis rests, and to strengthen the proofs which have already been laid before the public, by additional evidence, founded principally on the results of sexual selection.

The animals most nearly approaching man in organization are the apes; and, accordingly, if the doctrine of which we have spoken be founded on fact, it is from the apes that man derives his immediate descent. And here is the portrait which Mr Darwin draws of his ancestors:

> The early progenitors of man were no doubt once covered with hair, both sexes having beards; their ears were pointed, and capable of movement; and their bodies were provided with a tail, having the proper muscles. Their limbs and bodies were also acted on by many muscles which now only occasionally reappear, but are normally present in the quadrumans. The great artery and nerve of the humerus ran through a supra-condyloid foramen. At this or some earlier period the intestine gave forth a much larger diverticulum or caecum than that now existing. The foot, judging from the condition of the great toe in the foetus, was then prehensile; and our progenitors, no doubt, were arboreal in their habits frequenting some warm forest-clad land. The males were provided with great canine teeth which served them as formidable weapons.

The three main arguments on which the doctrine of evolution is founded are the bodily structure of man, his embryonic development, and the appearance in his body of the rudiments of organs which, in his advanced condition, are no longer required. First then, as regards bodily structure, there cannot be the smallest doubt that man is constructed on the same general model as other animals. All the bones in his skeleton, all his muscles, nerves, blood vessels, and internal organs may be compared with corresponding structures in monkeys, dogs, bats, or eels. There is likewise a close similarity in the composition of the tissues and blood of man and the lower animals; and various contagious diseases — such as hydrophobia, variols, and glanders — may be received from them, or communicated to them from him. Further:

Monkeys are liable to many of the same non-contagious diseases as we are. Thus Reagger, who carefully observed for a long time the Cebus Azarir in its native land, found it liable to catarrh, with the usual symptoms, and which when often recurrent led to consumption. These monkeys suffered also from apoplexy, inflammation of the bowels, and cataract in the eye. The younger ones when shedding their milk teeth often died from fever. Medicines produced the same effect on them as on us. Many kinds of monkeys have a strong taste for tea, coffee and spiritous liquors; they will also, as I have myself seen, smoke tobacco with pleasure. Brehm asserts that the natives of north-eastern Africa catch the wild baboons, with strong beer, by which they are made drunk. He had seen some of these animals, which he kept in confinement, in this state; and he gives a laughable account of their behaviour and grimaces. On the following morning they were very cross and dismal; they held their aching heads with both hands and wore a most pitiable expression; when beer or wine was offered them they turned away with disgust, but relished the juice of lemons. An American monkey, an Atalea, after getting drunk on brandy would never touch it again, and thus was wiser than many men. These trifling facts prove how similar the nerves of taste must be in monkeys and man and how similarly their whole nervous system is affected.

These details indicate not only structural but likewise mental affinity; and indeed, there can be no doubt that many of the lower animals — such as dogs, elephants and apes — possess considerable intellectual as well as moral endowments. The following anecdotes afford further proof of this assertion:

Brehm encountered in Abyssinia a great troop of baboons which were crossing a valley; some had already ascended the opposite

mountain and some were still in the valley; the latter were attacked
by the dogs but the old males immediately hurried down from
the rocks and with mouths widely opened roared so fearfully that
the dogs precipitately retreated. They were again encouraged to
attack; but by this time all the baboons had re-ascended the
heights, excepting a young one, about six months old, who, loudly
calling for aid climbed on a block of rock and was surrounded.
Now one of the largest males, a true hero, came down again
from the mountain, slowly went to the young one, coaxed him,
and triumphantly led him away – the dogs being too astonished
to make an attack.

I cannot resist giving another scene which was witnessed by this
same naturalist; an eagle seized a young Cercopithecus which, by
clinging to a branch, was not at once carried off; it cried loudly
for assistance, upon which other members of the troop with much
uproar rushed to the rescue, surrounded the eagle, and pulled out
so many feathers, that he no longer thought of his prey but only
how to escape. This faith in the theory of evolution to trace men
back not only to his ape progenitors, but to that far earlier period
when the common progenitors of man and of apes were aquatic
in their habits. For:

Morphology plainly tells us that the lungs consist of a modified
swim-bladder which once served as a float. The clefts on the neck
of the embryo show where the branchiae once existed. At about
this period, the true kidneys were replaced by the Corpora Wol-
fiana. The heart existed as a simple pulmonating vessel; and the
corda dorsalis took the place of a vertebral column. These early
predecessors of man, thus seen in the dim recesses of time, must
have been as lowly organized as the lancelet or amphioxus, or
even still more lowly organized.

Nevertheless, Mr Darwin sees no difficulty in the matter. Every
evolutionist will admit, he says, that the five great vertebrate classes
– namely, mammals, birds, reptiles, amphibia and fishes – are all
designed from one prototype; and as the class of fishes is the most
lowly organized and appeared before the others it may be concluded
that all the members of the vertebrate kingdom are derived from
one fish-like animal, less highly organized than any as yet found
in the lowest known formations.

Mr Darwin does not, however, maintain that man's immediate progenitors are to be found among any of the existing apes. They are, as it were, his cousins, not his ancestors; they both spring from the same stock, but, from such lucky accident, man got into a groove of progressive development, which led him to the highest place in creation, while his less fortunate relatives are still denizens of the forest or captive in menageries. But to this theory of evolution it has often been objected that the great break in the organic chain between man and his nearest allies cannot be bridged over by any extinct or living species. In Mr Darwin's opinion, however, this objection will not have much weight with those who, convinced by general reasons, believe in the general principle of evolution:

Breaks occur in all parts of the series, some being wide, sharp and defined, others less so in various degrees; so between the orang and the lemuridae – between the elephant and in a more striking manner between the Ornithorynchus or echidna and other mammals. But all these breaks depend merely on the number of related forms which have become extinct. At some future period not very distant as measured by centuries, the civilized races of man will almost certainly exterminate and replace throughout the world the savage races. At the same time the anthropomorphous apes, as Professor Schaeffhausen has remarked, will no doubt be exterminated. The break will then be rendered wider, for it will intervene between man in a more civilized state, as we may hope, than the Caucasian, and some ape as low as a baboon, instead of as at present between the negro or Australian and the gorilla.

With respect to the absence of fossil remains, serving to connect man with his ape-like progenitors, no one will lay much stress on this fact who will read Sir C. Lyell's discussion, in which he shows that in all the vertebrate classes the discovery of fossil remains has been an extremely slow and fortuitous process. Nor should it be forgotten that those regions which are the most likely to afford remains connecting man with some extinct ape-like creatures, have not as yet been searched by geologists.

But, granting all this, should we not expect a more gradual blending of the animal kingdom than is found to exist? If man is the successor of

some remote ape, why should the same causes which led to his origin
not ever since have continued in operation, and so have led to the
production of innumerable varieties not separated from each other by
broad lines of demarcation but passing insensibly from one form into
another, as little capable of distinct classification as infancy, childhood,
youth, maturity, and old age? And not only with man should this be
the case, but with the whole range of the vertebrates which derive their
origin from that fish-like animal which Mr Darwin's eye sees in the
dim obscurity of the past, 'as more like the larvae of our existing marine
Ascidians than any other known form'.

It should be noticed here that Matthew's statement is a precise
prediction of what indeed was found in the next hundred years. Anthropologists now consider there is a series of gradual development *Australopithecus ramidus*, *Australopithecus afarensis*, *Homo erectus*, Boxgrove man,
Neanderthal man, *Homo sapiens*. It is now estimated that man's beginnings
go back at least five million years and perhaps new discoveries will push
the time beyond five million years.

A large portion of the present work – and, indeed, its most novel
portion – is devoted to show the influence of sexual selection in modifying
structure, and bringing about progressive development. Strength and
beauty carry the day against weakness and ugliness and on this broad
principle the tendency is towards improvement. The weakest go to the
wall and only the strong flourish. The ugly are rejected and only the
best endowed are chosen. This is the rule among the lowest animals and
among savages, and many interesting details, collected from a variety of
sources, are given in its illustration by Mr Darwin; but among mankind
in civilized life there is from various causes a wide departure from this
practice:

> With savages the weak in body and mind are soon eliminated;
> and those who survive commonly exhibit a vigorous state of
> health. We civilized men, on the other hand, do our utmost to
> check the process of elimination; we build asylums for the imbe-
> ciles, the maimed and the sick; we institute poor laws; and our
> medical men exert their utmost skill to save life of everyone to
> the last moment. There is reason to believe that vaccination has
> preserved thousands who from a weak constitution would formerly
> have succumbed to smallpox. Thus the weak members of civilized

societies propagate their kind. No one who has attended to the breeding of domestic animals will doubt that this must be highly injurious to the race of man. It is surprising how soon a want of care, or care wrongly directed, leads to the degeneration of a domestic race, but excepting in the care of man himself hardly any one is so ignorant as to allow his worst animals to breed.

The aid which we felt impelled to give to the helpless is mainly an incidental result of the instinct of sympathy which was originally acquired as part of the social instincts, but subsequently rendered, in the manner previously indicated, more tender and more widely diffused. Nor could we check our sympathy, if so urged by hard reason, without deterioration in the noblest part of our nature. The surgeon may harden himself whilst performing an operation, for he knows he is acting for the good of his patient; but if we were intentionally to neglect the weak and helpless, it could only be for a contingent benefit with a certain and great present evil. Hence we must bear without complaining the undoubtedly bad effects of the weak surviving and propagating their kind; but there appears to be one check in steady action – namely, the weak and inferior members of society not marrying as freely as the sound; and this check might be indefinitely increased, though this is more to be hoped for than expected, by the weak in body and mind refraining from marriage.

In all civilized countries man accumulates property and bequeaths it to his children. Not that the children in the same country do not by any means start fair in the race for success. But this is far from an unmixed evil; for without the accumulation of capital the arts could not progress; and it is chiefly through their power that the civilized races have extended, and are now everywhere extending their range so as to take the place of the lower races. Nor does the moderate accumulation of wealth interfere with the process of selection. When a poor man becomes rich, the children enter trades or professions in which there is struggle enough, so that the able in body succeed best. The presence of a body of well-instructed men who have not to labour for their daily bread, is important to a degree which cannot be over-estimated; as all high intellectual work is carried out by them, and on such work material progress of all kinds mainly depends, not to mention other and higher advantages. No doubt wealth when very great tends to convert men into useless drones but their number is never very large; and some degree of elimination here occurs as we daily see rich men who happen to be fools or profligate, squandering away their wealth.

Although the doctrine of evolution has been for some years before the public, we have entered pretty fully into the consideration of the general subject, and by so doing have been obliged to say little of the new arguments in its favour contained in the work before us. This, however, is of less consequence as, however ingenious, they are not well calculated for analysis in our columns, and, moreover, would require more space than we can afford. The points which Mr Darwin apparently regards as the most difficult of his problems are the whole difference between man and the highest of the lowest animals is mental endowments, and the origin of the moral sense; but perhaps it would be just as difficult for him to explain in what manner intelligence and the moral sense are associated with man's present organization.

Mr Darwin is afraid that the conclusions at which he has arrived will be denounced by many people as highly irreligious, but he is unable to see why it should be more irreligious to explain the origin of man as a distinct species through the laws of variation and natural selection, than to explain the birth of the individual through the laws of ordinary reproduction. As manifestation of the wisdom of the Deity, it may assuredly be maintained that creation by evolution stand immeasurably higher than creation by individual acts. As regards the immortality of the soul, Mr Darwin believes that:

Few persons feel any anxiety from the impossibility of determining at what precise period in the development of the individual, from the first trace of the minute germinal vessels to the child either before or after birth, man becomes an immortal being; and there is no greater cause for anxiety because the period in the gradually ascending organic scale cannot possibly be determined.

Finally, Mr Darwin is of the opinion that a descent from apes is not one to be ashamed of:

He who has seen a savage in his native land will not feel much shame, if forced to acknowledge that the blood of some more humble creature flows in his veins. For my part I would as soon be descended from that heroic little monkey who braved his dreaded enemy in order to save the life of his keeper; or from that old baboon who, descended from the mountains, carried away in triumph his young comrade from a crowd of astonished dogs – as from a savage who delights to torture his enemies, offers up blood sacrifices, practices infanticide without remorse, treats his wives as slaves, knows no decency, and is haunted by the greatest superstition.

Man may be excused for feeling some pride at having risen, though not through his own exertions to the very summit of the organic scale; and the fact that having thus risen, instead of having been aboriginally placed there, may give him hope for a still higher destiny in the distant future. But we are not here concerned with hopes or fears, only with the truth as far as our reason allows us to discover it. I have given the evidence to the best of my ability; and we must acknowledge, as it seems to me that man with all his noble qualities, which feels for the most debased with benevolence which extends not only to other men but to the humblest living creature, with his god-like intellect which has penetrated into the movements and constitution of the solar system with all these exalted powers – man still bears in his bodily frame the indelible stamp of his lowly origin.

Text of Matthew's appendix to
Naval Timber and Arboriculture

Note A

It is only on the *Ocean* that *Universal Empire* is practicable – only by means of *Navigation* that all the world can be subdued or retained under One dominion. On land, the greatest numbers, and quantity of material, are unavailable, excepting around the spot where they are produced. The most powerful army is crippled by advancing a few degrees in an enemy's territory, unless when aided by some catching enthusiasm; its resources get distant, communication is obstructed – subjection does not extend beyond the range of its guns, and it quickly melts away. The impossibility of dominion extending over a great space, when communication is only by land, has often been proved. The rule of Cyrus, or Alexander, the Caesars, the Tartar conquerors,* or Bonaparte, did not extend over a tithe of the earth; and we may believe, that, by some of these chiefs, dominion was extended as widely as under land communication could be effected – further than it could be supported.

On the contrary, when a powerful nation has her war-like strength afloat, and possesses naval superiority, independent of being unassailable herself, every spot of the world, wherever a wave can roll, is accessible to her power and under her control. In a very short time she can throw an irresistible force, unexhausted by marches, and with every resource, upon any hostile point, the point of attack being in her own choice, and unknown to the enemy. In case of her dependent dominions being scattered over the two hemispheres, her means of communication, and consequent power of defending these and supporting authority, are more facile than what exists between the seat of government of any ordinary

---

* The very extended sway, the state of civilization considered, of the Tartar, was evidently the consequence of a great facility of communication from the plain open surface of the country, and the equestrian habits of the people.

sized continental kingdom and its provinces. Were a popular system of colonial government adopted, many islands and inferior states would find it their interest to become incorporated as part of the Empire.

Note B

There is a law universal in nature, tending to render every reproductive being the best possibly suited to its condition that its kind, or that organized matter, is susceptible of, which appears intended to model the physical and mental or instinctive powers, to their highest perfection, and to continue them so. This law sustains the lion in his strength, the hare in her swiftness, and the fox in his wiles. As Nature, in all her modifications of life, has a power of increase far beyond what is needed to supply the place of what falls by Time's decay, those individuals who possess not the requisite strength, swiftness, hardihood, or cunning, fall prematurely without reproducing – either a prey to their natural de-vourers, or sinking under disease, generally induced by want of nour-ishment, their place being occupied by the more perfect of their own kind, who are pressing on the means of subsistence. The law of entail, necessary to hereditary nobility, is an outrage on this law of nature which she will not pass unavenged – a law which has the most debasing influence upon the energies of a people, and will sooner or later lead to general subversion, more especially when the executive of a country remains for a considerable time efficient, and no effort is needed on the part of the nobility to protect their own, or no war to draw forth or preserve their powers by exertion. It is all very well, when, in stormy times, the baron has every faculty trained to its utmost ability in keeping his proud crest aloft. How far hereditary nobility, under effective gov-ernment, has operated to retard 'the march of intellect', and deteriorate the species in modern Europe, is an interesting and important question. We have seen it play its part in France; we see exhibition of its influence throughout the Iberian peninsula, to the utmost degradation of its victims. It has rendered the Italian peninsula, with its islands, a blank in the political map of Europe. Let the panegyrists of hereditary nobility, primogeniture, and entail, say what these countries might not have been but for the baneful influence of this unnatural custom. It is an eastern proverb, that no king is many removes from a shepherd. Most conquerors and founders of dynasties have followed the plough or the flock. Nobility, to be in the highest perfection, like the finer varieties of fruits,

independent of having its vigour excited by regular married alliance
with wilder stocks, would require stated complete renovation, by selection anew, from among the purest crab. In some places, this renovation
would not be so soon requisite as in others, and, judging from facts,
we would instance Britain as perhaps the soil where nobility will continue
the longest untainted. As we advance nearer to the equator, renovation
becomes sooner necessary, excepting at high elevation – in many places,
every third generation, at least with the Caucasian breed, although the
finest stocks be regularly imported. This renovation is required as well
physically as morally.

It is chiefly in regard to the interval of time between the period of
necessary feudal authority, and that when the body of the population
having acquired the power of self-government.

From the spread of knowledge, claim a community of rights, that we
have adverted to the use of war. The manufacturer, the merchant, the
sailor, the capitalist, whose mind is not corrupted by the indolence
induced under the law of entail, are too much occupied to require any
stimulant beyond what the game in the wide field of commercial adven-
ture affords. A great change in the circumstances of man is obviously at
hand. In the first step beyond the condition of the wandering savage,
while the lower classes from ignorance remained as helpless children,
mankind naturally fell into clans under paternal or feudal government;
but as children, when grown up to maturity, with the necessity for
protection, lose the subordination to parental authority, so the great mass
of the present population requiring no guidance from a particular class
of feudal lords, will not continue to tolerate any hereditary claims of
authority of one portion of the population over their fellow men; nor
any laws to keep up rank and wealth corresponding to this exclusive
power. It would be *wisdom* in the *noblesse* of Europe to abolish every
claim or law which serves to point them out a separate class, and, as
quickly as possible, to merge themselves into the mass of the population.
It is a law manifest in nature, that when the use of any thing is past, its
existence is no longer kept up.

Although the necessity for the existence of feudal lords is past, yet the
same does not hold in respect to a hereditary head or King; and the
stability of this head of the government will, in no way, be lessened by
such a change. In the present state of European society, perhaps no other
rule can be so mild and efficient as that of a liberal benevolent monarch,

assisted by a popular representative Parliament. The poorest man looks up to his king as his own, with affection and pride, and considers him a protector; while he only regards the antiquated feudal lord with contempt. The influence of a respected hereditary family, as head of a country, is also of great utility in forming a principle of union to the different members, and in giving unity and stability to the government.

In respect to our own great landholders themselves, we would ask, where is there that unnatural parent – that miserable victim of hereditary pride – who does not desire to see his domains equally divided among his own children? The high paid sinecures in church and state will not much longer be a great motive for keeping up a powerful family head, whose influence may burthen their fellow-citizens with the younger branches. Besides, when a portion of land is so large, that the owner cannot have an individual acquaintance and associations with every stream, and bush, and rock, and knoll, the deep enjoyment which the smaller native proprietor would have in the peculiar features, is not called forth, and is lost to man. The abolition of the law of entail and primogeniture, will, in the present state of civilization, not only add to the happiness of the proprietor, heighten morality, and give much greater stability to the social order, but will also give a general stimulus to industry and improvement, increasing the comforts and elevating the condition of the operative class.

In the new state of things which is near at hand, the proprietor and the mercantile class will amalgamize – employment in useful occupations will not continue to be held in scorn – the merchant and manufacturer will no longer be barely tolerated to exist, harassed at every turn by imposts and the interference of petty tyrants – Government, instead of forming an engine of oppression, being simplified and based on morality and justice, will become a cheap and efficient protection to person and property; and the necessary taxation being levied from property alone, every individual will purchase in the cheapest market, and sell the produce of his industry in the dearest. This period might, perhaps, be accelerated throughout Europe, did the merchants and capitalists only know their own strength. Let them, as citizens of the world, hold annual congress in some central place, and deliberate on the interests of man, which is their own, and throw the whole of their influence to support liberal and just governments, and to repress slavery, crime, bigotry – tyranny in all shapes. A Rothschild might earn an unstained fame, as great as yet has been attained by man, by organizing such a power, and presiding at its councils.

Note C

The influence of long continued impression, constituting instinct or habit of breed, is a curious phenomenon in the animal economy. Our population in the eastern maritime districts of Britain, descended principally from the Scandinavian rover, though devoted for a time to agricultural or mechanical occupation, betake themselves, when opportunity offers, to their old element, the ocean,* and launch out upon the 'wintry wave' with much of the same home-felt composure as does the white polar bear. They roam over every sea and every shore, from Behring's Straits to Magellan's, with as little solicitude as the Kelt over his own misty hill, overcoming, in endurance, the native of the torrid zone under his vertical sun, and the native of the frigid among his polar snows.

To what may we ascribe the superiority of this portion of the Caucasian breed – may it arise in part from its repeated change of place under favourable circumstances? Other races have migrated, but not like this, always as conqueror. The Jew has been a stroller in his time; but he has improved more in mental acumen and cunning – not so much in heroism and personal qualities: his proscribed condition will account for this.

The Caucasian in its progress, will also have mingled slightly, and, judging from analogy, perhaps advantageously, with the finer portion of those whom it has overwhelmed. This breed, by its wide move across the Atlantic, does not seem at all to have lost vigour, and retains the nautical and roving instinct unimpaired, although the American climate is certainly inferior to the European. It is there rapidly moving west, and may soon have described one of the earth's circles. A change of seed, that is, a change of place, within certain limits of latitude, is well known to be indispensable to the more sturdy growth and health of many

---

* The habit of breed is apparent in many places of the world. Where a fine river washes the walls of some of the internal towns of France, scarce a boat is to be seen, except the long tract-boats employed in the conveyance of firewood – nobody thinks of sailing for pleasure. The Esquimaux, and the Red Indian of North America, inhabiting the same country, shew an entirely distinct habit of breed. The Black and the Copper-coloured native of the Australian lands, are equally opposed in instinctive habit.

cultivated vegetables; it is probable that this also holds true of the human race. There are few countries where the old breed has not again and again sunk before the vigour of new immigration; we even see the worn out breed, chased from their homes to new location, return, after a time, superior to their former vanquishers, or gradually work their way back in peace, by superior subsisting power: this is visible in France, where the aboriginal sallow Kelt, distinguished by high satyr-like feature, deep-placed sparkling brown or grey eye, narrowed lower part of the face, short erect vertebral column, great mental acuteness, and restless vivacity, has emerged from the holes of the earth, the recesses of the forests and wastes, into which it had been swept before the more powerful blue-eyed Caucasian; and being a smaller, more easily subsisting animal, has, by starving and eating out, been gradually undermining the breed of its former conquerors. The changes which have been taking place in France, and which, in many places, leave now scarcely a trace of the fine race which existed twenty centuries ago, may, however, in part, be accounted for by the admixture of the Caucasian and Keltic tending more to the character of the latter, from the latter being a purer and more fixed variety, and nearer the original type or medium standard of man; and from the warm dry plains of France (much drier from cultivation and the reduction of the forests), having considerable influence to increase this bias: in some of the south-eastern departments, more immediately in the tide of the ingress of the Caucasian, where the purest current has latest flowed, and the climate is more suitable, and also in some of the maritime districts, where the air is moister, and to which they have been seaborn at a later period, the Caucasian character is still prominent. Something of this, yet not so general, is occurring in Britain, where the fair bright-blooded race is again giving place to the darker and more sallow. This may, however, be partly occasioned by more of artificial heat and shelter and other consequences of higher civilization. There seems to be something connected with confinement and sedentary life, with morbid action of the liver, or respiratory or transpiratory organs, which tends to change under dry and hot, and especially confined atmosphere. Perhaps imagination is also at work and the colour most regarded, as snow in cold countries, black among colliers, white among bleachers, or even the dark colour of dress, may produce its peculiar impression, and our much looked-up-to Calvinistic priesthood, from the pulpit, disseminate darkness as well as light.

Our own Kelt has indubitably improved much since, *par nécessité*, he took to the mountain; but, though steadily enduring, when there is mental excitement, he has acquired a distaste to dull hopeless unceasing labour, and would fare scantily and lie hard, rather than submit to the monotonous industry of the city operative, or the toil of the agricultural drudge. Though once a fugitive, the Kelt is now, in moral courage and hardihood, equal perhaps to any other, yet he still trembles to put foot on ocean.

Notwithstanding that change of place, simply, may have impression to improve the species, yet is it more to circumstances connected with this change, to which the chief part of the improvement must be referred. In the agitation which accompanies emigration, the ablest in mind and body, the most powerful varieties of the race will be thrown into their natural position as leaders, impressing the stamp of their character on the people at large, and constituting the more reproductive part; while the feebler or more improvident varieties will generally sink under the incidental hardships. When a swarm emigrates from a prosperous hive, it also will generally consist of the more adventurous stirring spirits, who, with the right of conquerors, will appropriate the finest of the *indigenae* which they overrun; their choice of these being regulated by personal qualities, not by the adventitious circumstances of wealth or high birth – a regard to which certainly tends to deteriorate the species, and is one of the causes which renders the *noblesse* of Europe comparatively inferior to the Asiatic, or rather the Christian *noblesse* to the Mahometan.

It has been remarked, that our finest, most acute population exist in the neutral ground, where the Caucasian and Keltic have mixed, but this may arise from other causes than admixture. Our healthiest and poorest country borders the Highlands, and the population enjoy more of the open air. Our eastern population, north of the natural division of Flamboroughead, are also harder and sharper featured, and keener witted, than those southward, who may be styled our fen-bred. There is no doubt more of Keltic blood mingled with the north division but the sea-born breeds have also been different, those more northerly being Scandinavian, and the more southerly consisting of the native of Lower Germany and the heavy Fleming. The placid-looking Englishman, more under the control of animal enjoyment, though perhaps not so readily acute, excels in the no less valuable qualities of constancy and bodily powers of exertion; and when properly taught under high division of labour, becomes a better operative in his particular employment, and even will sometimes extend scientific discovery further, than his more mercurial northern neighbour, who, from his quick wits being generally in advance of his manual practice, seldom attains to the dexterity which results from the combination of bodily action and restricted mental application. There exists, continued very considerable intellectual capacity in this English breed, but however, animal part, it too frequently is crushed under the preponderance of the affording that purest specimen of vulgarity the English clown. But, independently of climate, a great part of the low Englander's obtuseness is referable to his being entailed lord of the soil, under poor-rate law, contravening a natural law (see Note B), so that, when unsuccessful or out of employment, he, without effort to obtain some new means of independent subsistence, sinks into the parish or workhouse labourer. On the contrary, the Scotsman, with no resource but in himself, with famine always in the vista, as much in his view as a principle of action in material affairs as his strong perception of the right in moral, and also under the stimulus of a high pride, leaves no means untried at home; and, when fairly starved out of his native country, among various resources, often invades the territory of his more easy-minded southern neighbour, where his acuteness seldom fails to find out a convenient occupation, in which manual dexterity is second to economy and forethought – his success exciting the wonder and envy of the dull-witted native.

It would appear, that the finest portion, at least apparently so, of the north temperate zone, between the parallels of 30° and 48° latitude, when nearly of the level of the ocean, is not so favourable for human existence as the more northern part between 50° and 60°, or even the torrid zone. The native of the north of Europe has a superior development of person, and a much longer reproductory life than the native of the south, which more than counterbalances the earlier maturity of the latter in power of increase. Independent of the great current of population setting south in the northern part of the temperate zone, there seems even to be some tendency to a flux northward, from the confines of the torrid; but this arises rather from the unsteadiness of the seasons, and consequent deficit of food, at particular times, than from a steady increase of population.

Note D

Our milder moods, benevolence, gentleness, contemplation – our refinement in sentiment – our 'lovely dreams of peace and joy', have negative weight in the balance of national strength. The rougher excitement of hatred, ambition, pride, patriotism, and the more selfish passions, is necessary to the full and strong development of our active powers. That Britain is leaving the impress of her energy and morality on a considerable portion of the world, is owing to her having first borne fire and sword over these countries: the husbandman tears up the glebe, with all its covering of weeds and flowers, before he commits his good seed to the earth. Life and death – good and evil – pleasure and pain are the principles of impulse to the scheme or machine of nature, as heat and cold are to the steam-engine, thus moving in necessary alternate dependence. Our moral sense, our perception and love of good, could not exist without the knowledge of evil; yet, we shudder at the truth of evil being part and portion of nature.

Note E

There cannot be a more striking proof of the necessity of a better representation of the marine interest, than the fact that our trading vessels are constructed of an unsuitable figure, owing to the improper manner of measuring the register tonnage. In order to save a little trouble of calculation to the surveying officer in gauging the contents of the vessel, the law directs him merely to take the length and breadth at the widest place, and from these lines, by a regular formula, to compute the tonnage; the vessel paying the charges for lights and harbours, and other dues, in proportion to this measurement. The result is that, in order to lessen these dues individually, our vessels are constructed deep in proportion to breadth, consequently are sluggish sailors, and not nearly so safe and pleasant sea-boats as they otherwise would be – many a ship, especially with light cargo, getting on her beam-ends and foundering, or not standing up under canvas to weather a lee shore. The influence of this absurd measurement law is the more unlucky, as the ship-owner, from a deep vessel being, in proportion to the capacity of the hold, cheaper than one of shallower or longer dimensions, is already more disposed to construct his vessel deeper than is consistent with the safety of the seamen and security of the ship and cargo, the particular insurance of a deep vessel not being greater than that of one of safer proportions. The injurious effect from vessels being constructed on the principles of avoiding tolls or dues, rather than for sailing, will occur to everyone.

We need not say that all this flows from the ignorance or carelessness of the constructors of our Parliamentary acts, consequent to defective representation.

Note F

In the case of the upper carse on the Tay Firth, there is evidence, both from its vestiges and from records, that it had occupied, at least, the entire firth, or sea-basin, above Broughty Ferry, and that about 50 square miles of this carse has been carried out into the German Ocean by the strong sea-tide current, a consequence of the lowering of the German Ocean, and of the deepening of the outlet of this sea-basin at Broughty Ferry, apparently by this very rapid sea-tide current. This carse appears to have been a general deposition at the bottom of a lake having only a narrow outlet communicating with the sea, and probably did not rise much higher than the height of the bottom of the outlet at that time.

An increase of deposition of alluvium, or prevention of decrease, may, in many cases be accomplished by artificial means. The diminution of the carse of Tay was in rapid progress about 60 years ago, the sea-bank was being undermined by the waves of the basin, the clay tumbling down, diffused in the water and being carried out to sea, by every ebbing tide, purer water returning from the ocean the next tide flow.

This decrease was stopped by the adoption of stone embanking and dikes. A small extension of the carses of present high-water level, in the upper part of the firths of Tay and Forth, has lately been effected, by forming brushwood, stone and mud dikes, to promote the accumulation. In doing this, the whole art consists in placing obstructions to the current and waves, so that whatever deposition takes place at high-water, or at the beginning of the flood-tide, when the water is nearly still, may not again be raised and carried off.

Notwithstanding this accumulation, and also the prevention of further waste of the superior carse, the deepening of the Tay Firth, formerly carse, and of the gorge at Broughty Ferry, seems still in progress, and could not, without very considerable labour be prevented. In the case, however, of the sea-basin of Montrose, a little labour, from the narrowness of the gorges, would put it in a condition to become gradually filled with mud. Not a great deal more expenditure than what has sufficed to erect the suspension bridge over its largest outlet, would have entirely filled up this outlet, and the smaller outlet might have been also filled to within several feet of high-water, and made of sufficient breadth only, to emit the water of the river, which flows into the basin. The floated sand and mud of this river, thus prevented from being carried out to sea, would, in the course of years, completely fill up the basin.

From some vestiges of the upper carse, as well as of the lower or submarine carse, in situations where their formation cannot easily be traced to any local cause, it seems not improbable that the basin of the German sea itself, nearly as far north as the extent of Scotland, had at one time been occupied with a carse or delta, a continuation of Holland, formed by the accumulation of the diluvium of the rivers which flow into this basin, together with the molluscous exuviae of the North Sea, and the abrasion of the Norwegian coast and Scottish islands, borne downward by the heavy North Sea swell.

In the case of the delta of Holland having extended so far northward, a subsidence of the land or rising of the sea, so as to form a passage for the waters round Britain, must have occurred. The derangement, at several places, of the fine wavy stratification of these carses, and the confusedly heaped-up beds of broken sea-shells, shew that some great rush of water had taken place, probably when Belgium was disssevered from England. Since the opening of the bottom of the gulf, the accumulation may have been undergoing a gradual reduction, by more diffused mud* being carried off from the German Sea into the Atlantic and North Sea, than what the former is receiving – the same process taking place here as has been occurring in the basin of the Tay.

Throughout this volume, we have felt considerable inconvenience, from the adopted dogmatical classification of plants, and have all along been floundering between species and variety, which certainly under

---

* The sea water from Flamboroughhead, southward to the Straits of Dover, is generally discoloured with mud; and during every breeze takes up an addition from the bottom, which is an alluvium so unstable and loose, that no sea vegetation can hold in it. From not producing herbage, the general basis of animal life, few fishes or shells can find support in it.

The large sand-banks on the Dutch and English coast – in some places, such as the Goodwin Sands, certainly the heavier, less diffusable part of the former alluvial country, and portions of these alluvial districts being retained by artificial means – bear a striking resemblance to the sandbanks of the sea-basin of the Tay – the less diffusable remains of the removed portion of the alluvium which had once occupied all that basin, and to the remaining portion of the alluvium also retained by artificial means.

culture soften into each other. A particular conformity, each after its own kind, when in a state of nature, termed species, no doubt exists to a considerable degree. This conformity has existed during the last 40 centuries. Geologists discover a like particular conformity — fossil species — through the deep deposition of each great epoch, but they also discover an almost complete difference to exist between the species or stamp of life, of one epoch from that of every other. We are therefore led to admit, either of a repeated miraculous creation; or of a power of change, under a change of circumstances, to belong to living organized matter, or rather to the congeries of inferior life, which appears to form superior. The derangements and changes in organized existence, induced by a change of circumstance from the interference of man, affording us proof of the plastic quality of superior life, and the likelihood that circumstances have been very different in the different epochs, though steady in each, tend strongly to heighten the probability of the latter theory.

When we view the immense calcareous and bituminous formations, principally from the waters and atmosphere, and consider the oxidations and depositions which have taken place, either gradually, or during some of the great convulsions, it appears at least probable that the liquid elements containing life have varied considerably at different times in composition and in weight; that our atmosphere has contained a much greater proportion of carbonic acid or oxygen; and our waters, aided by excess of carbonic acid, and greater heat resulting from greater density of atmosphere, have contained a greater quantity of lime and other mineral solutions. Is the inference then unphilosophic, that living things which are proved to have a circumstance-suiting power — a very slight change of circumstance by culture inducing a corresponding change of character may have gradually accommodated themselves to the variations of the elements containing them, and, without new creation, have presented the diverging changeable phenomena of past and present organized existence.

The destructive liquid currents, before which the hardest mountains have been swept and comminuted into gravel, sand, and mud, which intervened between and divided these epochs, probably extending over the whole surface of the globe, and destroying all living things, must have reduced existence so much, that an unoccupied field would be formed for new diverging ramifications of life, which, from the connected sexual system of vegetables, and the natural instincts of animals, to herd and combine with their own kind, would fall into specific groups, these remnants, in the course of time, moulding and accommodating their being anew to the change of circumstances, and to every possible means of subsistence, and the millions of ages of regularity which appear to have followed between the epochs, probably after this accommodation was completed, affording fossil deposit of regular specific character.

There are only two probable ways of change – the above, and the still wider deviation from present occurrence – of indestructible or molecular life (which seems to resolve itself into powers of attraction and repulsion under mathematical figure and regulation, bearing a slight systematic similitude to the great aggregations of matter), gradually uniting and developing itself into new circumstance-suited living aggregates, without the presence of any mould or germ of former aggregates, but this scarcely differs from new creation, only it forms a portion of a continued scheme or system

In endeavouring to trace, in the former way, the principle of these changes of fashion which have taken place in the domiciles of life, the following questions occur: do they arise from admixture of species nearly allied producing intermediate species? Are they the diverging ramifications of the living principle under modification of circumstance? Or have they resulted from the combined agency of both? Is there only one living principle? Does organized existence, and perhaps all material existence, consist of one Proteus principle of life capable of gradual circumstance-suited modifications and aggregations, without bound under the solvent or motion-giving principle, heat or light? There is more beauty and unity of design in this continual balancing of life to circumstance, and greater conformity to those dispositions of nature which are manifest to us, than in total destruction and new creation. It is improbable that much of this diversification is owing to commixture of species nearly allied, all change by this appears very limited, and confined within the bounds of what is called Species; the progeny of the same parents, under great difference of circumstance, might, in several generations, even become distinct species, incapable of co-reproduction.

The self-regulating adaptive disposition of organized life may, in part, be traced to the extreme fecundity of Nature, who, as before stated, has, in all the varieties of her offspring, a prolific power much beyond (in many cases a thousandfold) what is necessary to fill up the vacancies caused by senile decay. As the field of existence is limited and preoccupied, it is only the hardier, more robust, better suited to circumstance individuals, who are able to struggle forward to maturity, these inhabiting only the situations to which they have superior adaptation and greater power of occupancy than any other kind; the weaker, less circumstance-suited, being prematurely destroyed. This principle is in constant action, it regulates the colour, the figure, the capacities, and instincts; those individuals of each species, whose colour and covering are best suited to concealment or protection from enemies, or defence from vicissitude and inclemencies of climate, whose figure is best accommodated to health, strength, defence, and support; whose capacities and instincts can best regulate the physical energies to self-advantage according to circumstances – in such immense waste of primary and youthful life, those only come forward to maturity from the strict ordeal by which Nature tests their adaptation to her standard of perfection and fitness to continue their kind by reproduction.

From the unremitting operation of this law acting in concert with the tendency which the progeny have to take the more particular qualities of the parents, together with the connected sexual system in vegetables, and instinctive limitation to its own kind in animals, a considerable uniformity of figure, colour, and character, is induced, constituting species; the breed gradually acquiring the very best possible adaptation of these to its condition which it is susceptible of, and when alteration of circumstance occurs, thus changing in character to suit these as far as its nature is susceptible of change.

This circumstance-adaptive law, operating upon the slight but natural disposition to sport in the progeny (seedling variety), does not preclude the supposed influence which volition or sensation may have over the configuration of the body. To examine into the disposition to sport in the progeny, even when there is only one parent, as in many vegetables, and to investigate how much variation is modified by the mind or nervous sensation of the parents, or of the living thing itself during its progress to maturity; how far it depends upon external circumstance, and how far on the will, irritability and muscular exertion, is open to examination and experiment. In the first place, we ought to investigate its dependency upon the preceding links of the particular chain of life, variety being often merely types or approximations of former parentage; thence the variation of the family, as well as of the individual, must be embraced by our experiments.

This continuation of family type, not broken by casual particular aberration, is mental as well as corporeal, and is exemplified in many of the dispositions or instincts of particular races of men. These innate or continuous ideas or habits, seem proportionally greater in the insect tribes, those especially of shorter revolution; and forming an abiding memory, may resolve much of the enigma of instinct, and the foreknowledge which these tribes have of what is necessary to completing their round of life, reducing this to knowledge, or impressions, and habits, acquired by a long experience. This greater continuity of existence, or rather continuity of perceptions and impressions, in insects, is highly probable; it is even difficult in some to ascertain the particular stops when each individuality commences, under the different phases of egg, larva, pupa, or if much consciousness of individuality exists. The continuation of reproduction for several generations by the females alone in some of these tribes, tends to the probability of the greater continuity of existence, and the subdivisions of life by cuttings, at any rate must stagger the advocate of individuality.

Among the millions of *specific varieties* of living things which occupy the humid portion of the surface of our planet, as far back as can be traced, there does not appear, with the exception of man, to have been any particular engrossing race, but a pretty fair balance of powers of occupancy – or rather, most wonderful variation of circumstance parallel to the nature of every species, as if circumstance and species had grown up together. There are indeed several races which have threatened ascendancy in some particular regions, but it is man alone from whom any imminent danger to the existence of his brethren is to be dreaded.

As far back as history reaches, man had already had considerable influence, and had made encroachments upon his fellow denizens, probably occasioning the destruction of many species, and the production and continuation of a number of varieties or even species, which he found more suited to supply his wants, but which, from the infirmity of their condition – not having undergone selection by the law of nature, of which we have spoken, cannot maintain their ground without his culture and protection.

It is, however, only in the present age that man has begun to reap the fruits of his tedious education, and has proven how much 'knowledge is power'. He has now acquired a dominion over the material world, and a consequent power of increase, so as to render it probable that the whole surface of the earth may soon be overrun by this engrossing anomaly, to the annihilation of every wonderful and beautiful variety of animated existence, which does not administer to his wants principally as laboratories of preparation to befit cruder elemental matter for assimilation by his organs.

In taking a retrospective glance at our pages from the press, we notice some inaccuracy and roughness, which a little more timely attention to *training and pruning* might have obviated; the facts and induction may, however, outbalance these.

We observe that Fig. *d*, p. 27, from the want of proper shading, and error in not marking the dotted lines, does not serve well to illustrate our purpose. This figure is intended to represent a tree of a short thick stem, dividing into four branches, springing out regularly in the manner of a cross, nearly at right angles with the stem. These branches cut over about three or four feet out from the division, form each one wing of a knee, and the stem, quartered longitudinally through the heart, forms the other wing. It is of great advantage to have four branches rather than two or three, as the stem, divided into four, by being twice cut down the middle, forms the wings nearly square; whereas, when divided into two, the halves are broad and flat, and a considerable loss of timber takes place, besides, the two branches afford a thicker wing than the flat half of the stem does when squared. When the tree separates into three branches, the stem does not saw out conveniently; and when divided, the cleft part is angular, and much loss of timber also takes place in the squaring. When the stem divides into four branches, each of these branches coincides in thickness with the quartered stem, and the knees are obtained equally thick throughout, without any loss of timber. The four branches, at six or eight feet above the division, may with a little attention be thrown into a rectangular bend, and thus give eight knees from each tree − knees are generally required of about eight inches in diameter, and three and a half feet in length of wing; but when they are to be had thicker and longer, a foot or more in thickness, and from four to ten feet in length of wing, they are equally in request, suiting for high rising floors or heel-knees.

The directions for forming larch roots into knees after the tree is grubbed, are also not very explicit. The stem of the tree is cut over nearly the same distance from the bulb as the length of the root spurs; this quartered through the heart (in the same manner as above), forms one wing of the knee, and the four spurs form the other wings. The same advantage results from having four regular root-spurs in larch, as in having four regular branches in oak; the two processes are quite similar, only the roots in the one case, and the branches in the other, form one wing of the knees.

We have given no directions for the bending of plank timber. In larch, the wind generally gives the slight necessary bend to a sufficient proportion; and in oak, the trees frequently grow a little bent of their own accord.

A foot-note has been omitted, stating, that the plan of bending young trees, by tying them to an adjacent tree, intended to be soon removed, belongs, as we are informed, to Mr Loudon.

We regret that our allusion to the lamented Mr Huskisson was printed off before we knew of his death.

Since this volume went to press, there has been some changes of scenery on the political European stage, *even rivalling* what has ever been accomplished of sylvan metamorphosis on the face of nature by Sir Henry Steuart. The intense interest excited by these efforts towards the regeneration of man has completely thrown into the shade our humbler subject – the regeneration of trees. We have even forgot it ourselves in the hands of the printer, while yet unborn. These sudden transformations altering the political and moral relations of man, also render a number of our observations not quite apposite, and our speculations, some of them, rather 'prophetic of the past'. They, by obliterating national distinctions, and diminishing the occasions for going to war, will, it is hoped, bring the European family closer into amity. At any rate, they have completely thrown out the calculations of our politicians regarding the balance of power and international connection as natural allies and foes, and bind the French and British together by ties on the surest principle of friendly sympathy, '*idem velle atque nolle*', which no Machiavellian policy of cabinets, nor waywardness of political head, will be able to sunder.

We had intended to bring out *Naval Timber and Arboriculture* as a portion of a work embracing Rural Economy in general, but this is not the time to think of rural affairs.

Letters exchanged between Patrick Matthew and Charles Darwin

Several of the letters from Patrick Matthew to Charles Darwin have not been found.

The Gardeners' Chronicle and Agricultural Gazette

17 April 1860

Nature's Law of Selection

Trusting to your desire that every man should have his own, I hope you will give place to the following communication in your number of March 3rd I observe a long quotation from *The Times*, stating that Mr Darwin 'professes to have discovered the existence and *modus operandi* of the natural law of selection', that is, 'the power in nature which takes the place of man and performs a selection, *sua sponte*, in organic life'. This discovery recently published as 'the results of 20 years' investigation and reflection' by Mr Darwin turns out to be what I published very fully and brought to apply practically to forestry in my work *Naval Timber and Arboriculture* published as far back as 1 January 1831, by Adam and Charles Black, Edinburgh and Longman & Co., London, and reviewed in numerous periodicals, so as to have full publicity in the *Metropolitan Magazine*, the *Quarterly Review*, the *Gardeners' Magazine*, by Loudon, who spoke of it as the book, and repeatedly in the *United Services Magazine* for 1831, &c. The following is an extract from this volume, which clearly proves the prior claim. The same volume contains the first proposal of the steam ram (also claimed since by several others, English, French, and Americans) and a navy of steam gun-boats as requisite in future maritime war, and which, like the organic selection law, are only as yet making way.

There is a law universal in Nature, tending to render every reproductive being the best possible suited to its condition that its kind, or that organized matter, is susceptible of, which appears intended to model the physical and mental or instinctive powers, to their highest perfection, and to continue them so. This law sustains the lion in his strength, the hare in her swiftness, and the fox in his wiles. As Nature, in all her modifications of life, has a power of increase far beyond what is needed to supply the place of what falls by Time's decay, those individuals who possess not the requisite strength, swiftness, hardihood or cunning, fall prematurely without reproducing — either a prey to their natural devourers, or sinking under disease, generally induced by want of nourishment, their place being occupied by the more perfect of their own kind, who are pressing on the means of subsistence.

Throughout this volume, we have felt considerable inconvenience, from the adopted dogmatical classification of plants, and have all along been floundering between species and variety, which certainly under culture soften into each other. A particular conformity, each after its own kind, when in a state of nature, termed species, no doubt exists to a considerable degree. This conformity has existed during the last 40 centuries. Geologists discover a like particular conformity — fossil species — through the deep deposition of each great epoch, but they also discover an almost complete difference to exist between the species or stamp of life of one epoch from that of every other. We are, therefore, led to admit, either of a repeated miraculous creation; or of a power of change, under a change of circumstances, to belong to living organized matter, or rather to the congeries of inferior life, which appears to form superior. The derangements and changes in organized existence, induced by a change of circumstances from the interference of man, affording us proof of the plastic quality of superior life, and the likelihood that circumstances have been very different in the different epochs, though steady in each, tend strongly to heighten the probability of the latter theory.

When we view the immense calcareous and bituminous formations, principally from the waters and atmosphere, and consider the oxidations and depositions which have taken place, either gradually, or during some of the great convulsions, it appears at least probable, that the liquid elements containing life have varied considerably at different times in composition and weight; that our atmosphere has contained a much greater proportion of carbonic acid or oxygen; and our waters aided by excess of carbonic acid, and greater heat resulting from greater density of atmosphere, have contained a greater quantity of lime and other mineral solutions. Is the inference then unphilosophic, that living things which have proved to have a circumstance-suiting power – a very slight change of circumstance by culture inducing a corresponding change of character – may have gradually accommodated themselves to the variations of the elements containing them, and, without new creation, have presented the diverging changeable phenomenon of past and present organised existence?

The destructive liquid currents, before which the hardest mountains have been swept and comminuted into gravel, sand, and mud, which intervened between and divided these epochs, probably extending over the whole surface of the globe, and destroying nearly all living things, must have reduced existence so much, that an unoccupied field would be formed for new diverging ramifications of life, which, from the connected sexual system of vegetables, and the natural instincts of animals to herd and combine with their own kind, would fall into specific groups, these remnants, in the course of time, moulding and accommodating their being anew to the change of circumstances, and to every possible means of subsistence, and the millions of ages of regularity which appear to have followed between the epochs, probably after this accommodation was completed, affording fossil deposit of regular specific character.

There are only two probable ways of change – the above, and the still wider deviation from present occurrence – of indestructible or molecular life (which seems to resolve itself into powers of attraction and repulsion under mathematical figure and regulation, bearing a slight systemic similitude to the great aggregations of matter), gradually uniting and developing itself into new circumstance-suited living aggregates, without the presence of any mould or germ of former aggregates, but this scarcely differs from new creation, only it forms a portion of a continued scheme or system.

In endeavouring to trace, in the former way, the principle of these changes of fashion which have taken place in the domiciles of life, the following questions occur: do they arise from admixture of species nearly allied producing intermediate species? Are the diverging ramifications of the living principle under modification of circumstance? Or have they resulted from the combined agency of both? Is there only one living principle? Does organized existence, and perhaps all material existence, consist of one Proteus principle of life capable of gradual circumstance-suited modifications and aggregations, without bound under the solvent or motion-giving principle, heat or light? There is more beauty and unity of design this continual balancing of life to circumstance, and greater conformity to those dispositions of nature which are manifest to us, than in total destruction and new creation. It is improbable that much of this diversification is owing to commixture of species nearly allied, all change by this appears very limited, and confined within the bounds of what is called species; the progeny of the same parents, under great difference of circumstance, might in several generations, even become distinct species, incapable of co-reproduction.

The self-regulating adaptive disposition of organized life may, in part, be traced to the extreme fecundity of Nature, who, as before stated, has, in all the varieties of her offspring, a prolific power much beyond (in many cases a thousandfold) what is necessary to fill up the vacancies caused by senile decay. As the field of existence is limited and pre-occupied, it is only the hardier, more robust, better suited to circumstance individuals, who are able to struggle forward to maturity, these inhabiting only the situations to which they have superior adaptation and greater power of occupancy than any other kind: the weaker, less circumstance-suited, being prematurely destroyed. This principle is in constant action, it regulates the colour, the figure, the capacities, and instincts; those individuals of each species, whose colour and covering are best suited to concealment or protection from enemies, of defence from vicissitude and inclemencies of climate, whose figure is best accommodated to health, strength, defence, and support; whose capacities and instincts can best regulate the physical energies self-advantage according to circumstances – in such immense waste of primary and youthful life, those only come forward to maturity from the strict ordeal by which Nature tests their adaptation to her standard of perfection and fitness to continue their kind by reproduction.

From the unremitting operation of this law acting in concert with the tendency which the progeny have to take the more particular quality of the parents, together with the connected sexual system in vegetables, and instinctive limitation to its own kind in animals, a considerable uniformity of figure, colour, and character, is induced, constituting species; the breed gradually acquiring the very best possible adaptation of these to its condition which it is susceptible of, and when alteration of circumstance occurs, thus changing in character to suit these as far as its nature is susceptible of change.

This circumstance-adaptive law, operating upon the slight but continued natural disposition to sport in the progeny (seedling variety), does not preclude the supposed influence which volition or sensation may have over the configuration of the body. To examine into the disposition to sport in any progeny, even when there is only one parent, as in many vegetables, and to investigate how much variation is modified by the mind or nervous sensation of the parents, or of the living thing itself during its progress to maturity; how far it depends upon external circumstance, and how far on the will, irritability, and muscular exertion, is open to examination and experiment. In the first place, we ought to investigate its dependency upon the preceding links of the particular chain of life, variety being often merely types or approximations of former parentage; thence the variation of the family, as well as of the individual, must be embraced by our experiments.

This continuation of family type, not broken by casual particular aberration, is mental as well as corporeal, and is exemplified in many of the dispositions or instincts of particular races of men. These innate or continuous ideas or habits, those especially of shorter revolution; and forming an abiding memory, may resolve much of the enigma of instinct, and the foreknowledge which these tribes have of what is necessary to completing their round of life, reducing by a long experience. This greater continuity of existence, or rather continuity of perceptions and impressions, in insects, is highly probable; it is even difficult in some to ascertain the particular stops when each individuality commences, under the different phases of egg, larva, pupa, or if much consciousness of individuality exists. The continuation of reproduction for several generations by the females alone in some of these tribes, tends to the probability of he greater continuity of existence, and the subdivisions of life by cuttings (even in animal life) at any rate must stagger the advocate of individuality.

Among the millions of specific varieties of living things which occupy the humid portion of the surface of our planet, as far back as can be traced, there does not appear, with the exception of man, to have been any particular engrossing race, but a pretty fair balance of powers of occupancy – or rather, most wonderful variation of circumstance parallel to the nature of every species, as if circumstance and species had grown up together.

There are indeed several races which have threatened ascendancy in some particular regions, but it is man alone from whom any general imminent danger to the existence of his brethren is to be dreaded.

As far back as history reaches, man had already had considerable influence, and had made encroachments upon his fellow denizens, probably occasioning the destruction of many species, which he found more suited to supply his wants, but which, from the infirmity of their condition – not having undergone selection by the law of nature, of which we have spoken, cannot maintain their ground without its culture and protection.

It is, however, only in the present age than man has begun to reap the fruits of his tedious education, and has proven how much 'knowledge is power'. He has now acquired dominion over the material world, and a consequent power of increase, so as to render it probable that the whole surface of the earth may soon be over run by this engrossing anomaly, to the annihilation of every wonderful and beautiful variety of animated existence, which does not administer to his wants principally as laboratories of preparation to befit cruder elemental matter for assimilation by his organs.

Much of the luxuriance and size of timber depending upon the particular variety of the species, upon the treatment of the seed before sowing, and upon the treatment of the young plant, and as this fundamental subject is neither much attended to nor generally misunderstood, we shall take it up *ab initio*.

The consequences are now being developed of our deplorable ignorance of, or inattention to, one of the most evident traits of natural history, that vegetables as well as animals are generally liable to an almost unlimited diversification, regulated by climate, soil, nourishment, and new commixture of already formed varieties. In those with which man is most intimate, and where his agency in throwing them from their natural locality and dispositions has brought out the power of diversification in stronger shades, it has been forced upon his notice, as in man himself, in the dog, horse, cow, sheep, poultry – in the Apple, Pear, Plum, Gooseberry, Potato, Pea, which sport in infinite varieties, differing considerably in size, colour, taste, firmness of texture, period of growth, almost in every recognizable quality. In all these kinds man is influential in preventing deterioration, by careful selection of the largest or most valuable as breeders; but in timber trees the opposite course has been pursued. The large growing varieties being so long of coming to seed, that many plantations are cut down before they reach their maturity, the small growing and weakly varieties, known by early and extreme seeding, have been continually selected as reproductive stock, from the ease and conveniency with which their seed could be procured; and the husks of several kinds of these invariably kiln-dried, in order that the seeds might be the more easily extracted. May we, then, wonder that our plantations are occupied by a sickly short-lived puny race, incapable of supporting existence in situations where their own kind had formerly flourished – particularly evinced in the genus Pinus, more particularly in the species Scots Fir, so much inferior to those of Nature's own rearing, where only the stronger, more hardy, soil-suited varieties can struggle forward to maturity and reproduction?

We say that the rural economist should pay as much regard to the breed or particular variety of his forest trees, as he does to that of his live stock of horses, cows, and sheep. That nurserymen should attest the variety of their timber plants, sowing no seeds but those gathered from the largest, most healthy, and luxuriant growing trees, abstaining from the seed of the prematurely productive, and also from that of the very aged and overmature; as they, from animal analogy, may be expected to give an infirm progeny subject to premature decay. See *Naval Timber and Arboriculture*, pages 364 and 365, 381 to 388, also 106 to 108.

Patrick Matthew
Gourdie Hill, Errol,
7 March.

Gardeners' Chronicle and Agricultural Gazette

1 April 1860

Natural Selection

I have been much interested by Mr Patrick Matthew's communication in the Number of your Paper, dated 7 April. I freely acknowledge that Mr Matthew has anticipated by many years the explanation which I have offered of the origin of species, under the name of natural selection. I think that no one will feel surprised that neither I, nor apparently any other naturalist, had heard of Mr Matthew's views, considering how briefly they are given, and that they appeared in the appendix to a work on *Naval Timber and Arboriculture*. I can do no more than offer my apologies to Mr Matthew for my entire ignorance of his publication. If another edition of my work is called for, I will insert a notice to the foregoing effect.

Charles Darwin
Downe Bromley, Kent.

Gardeners' Chronicle 12 May 1860

I notice in your Number of 21 April Mr Darwin's letter honourably acknowledging my prior claim relative to the origin of species. I have not the least doubt that, in publishing his late work, he believed he was the first discoverer of this Law of Nature. He is however wrong in thinking that no naturalist was aware of the previous discovery. I had occasion some 15 years ago to be conversing with a naturalist, a professor of a celebrated university, and he told me he had been reading my work *Naval Timber* but that he could not bring such views before his class or uphold them publicly from fear of the cutty-stool, a sort of pillory punishment, not in the market place and not devised for this offence, but generally practised a little more than a century ago. It was at least in part this spirit of resistance to scientific doctrine that caused my work to be voted unfit for the public library of the fair city itself. The age was not ripe for such ideas, nor do I believe is the present one, though Mr Darwin's formidable work is making way. As for the attempts made by many periodicals to throw doubt upon Nature's Law of selection having originated species, I consider their unbelief incurable and leave them to it. Belief here requires a certain grasp of mind. No direct proof of phenomena embracing so long a period of time is within the compass of short-lived man. To attempt to satisfy a school of ultra sceptics, who have a wonderfully limited power of perception of means to ends, of connecting the phenomena of Nature, or who perhaps have not the power of comprehending the subject, would be labour in vain. Were the exact sciences brought out as new discoveries they would deny the axioms upon which the exact sciences are based. They could not be brought to conceive the purpose of a handsaw though they saw its action, if the whole individual building it assisted to construct were not presented complete before their eyes, and even then they would deny that the senses could be trusted. Like the child looking upon the motion of a wheel in an engine they would only perceive and admire, and have their eyes dazzled and fascinated with the rapid and circular motion of the wheel, without noticing its agency in connection with the modifying power towards affecting the purposed end. Out of this class there could arise no Cuvier, able from a small fragmentary bone to determine the character and position in Nature of the extinct animal. To observers of Nature aware of the extent of the modifying power of man over organic life, and its variations in anterior time, not fettered by early prejudices, not biased by college-taught or closet-bred ideas, but with judgement free to act upon a comprehensive survey of Nature past and present, and a grasp of mind able to digest and generalize, I think that few will not see intuitively, unless they wish not to see, all that has been brought forward in regard to the origin of species. To me the conception of this law of Nature came intuitively as a self-evident fact, almost without an effort of concentrated thought. Mr Darwin here seems to have more merit in the discovery than I have had – to me it did not appear a discovery. He seems to have worked it out by inductive reason, slowly and with due caution to have made his way synthetically from fact to fact onwards; while with me it was by a general glance at the scheme of Nature that I estimated this select production of species as an a priori recognizable fact – an axiom, requiring only to be pointed out to be admitted by unprejudiced minds of sufficient grasp.

Patrick Matthew
Gourdiehill Errol
2 May

Letter to Patrick Matthew 13 June 1862

Dear Sir

I presume that I have the pleasure of addressing the Author of the work on Naval Architecture and the first enunciator of the theory of Natural Selection. Few things would give me greater pleasure than to see you; but my health is feeble, and I have at present a son ill and can receive no one here, nor leave home at present.

I wish to come up to London as soon as I can; if, therefore, you are going to stay for more than a week, would you be so kind as to let me hear, and if able to come up to London, I would endeavour to arrange an interview with you, which would afford me high satisfaction. With much respect, I remain, dear sir, yours very faithfully,

Charles Darwin
Down Bromley, Kent

Letter to Charles Darwin 3 December 1862

Dear Sir,

When in London last summer, it was only for a few days, engrossed with mercantile concerns so that I could not bestow that attention to scientific thought that I should have liked, I also learned from Prof. Huxley that by coming up to London you were sometimes rendered unwell. I would have been sorry to bring you from home lest I might do you injury, and, therefore, did not reply to your letter. I also could not but feel that I was an intruder and that there existed in scientific minds a strong *vis inertiae* and retiring inclination which I had no right to disturb, especially as I believe I could be of no service in advancing your pursuit. While you have been making advances in vegetable science, I have been attempting to promote a better system of land occupancy by the farmer – that there might be protection of property created by the farmer in enriching the vegetable mould. This is a question of the highest importance to the British Empire and race. My line lies more in the political and social, yours in tracing out the admirably balanced scheme of Nature all linked together in dependent connection – the vital endowed with a variation power in accommodation to material change. Althou' this is a grand field for contemplation, yet I am tired of it – of a world where my sympathies . . . intended to be bounded almost . . . to my own race and family.

I am not satisfied with my existence here to devour and to trample upon my fellow creature. I cannot pluck a flower without regarding myself a destroyer. At present we feel some enjoyment in tracing out the scheme of Nature. Since I have paid attention to the progress of discovery, so much has been done that comparatively little remains to do. What will become of man when all the great facts of material and vital science are pointed out?

We may be satisfied that we have lived in the great age of discovery and in the country and of the race in which and by whom these discoveries have been made. Man cannot advance much higher. A reaction such as attended Babylonian, Egyptian, Grecian and Roman civilization must soon ensue. The same powers that have reached high civilization cannot support it.

Fall we must.

We have had a very bleak and unpleasant summer in Scotland. Yet another season may be more propitious. Change of air and scene if the change is not too great acts a salutary part in the human constitution and a journey to Scotland might next summer be of service to you or any of your family. You mentioned you had a son unwell. I hope he has recovered. Should you think of a visit to Scotland I would be most happy in pointing out the little I know of the character of the country. There is something in the change of place which stimulates mental conception. I enclose one or two pieces which I have been amusing myself with and remain.

Dear Sir, Yours truly,
P Matthew
Gourdiehill Errol

Letter to Patrick Matthew, 21 November 1863

Dear Sir,

Mr Darwin begs me to thank you warmly for your letter, which has interested him very much. I am sorry to say that he is so unwell as not to be able to write himself.

With regard to Natural Selection, he says that he is not staggered by your striking remarks. He is more faithful to your own original child than you are yourself. He says you will understand what he means by the following metaphor.

Fragments of rock fallen from a lofty precipice assume an infinitude of shapes — these shapes being due to the nature of the rock, the law of gravity — by merely selecting the well-shaped an architect (called Nat. Selection) could make many and various noble buildings.

Mr Darwin is much obliged to you for sending him your photograph. He wished he could send you as good a one of himself. The enclosed was a good likeness taken by his eldest son, but the impression is faint.

You express yourself kindly interested about his family. We have five sons and two daughters, of these only two are grown up. Mr Darwin was very ill two months ago and his recovery is very slow, so that I am afraid it will be long before he can attend to any scientific subject.

Dear sir, yours truly,
E Darwin
Down Bromley Kent

(Letter 23) [Patrick Matthew to Charles Darwin]

Gourdiehill, Errol, Scotland, 12 March, 71.

To Charles Darwin Esq.

Dear Sir,

I am glad to see by the Newspapers that you have had health &
strength so as to be able to bring out full illustrations of the variation &
selection Laws of Nature. Of which I would desire to be able to write
a Critique, but am so much taken up with political and agricultural affairs
that I fear I will not have time, more especially as I intend in a few
weeks to go over to Germany where one of my sons has been settled
as an agriculturist for many years & has a large family, and as being
known quite as much in Germany as in Britain I may remain some time.
I also fear that I am not sufficiently a restricted Naturalist as to be able
to enter into the minutiae of the science. I am now engaged with the
cultivation of Peace & of Climate, also the philosophy of Agriculture,
in which being above 4 score it is probable I may not be able to complete,
as You have been able to do in Your province. I enclose an Article from
the *Scotsman* Newspaper which will shew I am not yet quite effete. I
hope your family are now all well, When you wrote to me long ago,
one of your sons was very unwell. I hope he recovered.

I have not had time to give the subject – the modification of life to
circumstances – sufficient attention. One strange character of Rye, acquired we may suppose by being so very long cultivated in field, of
taking a gregarious nature, was observed by me when over in Germany.
I [was] walking through Wheat fields searching for new varieties of wheat,
I found a few scattered plants of Rye, which being nearly ripe, had only
2 or 3 grains in the Ear, the other spaces being empty chaff. Also, in a
few solitary ears of Rye on the high way I found equally unfruitful. This
did not seem to be from bird depredation. At the blooming time of fields
of Rye, Rye grass, pinus sylvestris & pinaster, in time of a soft S. West
Zephyr, there is often seen a pollen mist [cloud] sweeping along, which
in the rye seems necessary to the fecundation probably from being so
long used to it.

There cannot be a doubt that in the scheme of Nature there exists
high design & constructive power carried out by general Laws, and the
great probability is that these laws are everlasting, as Nature itself is, tho'
under these laws subject to revolution. It is also probable that the spark
of life, like light & heat &c., is radiated from the Sun & has a power of
building up to itself a domicile suited to existing circumstances &

disseminating sparks of its own kind but possessed of a variation power. That there is a principle of beneficence operating here the dual parentage and family affection pervading all the higher animal kin[g]dom affords proof. A sentiment of beauty pervading Nature, with only some few exceptions affords evidence of intellect & benevolence in the scheme of Nature. This principle of beauty is clearly from design & cannot be accounted for by natural selection. Could any fitness of things contrive a rose, a lily, or the perfume of the violet. There is not doubt that man is left purposely in ignorance of a future existence. Their pretended revelations are wretched nonsense. It is a beautiful parable, the woman walking through the City of Damascus bearing fire in the one hand & water in the other, crying, with this water [*sic: recte* fire] I will burn heaven & with this water extinguish hell that man may worship God for his own sake & not as mercenary labourers. We are gifted with a moral sense & it is delightful to do good. It is a pleasure to me to wish you & Yours the enjoyment of doing good. I regret I cannot do more than wish it.

Patrick Matthew

P.S. I see it stated that account for useless parts by the laws of variation & competition, general laws cannot provide against accidents in all cases.

Letter to Patrick Matthew, 15 March 1871

Dear Sir,

I thank you for your kind letter. You show no signs of your fourscore years in your letter or in the newspaper article, which seem written with your pristine vigour. My health keeps very indifferent and every exertion fatigues me, so that I doubt whether I shall be good for much more. Your parable of the Damascus Woman is quite new to me and very striking. I sincerely wish you a happy meeting with your son. I have many letters to write, so pray excuse my brevity, and believe me, with respect, yours faithfully,

Charles Darwin

Down Beckenham, Kent

Matthew's letters to the press on scientific subjects

Gardeners' Chronicle and Agricultural Gazette, 28 May 1864

The Vegetable Mould

In the cooler portions of the temperate zone there is greater difficulty than in warmer regions in restoring the vegetable mould when much exhausted by improvident agriculture, or in improving it when naturally defective. Irrigation, the all powerful fertilizer in the warmer climates, is liable, if carried out extensively in our cooler localities, to have injurious effects by lowering the temperature, and at the same time disposing the cereals, grasses, legumes, potato, to blight – to disease caused by fungi or by animalcule destroyers. The cereals around a small lake in this neighbourhood were almost every season blighted by red and brown varieties of fungi, and the blighting removed by drawing all the water forming the lake by a tunnel. The same fungous disease termed mildew is well known to prevail around millponds, and stagnant pools, but apparently not so much near running water, or even extensive lakes. In the case of rapid streams the motion may affect the atmosphere favourably, while the force must increase the temperature; and in large lakes the commotion of the waves must produce something of the same effect, while in the small lakes and ponds very little wave commotion takes place. Moisture rises from stagnating pools often as an atmospheric change favourable to the growth of the fungi. Under extensive irrigation cereal blight will no doubt prevail, and the Gramineae might also suffer. The prevalence of fungi upon the leaves and stems of grasses has been found highly detrimental to cattle.

In some of the warmer sand districts in continental regions of higher latitude than 40°, irrigation during the hot dry season will be highly beneficial. In winter also, when the growth is dormant from cold, it is found advantageous, where easily practicable, to lay the old grass pastures under river water, more especially when the water contains lime in solution, or carries a little floated mud. This is a common practice in Holland, and other low countries. But generally in all the moister countries of low temperature, such as the British Isles, summer irrigation, except very partially carried out, or with the highly nutritious drainage of cities, may be quite as injurious as beneficial. If followed to any considerable extent, the loss by mildew and a lowered temperature may more than balance the gain of irrigation. Even Mechi's liquid dressings, if generally carried out, must act in the same direction. But this would have little influence compared to extensive grass-field irrigation effected by steam power or by windmill power, which latter I have seen in use in Holstein. Irrigation may also in cooler climates affect the health of the population, as it does in the warmer, though to a less extent. In the case of rivers or stagnating water giving out miasma, it has been found that muddy water, even water containing the washings of farmsteads, is more wholesome than clear water, probably from the deodorizing and purifying effects of earth matter or mud.

The natural high road to the improvement of the vegetable mould by irrigation not being generally judicious in the moist and cool climates of the British Isles, at least unless hot water be obtained by deep Artesian bores, the other means of improvement are various and much dependent upon local opportunities. To succeed in this the judicious farmer, having his improvements protected, will look around him and observe his opportunities. He will pursue an easy rotation of crops, have always heavy crops with the produce as much as possible returned as manure, proper drainage; clean and careful tilth; deep stirring especially when the subsoil is good, so that the air and roots of plants may penetrate deep into the soil; procure large manures where possible, and where large manures cannot be obtained, a judicious selection of small manures in order to obtain large manures; he will use plenty of cake with feeding stock, and especially have the grassland laid down rich of manure. Also in the case of light sand, claying the ground if good clay can be obtained near. On the coast, beach-sand composed of comminuted shells, as is found on some parts of the west coast of Ireland, forms an excellent manure. I have known this carted a considerable number of miles into the interior, and esteemed much more than seaweed, which, however, every farmer near the coast should do his utmost to secure when drifted ashore.

As an illustration of utilizing local opportunities I may here state the method pursued by one of my sons in Holstein, to improve the more arid sand portion of his ground, where, before his occupancy, the vegetable mould had been much exhausted. Having a considerable portion of land under coarse grass, Carices, etc., upon a formation of peat or peat earth, and where the dammed up water of mills prevent drainage and aeration, he adopts the plan of stripping off, as he requires it, the surface of a portion of the ground three inches deep, that is the coarse grass sward and a portion of the peat earth. That is taken to the dry sand fields and is well mixed with the horse and cattle manure from the farmstead, and with town manure from Altona, about two loads of the peaty sward for one of the manure, and a large bed foiled, fully five feet high, of the compound. This remains for about six weeks till it has thoroughly heated, when it is spread and ploughed in for a crop. Here the heating corrects the preservative acid of the peat, digests the mass, and the whole becomes an active manure. The portion of the meadow thus stripped of the sward, receives a surface dressing of the manure, and without ploughing is sown with proper seeds, and in two years becomes clothed with superior grasses to those of the original sward. As the moss is in some places accumulating, this supply will not soon fade. This system was once practised in Scotland, introduced by the North Frieslanders, when the greater part of their own country being submerged, they colonized the Lowlands of Scotland, bringing with them their language and customs, about the same time that the old Germans of Anglen, now Schleswig-Holstein, colonized and gave their language and name to England. I have found the language of the Island of Sylt, off the shore of Schleswig (a remnant of the ancient North Friesland), almost the same as our broad Scotch. For the purpose of making manure my son also keeps a flock of several hundred sheep. These during the day follow the shepherd (not driven) over the unenclosed pastures, and at night lodge in one of the old German barns the walls of which, for aeration, are of warped twigs. This barn is bedded with the same moss turf sward and the bedding renewed every few days till the depth of about four feet, when the heated moss is removed and immediately applied to the land (an excellent manure) and a new bedding begun. In the depth of winter the sheep are fed with hay, straw, turnips. Having good sea marl in different parts of the ground, in spare time, generally during strong frost, a portion of the ground receives a dressing of marl upon the old grass, about ten waggons to the acre. This is spread and is exposed for the atmosphere all summer, when the field is broken up in autumn for a cereal crop. This exposure to the air is necessary that the acridity of the marl may be corrected. This marling is seldom or never repeated. Without this application of marl, or being limed, the greater portion of the land will not grow clover. The only crop that does not benefit by the marling is oats, which apparently suffers by the marl rendering the soil too loose. This the pressing machine might perhaps correct. Numbers of old farmers are averse to marling. They say it enriches the father and impoverishes the son. No doubt it hastens the digestion of the vegetable mould, renders it more immediate food for the plant, and thus requires a greater supply of large manures to balance the greater consumption. It is, however, valuable as promoting the growth of clover and other lime plants, which are specially calculated to improve the quality and increase the bulk of the manure.

In going over last summer to Holstein, partly with a hope to meet and converse with Baron von Lisbig upon the vegetable mould, I observed a rather interesting fact respecting the rye plant, so much sown on the lighter soils of Germany, and the staff of life in the north of Europe. In going through several rye fields belonging to my son, of a superior kind of rye, I endeavoured to select the most prolific ears and best developed grains in this cereal, which presents, like other plants under the culture of man, considerable variety. I found it more disposed to have vacant space in the ear than any other kind of grain. This led me to examine more minutely into the cause of the vacancies, and I came to the conclusion that it was owing to defective fecundation. In fields of wheat I found a few ears of rye scattered amongst the wheat, with strong stems and large ears, but with very few or no grains in the ear. I also found a few scattered ears growing on the public roads in the same unfruitful condition, but especially given to the production of the fungus disease ergot. I also knew that in the blooming season, in time of a gentle breeze, smoke clouds of the pollen of rye are seen driving along rye fields, exactly the same as in this country we observe along fields of rye-grass. These facts led me to conclude that rye, and also rye-grass, are gregarious plants, that the pollen of a particular ear goes to fecundate other ears and not itself; that rye cannot exist like other cereals in solitude; that the pollen clouds are necessary to fecundation. Rye is perhaps the cereal that has been longest cultivated in fields by man, and this fact goes so far to prove the adaptation power of organic life to circumstances

Patrick Matthew
Gourdiehill
25 April 1864

Dundee Advertiser, 13 September 1867

Sir,

The conduct towards me of the *soi-disant* British Association for the Advancement of Science has been such that I consider it right to lay the subject before the public. I gave in to their Assistant-General Secretary nine papers to be read. Of these they rejected seven and admitted two, one of the latter, on Botany, I withdrew, as I thought it required the rejected to appear with it. The other I did not withdraw, as it had an immediate importance, but which the Society managed, by delaying the reading till the last, not to read.

I will match the importance of these nine papers, in a national point of view, against all that was read at the Dundee meeting, of which the public will have an opportunity to judge. With regard to one of these papers on what is termed Darwin's Theory of Natural Selection, but which theory was published by me about thirty years before Darwin (honourably acknowledged in his last edition by Darwin) at a time when man was scarcely ready for such thoughts, I surely had the best right to be heard upon this subject. Yet others were allowed to speak upon it, and its parent denied to do so. Such is the conduct of a Society terming itself the British Association for the Advancement of Science.

I am etc.
Patrick Matthew
Gourdiehill
12 September 1867

Dundee Advertiser, 25 April 1870

Sir,

Your able and useful article in the yesterday's Advertiser needs no comment, only that portion of it which proposes a settling tank to free the water of any mud which in time of heavy rains may be diffused in the water.

Here the reader requires rightly to understand the difference between diffused mud and dissolved minerals. It is a general fact that river water is wholesome nearly in proportion to the amount of earth matter especially clay, that is diffused in the stream. This arises from the deodorizing effect of earth or clay in correcting any putrid organic matter in the water, or even in the fluids of the individual who may use it; that is when the earth is only diffused, not dissolved, such as lime or silex, when much of it becomes pernicious, though invisible, even giving the water a brighter, more crystalline appearance. Long-continued boiling of water increasing its power of solution of earthy minerals, and diminishing the quantity of water, is therefore to be guarded against. In the more unwholesome climates, where fever malaria abounds, it is found that the banks of muddy streams are much more wholesome than the banks of streams transparent as crystal. This is due to the deodorizing effect of the diffused mud, chiefly clay, which seems to prevent any malaria miasma and neutralizing them. The horse, one of the most delicate of animals in the digestive organs, and which is strongly guided by instinct, raises the mud in the water where he drinks by pawing it before he drinks. This serves a double purpose – it frightens away any injurious insect or animal he might drink up with the water, and also raises the mud.

In America, the St Lawrence, which has the great American Lakes as compensation ponds and clarifying banks, and having its waters from a basin chiefly consisting of lime stone and strata, has so much lime in solution as to be unwholesome, though clear as crystal. So beautiful is the water that emigrants from Europe going up in vessels to Quebec, Montreal, and other ports after entering the St Lawrence, having had impure, slightly putrid water on the voyage, and seeing the crystal water of the St Lawrence so tempting can scarcely be prevented from drinking it, and becoming very unwell. The Mississippi also coming in part from the same limestone region before its junction with the Missouri, is also of pure crystal water, but its banks are subject to fever and ague while the banks of the Missouri, an extremely muddy river, are comparatively free from fever. In Spain I have seen beautiful green hills and valleys, streams as clear as crystal, with clean beds and banks of gravel or sand, no marsh or spot of mud – just such a dry country as you would suppose pre-eminently healthy, yet subject to remittent and intermittent fever. It is a well known fact, though the means of extending infectious disease in towns is much greater than in hamlets and villages, yet scarlatina, measles, and even cholera are generally more infectious and fatal, and easier communicated in the latter. This seems owing to the great disinfectant power of the coal smoke of cities, which acts unfavourably to the extension of the animalcule of the infectious disease – in fact, poisons it; while at the same time, like the clay in diffusion in water, smoke in diffusion in air deodorizes it – corrects the putrescency.

The balancings of Nature are admirable, though sometimes not understood by man, who, from ignorance, runs counter to them. When rivers are in flood, there is much organic matter carried down as well as diffused minerals – clay (alumina) being the most abundant, mud which effects a most powerful deodorizing effect in neutralizing the corrupting organic matter. Man, however, in the water he uses, is afraid of and endeavours to get rid of the diffused clay which he sees; but he is ignorant of the more injurious minerals which spring water, and to some extent river water, often contains dissolved in the water, such as lime, silex, etc. which even renders the water clearer than when pure. Water containing these solutions is, however, unwholesome; while clay in diffusion is often advantageous from its antiseptic quality. Another common error, as I have said, is not being aware that much boiling renders water less wholesome by expelling the air it contains, also by diminishing the quantity of water, while it does not diminish the mineral solutions. There are thus other ways of spoiling good water besides mixing it with mischievous ingredients: alcohol, poisons, *coculus indicus*, nux vomica, sulphuric acid, lime, acetate of lead, etc., or even sugar, tea, coffee. Wise Nature has adapted pure water so as to be relished by man when he needs it; while, when he does not need it, it tastes insipid (Scotch, wersh). When water is mixed with other ingredients whether injuriously stimulated or pleasing to the taste, man is often induced to drink more liquid than he requires, and, in consequence he becomes of soft, flabby consistency, defective in muscular strength and disposed to disease.

The water of the Nile in Egypt is said to be the most salubrious in the world, not only for drinking, but also in sailing upon, not giving out malaria, like most other rivers in hot climates. This appears to be caused by the mud it contains and the complete deodorizing the water sustains in a course of 1,500 miles after it has received all its water, little or no rain and no springs being received during its long extended course, so that the deodorizing power of the mud has time to act completely to sweeten it. In the case of a pond to remove the mud as sediment, not only what is highly useful abstracted, but in a day or two the mud subsides before it has time to deodorize the water completely, while, along with the dissolved minerals a considerable quantity of organic matter remains which had been at first carried down with the diffused minerals, but which not being so heavy as the diffused minerals does not subside, and is left to corrupt the water, generating animalcule life to increase the corruption. This goes to prove that a settling pond can well be spared, at least where the amount of water supply is of itself always abundant. In the case of the Isla water, coming from a cold alpine country there is not much diffused organic matter except peat, a little of which may perhaps be useful, acting as a deodorizer to prevent corruption, though, when abundant, injurious to animal life. There is a strong presumption that mud in the water we use, being chiefly clay, has a wholesome effect upon the human organism in correcting any disposition to putrescence in the digestive organs in the general system, which, especially in the corrupt atmosphere of cities, is not infrequently the case. Clay may also remove dissolved lime or silex in water, as it does ingredients in sewage by combining with them and subsiding.

I forward the above as in my last I objected to the Dundee magistracy as being, 'More intent upon wild costly scheming than useful improvement. Instance their neglect of the sanitary dwellings of the working men.' In this case, though costly, it is a most valuable object, almost a necessity alike advantageous to rich and poor. It must be remembered that water constitutes nearly three fourths of the materials of organic life, and at the same time acts as the liquid element or floating power in the canals of life, of the other materials to where they are required to build up the organism, to supply fuel to the fire of life, and to carry off the life-exhausted materials. It is thus above all necessary to procure it of the best and most wholesome quality and in abundant supply.

Yours etc.,
Patrick Matthew
Gourdiehill Errol
16 April 1870

Matthew's views on the
annexation of Schleswig-Holstein
and the Franco-Prussian war

Commentary; Letters to the Press

In the appendix to *Naval Timber and Arboriculture* Patrick Matthew devoted a section to the characteristics of various breeds of *Homo sapiens*. He makes the point that the breed occupying the eastern coastline of the United Kingdom is largely derived from the 'Scandinavian rover' who, 'though devoted for a time to agriculture or mechanical occupation, betake themselves, when opportunity offers, to their old element, the ocean.' Patrick Matthew then proceeds to try to analyse the factors which permit certain breeds to retain their vigour and the Caucasian instinct to roam the seas. Since the retention of a strong navy to defend British interests appeared to be the main reason for writing *Naval Timber* this instinct to roam the seas was welcomed by Patrick Matthew especially because this same breed seemed to be populating America with success. Later on, however, Patrick Matthew came to value the breed of Angles above all other breeds especially the Scandinavian rovers whom he regarded as mere despoilers of property. The Angles were valued for their horticultural ability, their honesty and hard-working characteristics. After much travelling around the continent of Europe, Patrick Matthew came to respect highly the inhabitants of Schleswig-Holstein, where the Angles originated, and bought some farms which were left in the charge of one of his sons. So, when Bismarck in January 1864 marched the Prussian and Austrian forces into the two Duchies and forced the Danes to withdraw, Patrick Matthew rushed to the defence of this act.

Patrick Matthew wrote out the reasons for his support for the German take-over in a booklet entitled 'Schleswig-Holstein', containing five long letters, and in long letters to the *Dundee Advertiser*. Strangely, Patrick

Matthew announced at this time in a letter to Darwin, of all people, his intentions to combat and expose 'the shameful misstatements of the British Press'. In the same letter to Darwin, Matthew drew attention to the other subject which occupied his mind at that time – the vegetable mould about which he had recently written in the *Gardeners' Chronicle*. Darwin was also interested in this subject about this time with reference to the work of earthworms in the upper inches of the soil. There is no evidence that Darwin ever read the book when a copy arrived. It is not amongst the Darwinia stored in Cambridge University Library. That a copy did arrive is proved by the one comment Darwin made in a letter to Hooker after hearing that Wells had anticipated Matthew: 'So poor old Patrick Matthew is not the first and he cannot, or ought not, any longer put on his title pages, "Discoverer of the principle of Natural Selection".' What Matthew had written on the title page of Schleswig-Holstein was 'Solver of the problem of species'.

Patrick Matthew had become alarmed by the bellicose utterances of Prime Minister Palmerston when the threat of a Prussian invasion became obvious. So did Queen Victoria who, in spite of the recent marriage of the Prince of Wales with a Danish princess, was sympathetic to the Germans over Schleswig-Holstein. Historians try to make out that the English public sympathy for the relatively weak Danish forces was the traditional sympathy for the underdog. This alleged English sentimentality was as much a myth then as it is today as anyone could see in relation to the fish disputes with Iceland. Public opinion was misinformed by the Press and the Government and to set the record straight Matthew wrote out long historical arguments to counter the misunderstanding. England, in 1864, was in no state of readiness to stop Bismarck; she had no allies because Palmerston and Russell had antagonized both Russia and France whose power, it was alleged, could upset the balance of Europe. Germany, up until this time, had never been regarded as a threat to the balance of power. The French army was pitifully weak and the whole country demoralized over the recent farce in Mexico when the French puppet Maximilian was deposed. *The Times* and Thomas Carlyle campaigned for the German right to occupation. The Schleswig-Holsteiners had tried in 1852 to rid themselves of the Danes but were too weak to win through when their allies the Prussian forces withdrew after a threat from Russia. No support for the underdog came from England in this encounter.

Although Bismarck and his Prussian forces had no legal historical right, as had the German Bund, to invade and incorporate the German-speaking twin Duchy of Schleswig-Holstein, Matthew regarded it the duty of any German-speaking state to arrange this integration. Matthew's support for the Schleswig-Holsteiners was not only on account of his having farm estates there but because the Anglen-Sachsen was the '. . . brood-ground of the purest, most energetic German race. The population, with some few exceptions, speak the low-country German (parent of the modern English), a purer, terser, and more expressive language than the high-country German. The people of this territory, by their colonisation of England, giving to England their name and language, while England again, along with the lowlands of Scotland (colonized by the north Frieslanders) has colonized North America, Australia, New Zealand, etc. the Duchies may thus be regarded the remarkable brood-ground of the most extending race on earth, a race who will probably lay the foundation of a universal language for civilized men.' On the other hand, Matthew regarded the Danes as an inferior variety of *Homo sapiens* because they were descendants of the Vikings who were mere despoilers and marauders and not given to building up a civilization. The only asset such a race passed on to their descendants in England was the ability to rove the seas with preternatural skill. Matthew did not rate the Celts highly because they feared to rove the seas; such a variety of *Homo sapiens* could never hope to maintain a global empire.

If Matthew's support for Bismarck's invasion of Schleswig-Holstein ran counter to English public opinion, his quick defence of the Germans in the Franco-Prussian war of 1870 was even more divorced from the surprising sympathy showed by the English for the French aggressors. His first letter to the *Dundee Advertiser* (11 October 1870) clearly branded France as the aggressor: 'Louis the XIV in an unjust war tore Alsace and Lorraine from Germany. In an unjust war declared against them by the French the Germans have taken the territory back . . .' The response by the editor of the *Dundee Advertiser* was surprising since earlier in 1870 Napoleon III was severely castigated by the same paper: 'That a day of reckoning must come for the treacherous act which established the existing throne is possible enough . . .' (3 May 1870).

It is perhaps just as well that Matthew did not live long enough to witness what the new German imperialism would turn into. During his lifetime the moves made by Bismarck towards German unification were legitimate enough. But the soulful, honest, hardworking German of

Matthew's youth was a fast disappearing type and being rapidly replaced by a highly efficient military type. The early Matthew of *Naval Timber* would have rejoiced at this adaptation to circumstances '. . . the periodical return of war is indispensable to the heroic chivalrous character and love of freedom . . . It is by the jar and struggle of the conflict that the baser alloy and rust of our manners and institutions must be removed and rubbed away.' But the years between 1831 and 1870 produced great change in the martial philosophy of Patrick Matthew. He was now a crusader for peace and understanding between nations although in typical Victorian insensitivity he saw no immorality in the Europeans eliminating a few roving savages in their progress west on the North American continent. It was known in the area of Gourdiehill that Patrick Matthew would not allow anyone to shoot blackbirds which raided his orchard every season. It is possible that his martial outlook was softened by his association with the Schleswig-Holsteiners whom he came to know well when visiting his estates there. There is a footnote in his book Schleswig-Holstein which is very revealing: 'In Germany the innocent small birds are held sacred . . . It is held criminal in Germany to steal from an innocent bird that does not destroy the crops . . . and is punishable by fine and imprisonment . . . How different this from the Wren-hunt in Celtic Ireland . . .'

Dundee Advertiser, 1 July 1864

Sir,

I observe in your leading article of last Saturday some notice of my pamphlet Schleswig-Holstein, in which you quote my 'epithets' descriptive of the parties concerned, placing them in italics, for admiration, no doubt, as mere flourishes of speech, like your own upon this question, without giving in a direct, intelligent manner the undeniable facts which I adduce as proof of the correctness of the epithets I employ. This, however, may be passed over, as the few hints you do give regarding my facts are a sort of acknowledgement that something is wrong 'in the State of Denmark' – an admission that few of your brethren would have had the honesty to admit, their role on this subject being to keep facts as much as possible out of sight.

Passing, then, this little unfairness, as well as the insinuation that, from being connected with the Duchies, I may have a selfish bias in their favour. Here, it is true, I have a bias, from a knowledge of facts which mark the conduct of Denmark as dishonest, aggressive, and rapacious, and the Germans long-suffering to a blameable extent in not checking the Danish usurpation of the Duchies sooner. In your critique, you go on to state, 'Mr Matthew's pleadings (my statements are facts, not pleadings) for Schleswig-Holstein are now out of date(!) His exposition of facts has been left behind in the rapid march of affairs(!)' – as if the fact of the attempt of usurpation of the Duchies by the Danes, and the plunder and enslavement of its indigenous German population were out of date. As well might say that a murder and robbery committed in Dundee last autumn was out of date. The Duchies were German from time immemorial, and united in one state for nearly five centuries. Here I am tempted to quote from my pamphlet: 'In the year 1375, the reigning Duke Henry dying without issue, Schleswig-Holstein fell by heritage to the Count of Holstein, and from that period dates the connection or union of Schleswig with Holstein. In the beginning of the fifteenth century King Erich of Denmark attempted to dissever Schleswig from Holstein, but was defeated. From that time the independence and union of the Duchies was acknowledged by Denmark till the recent usurpation.

'In 1448 the Count Christian of Eldenburg became King of Denmark by election of the Danish Council of State and in 1469 became absolute monarch of Denmark, and about the same time was elected Duke of Duchies, limited by a Constitution, which has been maintained till the recent Danish usurpation, while Denmark remained an absolute monarchy. On being elected Duke of Schleswig-Holstein, Christian I solemnly pledged himself to maintain the following conditions, which all his followers, till the last three reigns, upon ascending the throne, also pledged to maintain.

1. The succession to the Duchies to be in the male line only (the succession in Denmark to heirs male and female was decreed in 1665).

2. Schleswig-Holstein shall for ever remain united (*ewig zusammen bleiben*).

3. The inhabitants of Schleswig-Holstein, without their own consent, shall have no new taxes laid upon them.

4. The internal administration of affairs in the Duchies and everything regarding their own welfare, is to be conducted by themselves in conjunction with the *Landtag*.

5. All the authorities of Schleswig-Holstein must be natives of the country.
6. No foreign war can be commenced without the consent of the Schleswig-Holstein Council of State.
7. No Schleswig-Holsteiner is to be forced to serve the King of Denmark out of the Duchies.

'That all these constitutional pledges have been violated by Denmark every one knows . . . The regular taxes imposed upon the Duchies at the will of the Danish Government, and which only could be paid through the extreme industry of the German population, was not enough. In 1813 a contribution of more than eighteen millions of dollars was imposed on the Duchies, to support the sinking credit of Denmark, and levied in a manner upon the heritable property of the country, as to produce incalculable evil, amounting almost to a general bankruptcy, and which the landed interest at this day has scarcely got above. The extraordinary impost upon the land of the Duchies took precedence of all heritable bonds, and the monied interest of Hamburg, etc., refused to allow their capital to be lent on Schleswig-Holstein property upon such doubtful security – when a Danish king could come in and say "Though your bond was the first registered, yet my impost shall take precedence of your bond". In justice this contribution must be paid back.'

This enormous financial robbery was not enough – was only one item of the whole amount of plunder. For a number of years back the pillage of the Duchies by Denmark has been maturing to a complete system, and has been brought to as high perfection as anything of human construction can well reach. Every encroachment the needy place-hunters of Copenhagen could contrive has been sedulously followed out. The German population of the Duchies are comparatively a more industrious people than the Dane, and the powerful Danish fleet of men-of-war, far too great for any purpose of good, and quite beyond Denmark's own means, has in fact been constructed by the wealth and money produced by German industry, and indeed maintained, and to a considerable extent manned from German shores.

The Danes, originally sea-robbers, and comparatively averse to honest industry, could never of themselves by honest means have put this fleet upon the ocean. In former times the sea kings of Denmark plundered in a bold above-board manner. But the modern Dane has resorted to other means in carrying out his predatory instincts. The Dane has succeeded for a length of time in turning the industry of the patient German to account. But patience has its limits even among Germans.

When Hanover and Britain came, much in the same manner as the Duchies and Denmark, to be under the same monarch, no advantage, no usurpation on the part of the stronger state took place to render the weaker subservient as a field for pillage, or to interfere with its nationality as one of the German Bund. How, then, is Denmark to be permitted this usurpation? Where would the honour and prestige of Germany be, were she to submit to such treatment of one of her own body? . . . the young men of from 20 to 21 years of age taken away from their homes to man the fortresses and fleet at Copenhagen principally under Danish officers, and to work in the dockyards, and so insufficiently paid that their fathers (working men) were under necessity to remit money to their sons to keep them from starving, etc., etc., . . . As the Duchies were regarded only as a field of plunder by the Danes, no wonder the Danes in Copenhagen are in consternation and wrath.

I may add – is Britain to become the tool of Denmark in an attempt to carry out this iniquity?

But to return to your critique. In the first half, impartiality, sense, judgement, are not wanting; but in the second half you bring forward Denmark in a position even worse than I have described her – as a demon of evil placed at the mouth of the Baltic to repress the commerce and progress of the Baltic nations, by blocking the water highway kind Nature has afforded them (as she has till recently, bribed not to do, so far followed out); and you wish to protect her in continuing to hold a portion of her neighbour's territory she had usurped, that, by your own account, she may be the more able to carry out this diabolical end. This is the whole scope, bearing, and purpose of the latter half of your critique, which I am really sorry to observe.

In perusing the pitiful and lame speeches of our two leading diplomatists in your paper of yesterday I also deeply regret the degradation to which the insolent and unjust threats these wiseacres have made (and happily been obliged to recede from) have reduced us. Here the unprincipled pet plan of our intermeddling scheming Prime Minister has fortunately been wrecked, ruining his future prestige as a successful diplomatist – now no longer to be trusted in the position he has too long occupied for his country's reputation. Here we pity his coadjutor's position, whom he seems to have dragged through the mud. The present degradation of Britain exemplifies the fact that straight-forward honesty is the best policy, and that the cunning manoeuvring statecraft of unprincipled politicians only leads to mischief or disgrace. Why did our two unsuccessful diplomatists not at once own they had mistaken the nature of the Schleswig-Holstein question, and that they, upon fuller enquiry, had found Germany justified in her proceedings, and that they were sorry for their error. But this would have implied a consciousness of ignorance upon a subject they ought to have had a correct knowledge of before they resorted to threaten – a humiliation that their pride would not bend to. They preferred the humiliation of their country. How differently would these two ministers have been estimated by the present age and by posterity had they come forward and ingenuously owned they had erred from misconception of the subject.

In your leading article of yesterday I observe a statement which I think deserves some notice. You say, 'The time was when British Ministers would have been ashamed to face Parliament with the confession that they had no foreign ally to help them, or, having to make that confession, that they were afraid to do what was right unaided. The time was when British statement, the more they distrusted other Powers, trusted more in the power of their own nation. Now, however, the most boastful Ministers of the proudest people on earth humble themselves and their country by declaring that, because other Governments are treacherous, they dare not be steadfast and true.' Does this mean to express that because other nations will not join Britain against Germany that they are treacherous, or that our Government declares they are treacherous? I am not aware that our Government has declared this. No doubt other nations are not possessed like Britain with the Danish mania. But that, they, on this account, are treacherous, can only be received as a maniacal conclusion.

There are two principles upon which legitimate government is based: constitutional rights and nationality. By the former, Schleswig-Holstein is fixed, independent, and indivisible, a limited Dukedom Monarchy, which can only be changed by the general-will of the people themselves. Should ancient constitutional right be here impracticable, the principle of nationality must be fallen back upon, and rigidly followed out, and the people choose their own government as a portion of ancient Germany only with the Holstein half under sanction of the Imperial Diet – of course the Danish usurpation an imposition of force, justly to be repelled by force by Germans.

Patrick Matthew
Gourdiehill
29 June, 1864.

Dundee Advertiser, 11 October 1870

Sir,

Can any claim of national property be stronger than this? Louis the XIV in an unjust war tore Alsace and Lorraine from Germany. In an unjust war declared against them by the French the Germans have taken the territory back. The people are of German race, speaking the German language. The French right was that of unjust conquest only. The German right is that of just reconquest. Which right preponderates in national law.

Patrick Matthew
Gourdiehill, Errol.

Dundee Advertiser 18 October 1870

Sir,

In a late number of your paper a Southern German, a little jealous, it would seem, of the great energy of the Northern Germans, has attempted to mystify the state of things betwixt France and Germany, ignoring facts, and speaking of his brother Germans in terms which every German will be ashamed to see. All Europe knew the preparation by France of a vast army and navy in time of peace. This vast war preparation was evidently intended, after the fashion of the legions of ancient Rome, to overawe the other nations, render France military superior of Europe, and to fulfil her views of aggressive intention wherever she coveted an accession of territory. How the other nations of Europe submitted to have their independence thus interfered with, in a manner constrained by the late domineering war power of France to be her vassal, is the result of the want of combination. The constant boasting of this great army, their menace of a march to Berlin, countenanced by the Government, the press, and the people of France, has, however, united Germany in self-defence. A few years ago, we in Britain had similar threats of a French invasion and a march to London, which, however, were not carried out from the Channel difficulty but which originated our

Volunteer organization and our fire-precision matches. This vast military preparation, and threats of the invasion of Germany, were enough to be a just *casus belli* on the part of united Germany against France. But the Germans, long suffering and slow to anger, remained without any disposition whatever or thought of attacking France. As proof of this – of their strong disposition to peaceful industry, to 'live and let live' – the withdrawing of a member of the Hohenzollern family to be King of Spain, owing to the French Government declaring that such would be followed by a declaration of war by France, is sufficient. This being yielded by Germany, the only reason that France could adduce for a declaration of war was that the self-defence union of Germany had interfered with the balance of power in Europe not, however, mentioning that this union was caused by menaces of her own creating. What should we think of France declaring war against Britain because she had organized an army of volunteers? How often has France tried to upset the balance of power in Europe? The right balance of power in the eye of the French is, at least was, all Europe at the feet of France. The war preparation – the vast army of more than 500,000 soldiers – which was the chief business of Napoleon III to create, was on purpose to effect this. In choosing a King what right had France to dictate to Spain? I have seen a good deal of Europe, and at times of great political excitement, and have found the governing power or executive most beneficially carried out in Prussia. In the north of Germany the science of Government, the sciences necessary to be known to officials, are taught in the Universities. No wonder, therefore, that Spain, so much requiring an efficient Government, should desire a leading magistrate from a country where the science of Government is most studied and the executive most beneficially exerted.

The vast French army created by Napoleon III in time of peace, prepared for aggression wherever an enlargement of territory or opportunity for plunder presented itself, has cost the other nations of Europe several hundred millions sterling in military and naval preparations for self-defence, repressing industry and promoting misery in most cases to an equal amount. The recent declaration of war by France shows how flimsy a pretext will be seized upon. This declaration was regarded as a godsend by the French army, which delighted in bloody wars and quick promotion, accompanied by plunder at will. In the time of the grandfather of the present French soldier, rich, industrious Germany was regarded as a brigand's paradise. In marching eastwards, each little potentate's domain and Court-City afforded a sort of caravansary on the way, while the danger of a skirmish-fight was not greater than gave excitement and zest to life to the French soldier. There was always in the vista a return victorious to Paris; and if all had not won a Marshall's baton, most were loaded with plunder and glory, with breast covered with Orders and medals. A return to Paris, to enjoy triumphal processions and the smile of beauty in the capital of the civilized world, was their Heaven.

The truth is, this army, the child of the Emperor, had come to feel his master. If agreeable work was not provided by their creator, the soldiers would have amused themselves by plucking him down and putting up a more active Emperor. So the Emperor was selfishly forced to hound his army on to capture Germany, neither he nor them having a thought of guilt. Military glory would cover all. The little affairs of the Crimea and Mexico, mere interludes, did not afford much glory or plunder; nor did the arduous duties of Algiers, only acting as a military school and teaching savage inhumanity. The conquest and plunder of Germany would, however, atone for all, would load the French with glory and riches, and raise the Emperor Napoleon the Third to be the greatest man of the age. To Berlin Ho! was the cry that resounded throughout France. What is the Emperor? What is the invincible army now? I would ask of this Southern German correspondent: Who is it that has effected this astonishing metamorphosis? Do they merit the terms he has twitted them with? As to Alsace and Lorraine, is it not necessary to the future peace of Europe that France, long the disturber of Europe, be compelled to restore the territory she had robbed from her neighbours and be in future limited to her own territory? The nations of Europe, in humanity should demand fighting to cease, on these conditions, with payment of the cost of the war to Germany.

Yours, etc.

Patrick Matthew

Gourdiehill Errol

18 October 1870

Dundee Advertiser, 3 November 1870

Sir,

It has long been a maxim that Republics – that is equality of political rights and representative Government – required a high morality, a probity in the great body of the people as well as in the Government officials. Judging of France by the past, where within my memory, a Republic has been twice tried, and twice found impracticable, we must conclude that the amount of probity has been defective, or the ignorance too gross. In the case of ancient Rome, which France so covets to imitate, a pure republic never existed. An aristocracy sufficiently defective in morality, and a people grossly ignorant, along with slavery, prevailed. This was naturally suited to a robber nation, which acted on the brute force system – that might was right. France mistaking her fighting power, and acting upon the brute force principle, proclaimed a war of aggression and plunder against her quiet neighbour, and being beaten in the field in her attempt to conquer Germany, instead of accepting her defeat as a merited punishment – some well believe a judgement – has raised an outcry that honour calls her to carry out to the knife (be it remembered a guilty war of her own creating). France only regards honour in the brute force view – that is, fighting success, quite apart from justice, morality, humanity; as if the knowledge of good and evil in her case had been lost. At present, when actually at the mercy of Germany, France will listen to no peace which embraces the restoration of territory she has seized from her neighbours, Germany and Italy. She also attempted to seize upon Spain in a most treacherous manner, and Mexico by a sleight of hand dexterity, but, with the assistance of Britain to Spain and of the United States to Mexico, was baffled. The last manoeuvre is to recommence a Republic, make their own Emperor, whom they had so recently confirmed in his Government by a plebiscite vote, the scapegoat of the German war and defeats, but who had been driven, by the enthusiastic desire of the army and people, into the guilty war of aggression. Will France under any Government be less the disturber of Europe?

The French nation seem to think that the adoption of a Republic is an atonement for all previous sins of commission, as if a white surplice was enough to change the nature of what is covered; expel demoniac possession of restless, reckless ambition; cupidity of the property of others; and fighting propensities. How can France go on as a Republic without anarchy or foreign war with the sparse morality which at present she exhibits, when the passions of bitter hate and revenge at being curbed in her boasted aggressive march to Berlin are so furiously raging, it is not easy to predicate. May we hope that the ancient Romish brigand fashion – desire of plunder, foreign dominion, and turbulency – will give place to the improvement of her home resources and industries, which are far from being exhausted. On the contrary, how is Germany to act when France, fairly beaten in her aggressive attempts to conquer and plunder Germany, instead of mending her ways, like a mangled viper, gets careless of her own life being trampled out, and only attempts the destruction other opponent? Such would only be giving time for France to prepare a new army of aggression, and a fourth march to Paris be necessary. Germany has only one resource – to lessen the territory of her implacable neighbour and to procure an impregnable frontier on the side of France, with a war navy able to cope with France.

Patrick Matthew
Gourdiehill Errol
3 November 1870

Schleswig-Holstein

Letter I To the right hon. Lord Palmerston, Attempted Dismemberment of Germany

Letter II To the British people. The British Press Versus Constitutional Rights and Nationalities.

Letter III Hurried Glance at History of Man in Europe.

Letter IV Respect to Nationalities Necessary to Peace and Progress in Europe.

Letter V The Necessity for the Removal of the Malign Influences which Repress Human Progress.

by
Patrick Matthew
Author of *Emigration Fields* & *Naval Timber and Arboriculture*,
solver of the problem of species; first proposer of steam rams,
metallic cover, sloping sides, heavy gun boats, etc.
London
Spottiswoode & Co. New Street Square, E C
1864

At no period, for more than half a century past, have I observed so much spleen and low abuse vented upon any people, as recently by the British Press upon the Germans; and that without any cause given by that honest, highly moral, long-suffering, but determined race. In the following letters, I attempt to disabuse my countrymen of the wrong impressions they have taken regarding the German people and the

Schleswig-Holstein question. This unfortunate misconception arises, in a great measure, from the gross misrepresentations of a partial, disingenuous, and sneering Press, who seem to regard public feeling as an instrument it is their calling to play upon 'what stops they please', and, like the dissenting priest, find that cultivating the passions, especially that of political antagonism as the other does religious antagonism, pays better than cultivating kind feeling and kindred affection.

Taking advantage of the natural disposition of humanity to protect the weak against the strong, the oppressed against the oppressor (a feeling which has actuated Germany to come forward to protect the German Duchies from the Danish usurpation, plunder, and oppression), the gentlemen of the British Press, with, it is true, some honourable exceptions, have done their utmost to raise up a hatred of Germany and affection for Denmark, without regard to truth right, or justice, making up for adverse facts by abuse of everything German, and praise of everything Danish. *In this case their twisting the robber into the robbed is a specimen of their ingenuity, and is on a par with their general misrepresentation.*

I lay before the public the following Letters (intended for the London Press, but refused), in the hope that a plain statement of facts by a plain country farmer of fifty-seven years practice, who has seen more years than men of the Press, from their arduous employment, usually reach, who has had more opportunity to obtain a knowledge of facts, and more time to reflect, may have a beneficial impression in removing animosities from two kindred peoples. Should current prejudices be too strong for removal, I rest confident that posterity – that future gentlemen of the Press – will recognize that truth of my statements, and accuracy of my views, as the present age is beginning to do I regard to other very different subjects which an age ago I had laid before the public – so long to be neglected.

Patrick Matthew
London
May 30, 1864.

Letter I
Attempted Dismemberment of Germany

To the Right Hon. Lord Palmerston

My Lord, I have seen it stated that your Lordship declares that none in Britain comprehend the Schleswig-Holstein question except yourself

– that at least you did so once, but that now it may have escaped your Lordship's memory. Perhaps in the actual experience and knowledge of the subject, I am not far behind what your Lordship may once have been. However that may be, however much your Lordship may have forgotten your Lordship must be sensible that no person or persons whatever have a right, contrary to the will of an independent state or states, to transfer it or them in subjection to another nation, even though that nation were not deservedly hated by the state or states attempted to be transferred. This is what has been attempted to be done in the case of Schleswig-Holstein, in the face of opposed nationalities, language, and hatred of races; and it would appear that your Lordship, as Prime Minister of Britain, had given it your sanction, probably from being aware of the pledges given by Denmark to Austria and Prussia, previous to signing the protocol of 1852, that the rights of the Duchies would be respected.

Holstein, as everyone knows, is an integral portion of the German Bund, though, till lately, usurped for a time by the Danes. It, along with Schleswig, constitutes the Dukedom of Schleswig-Holstein. This ancient Anglo-Saxon territory, Schleswig-Holstein, comprising the ancient Anglen, may be regarded as the brood-ground of the purest, most energetic German race. The population, with some few exceptions, speak the low-country German (parent of the modern English), a purer, terser, and more expressive language than the high-country German. The people of this territory, by their colonization of England, giving to England their name and language, while England again, along with the lowlands of Scotland (colonized by the north Frieze), has colonized North America, Australia, New Zealand, etc. – the Duchies may thus be regarded the remarkable brood-ground of the most extending race on earth a race who will probably lay the foundation of a universal language for civilized men.

Schleswig, partly ancient Anglen; partly a portion of the ancient north Friezeland, the greater part of which is now submerged; partly, upon the northern border, Danish (originally Cimbric), is about two-thirds German, and one-third Danish, the towns and leading portion of the people being almost wholly German. Schleswig has been subject to inroads by the less civilized Dane of Jutland, assisted by the Islands, the same as the more civilized portion of Scotland by the highland Celts. Still it is evident that Jutland and the Danish Islands had, at some past era, been subject to German sway, as the Cimbric language had wholly disappeared before the era of historic records, replaced by a branch of the Teuton or German, though much of the Cimbric blood may have remained.

To reduce the people of Schleswig to be subject to the Dane, would be much the same as to reduce the people of the lowlands of Scotland to the government, language, manners, and social standing of the highland Celt. It may be asked, what right has the German Bund to drive out the usurping Danes from Schleswig? The right and duty is clear and undeniable, not any of the German Bund, but of any of the German States, to protect their kindred in their own country Schleswig constitutes a half of the Schleswig-Holstein Dukedom, constitutionally under a German Duke; and surely by nationality, by language, by constitution, Germans have a right – if anything whatever can constitute a right – to defend Germany and German people, while Denmark has no right whatever, but that of force, which is rightly met by force.

The connection between Britain and Hanover afforded a case almost identical with that of Denmark and the Duchies. In Britain and Denmark the succession, when not elective, is to heirs male and female, while in Hanover and the Duchies it is to heirs male. Hence, upon the death of the late King of Denmark and Duke of Schleswig-Holstein, the succession of the Duchies falls to the eldest male line, the Augustenberg family, and if not elective, in Denmark to the nearest of kin by the female side, as took place in Britain and Hanover upon the death of William IV. There might be however one slight difference. As far as I know, the British kings never came under any solemn obligation not to mix the two governments, while the King Christian of Denmark, when he was elected to be Duke of the Duchies in 1460, came under the most solemn obligations that the two nations or states should have the governments entirely distinct, and that the Duchies of Schleswig-Holstein should remain for ever undivided. This oath was taken by all the succeeding sovereigns previous to the three last. This shows that, from the first, the danger of Danish aggression was foreseen, and as far as possible means adopted to prevent it. In defiance of this constitutional stipulation, the encroachment by Denmark upon the constitutional rights of the Duchies has been going on for a number of years back, till it came last autumn to the climax of Denmark declaring Schleswig to be an integral part of Denmark, and to treat Holstein as a conquered province, occupied by Danish troops, and a large emblazoned shield of the Danish arms, with the words, *Königliche Zoll* – King's Custom House – placed before the

Altona Custom House, a display to brave the German Bund, and mock the constitution of the Duchies.

In this case, seeing that, Holstein is one of the German Bund, thoroughly German in race language, literature, and feeling, and that Holstein and Schleswig constitutionally form a twin Dukedom, and besides that, though there is a part of the population of Schleswig on the northern frontier Danish, that the great proportion, including nearly the whole of the leading classes, with the exception of the Danish officials, are thoroughly German, can there be a doubt of the right of the Duchies to demand complete separation from Denmark as an independent state, like Austria and Prussia, and Holland, in part connected with the German Bund? Instead of taking part with the usurper, should Britain see any other nation attempt to dismember Germany (the neighbour, kindred and ally of Britain), or interfere to assist Denmark in her attempted usurpation, it is the duty of Britain to resist such an outrage against national rights. Should Britain fail in her duty towards Germany, she may lose the favour of her old friends – perhaps miss their assistance should she require it at some future time.

The best friends of Denmark must agree with me here. I am the well-wisher and sincere friend of Denmark in all that is right and advantageous for herself. I rejoice in the prosperity of her agriculture, and her great increase in wealth so derived, favoured by the abolition of the Corn Bill in Britain. I will also rejoice in her improved representative government, should it take a just and improving course. Wherever there is a Danish population in Schleswig desiring to be attached to Denmark, I would be the last man who would wish them placed under German rule. But I am not the less a friend to justice and of Germany. The true interest of Denmark is to make a commercial league with Britain – entire free trade betwixt the two nations – perhaps articles of mischievous tendency, alcohol compounds, tobacco, opium, excepted. This would render the two countries necessary to each other, and friends lastingly.

The heir to Schleswig-Holstein by the constitution of the Duchies, which no power but the will of the people has a right to change, has stated in his manifesto, in speaking of the usurpation of the Duchies by the Danes: *'The people's sense of right is the best guarantee of the rights of princes. Under pretence of the rights of princes the Duchies have been oppressed by the Dane, and under a prince they shall be righted.'*

It may be proper to state to your Lordship, at least to recall to your

Lordship's memory, how the oppression of the Duchies by the Dane has been carried out, the people treated more like sheep to be shorn than men to be justly governed. Independently of a high tax, both upon imports and land, an extraordinary contribution of 18 million dollars was some years back levied upon the Duchies to pay Danish debt, reducing numbers of landholders to bankruptcy, for the repayment of which the Duchies have just claim; the youth of the Duchies, the German youth, have been forced away to Copenhagen to man the Danish forts, serve in the war vessels, and work in the dockyards, constructing a war fleet to overawe Germany by threatening her commercial navy and to retain the Duchies in thrall; while so low was their pay, that their parent in the Duchies – often poor men obliged to borrow funds – had to forward money to their sons at Copenhagen to prevent them from starving. Such is the horror the young Germans have of being taken to Copenhagen by the Danes, that they fly their country rather than submit thus to be made work against their sense of patriotism.

Lately, upon the anniversary of one of the battles on which the Holsteiners were worsted by the Danes, after they were deserted by the Prussians at the threat of Russia, and by which the Danes say they conquered the Duchies and made them their own, some of the friends of the slain Holsteiners buried at Altona hung a few wreaths of flowers upon the graves of the slain. The result was that about 4,000 Danish troops with a park of artillery were immediately sent to occupy Altona. How could Germany submit to allow a portion of herself to be thus insulted and trampled upon? Did the absurd protocol of 1852 authorize this? Did it stipulate that tribute in money and young men as slaves should be paid? Did it stipulate that the Duchies should pay the Danish debt? And that the tribute should be paid in Danish coin only – German coin being the usual circulating medium of the Duchies? Did it stipulate the use of the Danish language in the schools and law courts of the German towns of Schleswig? It might as well have done so as what it did.

Is this system of oppression to be supported by Britain against all constitutional right and justice, and only to be upheld by the right of force? Of late the tyranny (see *Dundee Advertiser*) was carried so far that any person found to have in his possession any of the smaller German currency, was liable not only to have such money confiscated, but to be fined or imprisoned for the offence, while the police were empowered to seize purses, search shops, break open tills, in quest of German coin, and that these measures were recklessly enforced in Altona, which is by position a mere suburb of German Hamburg. Still more galling is it that the Danish Government should wage a perpetual crusade against the German tongue in the churches, the schools, the universities and the services in Schleswig, thus endeavouring to metamorphose German people into Danes! Is your Lordship to send off a British fleet and army to assist the Danes in this sort of work? Your Lordship may depend upon it, that this act and its perpetrators would receive a meet award from posterity.

I am almost ashamed to detail the numerous ways that 'poor brave' Denmark has taken to repress the energies and the capacities of improvement of the Duchies, but an example or two will suffice to show the character. In the case of the university of Kiel, which formerly had a high standing as one of the centres of education and science in the north of Europe, especially as having the purest *Hoch Deutsch* spoken, and to which the youth from the Duchies resorted, this seat of high education has been in every possible manner depressed by the influence of the Danish Government, chiefly restricting the government patronage and place to the youth who had studied at Copenhagen, while those who had studied at Kiel were looked askance upon. This was entirely opposed to the constitutional law of the Duchies by which the study during two years at Kiel university was required to render the student eligible as a candidate for any of the learned professions or official situations. This illegal and shameful centralization towards Copenhagen had the most injurious effect upon the Kiel university as having studied there was found to be a bar to advancement, the number of students naturally fell off from low salaries attached to the professorships, and the diminished number of fees, the emolument as insufficient to call forth men of the highest standing, while one of the most important branches of study to befit the student from the Duchies had first to learn Danish before he could follow it out. Also a professorship of agriculture, so important in the almost entirely agricultural Duchies and for which funds were collected to endow, when solicited for the Kiel university, was refused to be permitted by the Danish usurpers.

The same insidious means were taken to repress the material advancement as the mental. The rising commerce of the nations bordering on the Baltic eastward with the rest of the world has been under the necessity of circumnavigating the Cimbrian peninsula, increasing the length of the voyage in dangerous seas about 1,000 miles to what it would be were a convenient canal cut across the Duchies – the Kiel canal of an old date being very circuitous, inconvenient, and only suited for small craft. Canals have been proposed at three or four different places across from the Baltic to the German Ocean, either of which would be of immense importance to the Duchies and the Baltic nations; but Denmark, in order to render Copenhagen an entrée port for the Baltic, and till lately to enhance the blackmail she levied on the Baltic trade, has denied permission for such a canal. The wonder is that Russia, Prussia, Mecklenburg, etc., and Britain permitted such an imposition as this levying of blackmail, called Sound dues, at Elsinore, or such an obstruction to the commerce of the north of Europe as the want of a convenient canal across the neck of the Jutland peninsula. It is probable that the proposed canal from the excellent entrance harbour at Neustadt on the Baltic side to a little east of Brunsbuttel on the lower Elbe, would prove the most advantageous. With a railway line at each side and two steam drags, vessels might make the transit in a few hours without any risk; while proceeding round by the Skager Rack and Skaw as many weeks might be required, and danger incurred.

In the present involved state of affairs in Europe which the British diplomacy has to meet, it is above all things necessary to cultivate the friendship of Germany. We have seen a danger resulting from Denmark being influenced to act against us. We have to guard against the restlessness and warlike bent of the French, and the intrigue and cunning of Russia – to restrain the grasping ambition of both – that of the former to absorb Belgium, Egypt, Sardinia, and make the boundary of France on the northeast the Rhine – that of the latter to seize the entrance of the Baltic and the Dardanelles. These are the objects of each, and if they combine to carry these, it will require all the power of Britain and an united instead of a dismembered Germany to prevent their success.

It affords a melancholy view of humanity in its highest development to observe right, justice, every sentiment of patriotism outraged by the leading governments of Europe – the greater, the stronger being the most guilty – instance the protocol of 1852. We naturally ask ourselves, Can it be possible that the governments had a knowledge of good and evil, and that the German portion of them did even sign such a document stipulating the dismemberment of Germany – holding as nought the liberties of nearly a million of the most ancient branch of the German race, recklessly breaking the old constitutional rights, upon which their own governments were based. It is with difficulty that we can believe that Austria, Prussia, Mecklenburg, and their old ally Britain could be guilty of this. They well knew, they had already seen, how the usurped power over the Duchies by Denmark had been exercised. They well knew that by authorizing this usurpation, they were devoting the Schleswig-Holstein people to the most possible domination – to be the slaves of another people speaking a different language, different in literature, feeling, manners and customs; and more, that the ruling nation was of a lower grade in civilization than the subjects. The governments signing the protocol could not surely be ignorant that, where a people is different in language from the people and nation by whom they are governed, the subjection is the most galling and unwholesome of all, and should the people trampled upon not right themselves by force, that a decline of energy of race in the subordinate is in time the certain sequence – that under continued slavery the mind of the race becomes debased. Hitherto the domination of Denmark over the Duchies has only tended, not to humble the people of Schleswig-Holstein, but rather to strengthen the love of liberty and to exasperate them against their oppressors. Can any maltreatment exceed that which I have pointed out – the Duchies taxed for the means of keeping up a large naval and military force, quite disproportionate to the population and means of Denmark, in order to retain the Duchies in subjection – the officials in Schleswig generally Danes – the young men of the Duchies taken to Denmark as slaves and subjected to severe drudgery, not even receiving sufficient food to save them from starvation? The signers of the protocol knew, or if not they ought to have known, that to have the conditions of the protocol observed by the Danes, at least those promised by Denmark to Prussia and Austria, would require a large army to watch their conduct constantly kept up.

In order to flatter the governing families of Germany, that they might be led to give their concurrence, the intriguers who planned the protocol got a German prince, a relation of the late king, but not the heir to the Duchies, nor I believe to the crown of Denmark, protocol-appointed to be king of Denmark and duke of Schleswig-Holstein, should the late king have no direct heir. This might also be the view to render the German people more complying as well in the Duchies as in the rest of Germany. Here it is evident that, from the new constitution of Denmark, the influence of the king, though with German predilections, would not be great to befriend the Duchies, and that, in another generation, any German leaning would disappear, when the Duchies would be left to the tender mercies of the Dane.

It happened rather unluckily for the success of the protocol, but luckily for human rights and the future peace of Europe, that the signing of the protocol by Prussia and Austria was on certain stipulations regarding the manner the Duchies were to be governed, and to come into operation from the time the protocol was signed. To these stipulations the Danes, in their unbridled lust of power, gave no heed, only looking upon the Duchies as a conquered subordinate dependency of Denmark. The Prussian and Austrian parts to the protocol are thus relieved from their gage, unlawful though it was. *In the case of the Danish usurpation it is only the German people who are entitled to see the Duchies righted, as being a portion of themselves, whether in Schleswig or Holstein.* It is stated that Prussia has withdrawn her name from the protocol; the other governments who have signed the protocol seem to be proud to admit of error, though aware they have erred – not to possess honesty or courage to repair what they have done, though opposed to justice, patriotism, and in part to the strong feeling of their subjects. This is a dangerous position they have placed themselves in, and if ill befall, they will know whom to blame. In the case of the German nation not being able to assert the rights of Schleswig-Holstein, then the European nations, under the plea of the preservation of the balance of power, might have a right to interpose to prevent the Danish usurpation, but no right whatever to decree by protocol the usurpation.

Earnestly desiring the well-being of Denmark, I would strongly rec-ommend her to arrange the affair of the Duchies without delay. The protocol arrangement will not suffice. Can it make Danes of Germans? A complete clearance from the Duchies is necessary. Should any con-nection remain, constant quarrels will take place. Denmark would be like a bird with a broken wing, and her king would be *Christian with his burthen of sin.* The Duchies would prove a thorn in her side, disturbing her and ready to combine with her enemy should war take place. Besides, the connection would entail the hatred of Germany. She sees in the case of Poland that the sense of injustice and usurpation can never die – at least under the extending education and knowledge of modern Europe – but on the contrary, increase till nationalities prevail. If she attempt by force to oppose Germany, being the weaker party and in the wrong, she may depend, sooner or later, upon condign punishment, great destruction of Danish life and property, to end in a compulsory giving up of her unjust claim, and, after the French fashion, being made to pay the expense of war. With regard to those governments that have given their sanction to the unjust London protocol of 1852, they must, like others who have done wrong, and who may have any moral sense left, repair the evil as quickly as possible. They cannot do away with the fact that the people in the Duchies are Germans, and that to force them to be slaves to the Danes would be one of the greatest crimes perpetrated in modern times, and like slavery in the United States, not abolished in time, eventually to meet its reward.

Need I remind your Lordship that, under the existing and increasing moral sense of modern Europe, the only means of providing for peace and prosperity is a strict observance of nationalities? There is a knowledge of good and evil in civilized man progressive as civilization progresses, which cannot be overcome and which well regulate governments by nationalities in spite of unjust protocols. Schleswig-Holstein, from the difference of the language alone, can never incorporate with Denmark, unless the language of Denmark change to German, which is not improbable, at least more probable than that the Duchies should remain under Danish rule. The necessity of a common nationality and language was seen in the unworkable incongruity and consequent separation of Belgium from Holland, proving the absurdity of protocols made by ignorant unprincipled men at Vienna as well as at London. It is also seen in the expediency of Britain giving up the Ionic Islands, and the further expediency of Austria giving up Venice, and France Rome.

As regards Germany, once so much torn by religious antagonism, it is well that this cause of division is nearly extinct. It is also to be hoped that jealousy between the Austrian, Prussian, and smaller states party will not blind her better judgement to the necessity of uniting to resist the dismemberment of the empire. This affair of the Duchies is, I believe, destined to have a valuable combining effect upon Germany, that is, provided the signers of the protocol so not remain bigoted to persist in wrong. It will, in Germany, afford a sort of useful drill, or school of unity of feeling and action. Lying in the centre of Europe, able, if united, to sway the destinies of Europe to peace, order, progress, and the establishment of industrial liberty, equally important as political liberty to the well-being of the species – shame upon the degenerate German, if such there be, who from paltry jealousy would stand idly by and see his fatherland dismembered! And shame upon the English branch, the Angles, originally from this ancient Angel-Sachsen – this very Schleswig-Holstein – who would forget the claim of parentage, of kindred! Are they to be as regardless of the ties of blood as the Anglo-Americans?

The Germans had an example in the French conquest and occupation of Germany of the consequence of the want of unity. Let this never be forgotten. If complete unity of action and organization be not previously arranged, all ready to rise as one man to resist any attempt at dismemberment of interference with German territory, it is not impossible Germany may again be reduced under foreign yoke, and perhaps be unable a second time to rise and retrieve her liberties.

In closing this letter, I cannot help again adverting to the character of the protocol of London, with which your Lordship was connected. Judged aright, it is a combination of a number of governments, so far despots as despotically to interfere with what they had no business whatever, and in doing which they outraged every principle of constitutional right and of human liberty. The Schleswig-Holstein affair is merely a dispute between the Danish Government and the Duchies, the half of which forms a part of the German Bund, which the German people, the observance of the constitution of the Duchies, and the law of nations, will quite suffice to arrange. There is, however, an observation attributed to your Lordship, which I hope is not correct, to which I have already alluded, that your Lordship had said you had perhaps forgotten the bearing of the question of the Duchies. This will be taken as implying that you consider the dismemberment of the German Empire, the nationalities of the Duchies, the liberties of nearly a million of German people of the same blood as ourselves, as not of sufficient importance to merit your Lordship's recollection – is forgotten by the Prime Minister of England. I sincerely hope that this marked slight upon the importance of the liberty of the Duchies, of the integrity of the German Empire, of nationalities, is untrue, and that it will be denied by your Lordship.

I remain, my Lord,
Your obedient Servant,
Patrick Matthew
Gourdiehill: 21 December 1863.

Letter II
To the British People

Friends and Countrymen,

Having left my home in the Carse of Gowerie, Perthshire, about three weeks ago, and taken a run through Schleswig-Holstein, a country I have long had an intimate knowledge of, I have hastened back to London to try if possible to disabuse you of the wrong impressions you have received from the gross misrepresentations of the British Press in favour of the attempt by the Danes to usurp the German Duchies. That this is, or rather was, a most unjust attempt at usurpation – entirely evil in its origin, purpose, progress, and tendency – directly opposed to nationalities, constitutional rights, and the natural rights of man – I am certain to have your verdict as soon as you come to have a knowledge of the facts. These I will try to lay honestly before you. In the first place I will mention my journey.

On coming in sight of Heligoland in the Leith steamer, we observed a British frigate (the *Aurora*), under steam, come rapidly round from the northward by the west side of the island and anchor on the east side. About the same time, between twelve and one o'clock, slight concussions of guns were felt, the noise reverberating downward to the deck from the sails of our vessel. On advancing a little farther we could distinguish through a smoke-haze the German and Danish fleets in action, about twelve or fifteen miles north-east of the island, the noise of the cannonade becoming, as we advanced, louder and continuous. This had a strong exciting effect upon our seamen aboard, causing their eyes to open wide and flash in a remarkable manner, as if none had the right to fight upon the sea but themselves. After the action had continued about two hours, we observed a dense column of smoke arise high up from one of the largest vessels. A portion of her rigging was on fire, and some of her spars appeared either broken or burned. Upon this two of the large ships, the one on fire and another and three of the gun-boats (the German force), retired south-west to within the British waters of Heligoland, and cast anchor, no doubt to repair the damage of the vessel which had caught fire while the three remaining large vessels (the Danish force), after a little delay, bore away northward. On my return I had opportunity at Cookshaven of seeing the two large German vessels which had been in the action. One of them, the *Schwarzenberg*, the rigging of which had been on fire, had a few brown spots on her sides, but neither seemed to have received serious damage. It was said that the kindling of a portion of the rigging was owing to the very foolish act of bringing upon deck in the hurry a number of shells, which, lying in a heap accidentally exploded, kindling the rigging and killing and wounding numbers of the men. This accounts for the great loss of men in the *Schwarzenberg*, and the slight loss in the others.

Upon reaching Altona and proceeding inward, German and Schleswig-Holstein flags were waving everywhere; the utmost order and regulation prevailed Austrians, Prussians, soldiers of the Bund and of Schleswig-Holstein being on the most friendly terms mutually and with the country people; the soldiers billeted on the farmers seeming a portion of the family, and playing with the children. Holstein appeared the land of harmony and kindness; all was right – the hated Dane was expelled.

Although having witnessed several German springs reclothe the land in verdure, I never observed spring so genial and grand as the present. A little longer delayed than usual, the sun, having attained greater strength, roused nature up with a bound from her winter sleep. When I left Scotland the trees and country were green. On April 28, more than a week before I left, I measured my own rye-grass in the field thirty-one inches long. In Holstein, three degrees farther south, on May 10, nakedness and barrenness prevailed; but in a few days the whole face of nature was changed, as if by enchanter's wand – exuberance of expanded leaves and flowers. Summer was come, 'the meadows painted with delight', the summer birds were come, and every garden resounded day and night with the nightingale's song – the poor little thing transported with joy! Such a change had occurred with man.

May I hope that this most genial spring is a good augury of the future of this beautiful country – that there will in future be protection to person and property – that no more forced contributions will be levied on the Duchies to pay the Danish debt, and that the young men will no longer be forced to flee their country, to escape being sent as slaves to work in the Copenhagen dockyards, and starved of sufficient pay to procure food?

While in the neighbourhood of Altona I saw at Blankenese the reception, by the assembled people, of the Duke Frederick of Augustenburg as their future sovereign. The whole country population, for many miles around, turned out to welcome him; music playing, banners flying, the men of the numerous agricultural villages, all well-dressed men, marching in order, each village distinct under its own banner, and with the white ring round the arm as pledge of their faith and readiness to take the field. Here the whole population was unanimous. The day was splendid. All the roads around were filled with people, and the reception most enthusiastic. Duke Frederick of Schleswig-Holstein is a man of 'manly make', tall and handsome. A face indicative of firmness without much play feature – a quiet determined look, as if he would know and do his duty without words in the Leopold fashion never become the slave of luxury and sensual enjoyment – perhaps rather too much of a military bearing, but that may be useful.

The only cloud to the general brightness was the sight of Danish prisoners. Why did they not all run home, as they ought? They had no right to be in Schleswig-Holstein. The effect of sympathy mastering the better judgement was exemplified a few days ago in myself, upon meeting a detachment of Prussians escorting Danish prisoners. I could not help feeling strongly for the poor men under their misfortune; but when, at the cemetery at Kiel, I passed the burial military procession of a Prussian soldier of the liberating army, who had been severely wounded, my feelings took a different direction. The prisoners were in German hands, the kindest people in Europe, and would be better treated than they merited. They had been the aggressors they had fought on the anti-nationality side, they had been guilty, at least, of attempted murder of those who had never injured them – of those protecting their native land against a foreign usurpation. They, if only poor instruments in the hands of others, were yet so far guilty in having allowed themselves to be made tools of unprincipled Copenhagen politicians, who have been existing upon the spoils of the Duchies. The public feeling in Britain, taking part with Poland against foreign usurpation, and with Denmark in favour of foreign usurpation, must arise from some strange confusion of ideas.

In nations, as in the individual, certain provisions are necessary for the maintenance of health and capacity of development. Even rare fertility of soil, superiority of climate and position are not of themselves sufficient without these. Of these provisions, home-government is the most essential. In the case of the Duchies, nature has been highly propitious. In race we have the old pure German Teuton, offsets from which have gone to form the leading portion of the English and Scotch peoples, and, at the second remove, that of the American United States. In climate, that sea air tropical current from the south-west which passes over the British Islands sweeps across the Duchies into the Baltic Channel, greatly modifies the climate, and affords more regular showers to the growing crops than in more continental positions, giving greater certainty of production. The rich silt deposit of the west side of the Duchies and along the Elbe border affords the finest pastures in Europe, producing breeds of horned cattle and horses primarily superior to any other, and of which Britain has availed herself as a bases of her improved breeds, as well as of the superior race of man. The eastern side of the Duchies, rising into beautiful undulations, the highest not exceeding 300 feet, consists generally of a rich deep clay loam, over a sand and gravel bottom affording natural drainage. This eastern portion, the ancient Angle land, is peculiarly fertile in the cereals, grasses, and legumes, producing great quantities of that superior butter with which London is chiefly supplied. In position the Duchies partake much of that of Britain, both lying as natural entrepôts on the west side – to seaward – of the European continent.

The central portion or backbone of the Cimbrian Peninsula, including Schleswig-Holstein, running from the Elbe northward almost to the Norway coast, is the sand-bar of the Baltic. Most gulfs and rivers have a similar bar where the sea waves break. This Baltic Bar, thrown up when the sea was from 50 to 100 feet higher, or the land lower, and where not only the Atlantic wave broke, but also where the north-east Baltic wave would strike the Atlantic west-wave, both laying down or rather heaping up their wafted materials, forms the basis of the Cimbrian Peninsula. This sand-bar from 50 to 100 miles broad, and near 400 long, is curiously twisted in the stratification, from the whirlings of the impinging waves and currents meeting from east and west; and the mud or clay wafted matter not being deposited where there was so much water commotion, the soil in this central portion is too silicious and much of it uncultivated, partly covered with peat deposit, formed by and bearing heath, mosses, and poor grass. On the west side of the Duchies, a later deposit of silt covers up this sand basis. This silt land, not above a few feet higher than high-water level, much of it below that level with the sea walled out, forms the rich marsh pastures where the cattle reared in Jutland are fed off. On the east side of the peninsula we have the very interesting rich loam formation covering the basic sand, in some places to a great depth, in others only a few feet. This clayey formation, in

some places with boulders, seems a glacier moraine, deposited when the
Baltic was a vast glacier river, the rich clayey mould being the glacier
scourings of the mud bottom of the Baltic Sea. This material has to some
extent suffered displacement by earthquake movement, but the inequalities of the surface are chiefly the result of the scooping out of the
streamlets. This beautiful undulating eastern division is much more
extensive than the flat silt western division now is. But at a former period,
when North Friezeland existed, they might probably be about equal.
The poor central sand and gravel division, nearly level, fully equals the
rich eastern in extent; the former is also in some places modified by
earthquake commotion bringing up clay, marl and various mixtures. The
whole peninsula seems here and there to have received deposits from
icebergs, and is entirely a modern drift formation, no rock except a little
chalk and some other recent calcareous agglutinations being reached by
boring or digging.

From the situation of the Duchies, barring up what would seem the
natural mouth of the Baltic, and throwing the Baltic navigation northward
round the Cimbrian Peninsula, as I have before stated, a deep convenient
canal, long projected, and easily practicable across the Duchies, would
be highly advantageous to the nations eastward which bound the Baltic.
It is dread of this, which would throw Copenhagen, and Denmark
generally, out of the line of Baltic trade, that renders Denmark so covetous
of the Duchies, that she may prevent this, crush the improvement of the
Duchies, prevent the development of their natural capabilities, and their
becoming the channel of the Baltic commerce, laying Denmark, and
more especially Copenhagen, in the background.

This solves the question of the Duchies, account for the policy of the
gradual step-by-step usurpation, and the pertinacity with which Denmark
has kept hold of her prey, till wrung from her by main force. Are the
British to allow themselves to be made her tool in attempting to get
back to Denmark what she had stolen? Abroad, it is said, some of the
British Press have been bribed – they themselves best know. This may
have given the cue, and they followed each other like a flock of sheep.
They might with equal justice and chance of success attempt to re-establish
the 'Algerine pirates as Danish slavery over the Duchies.

I mention here that, about fourteen years ago, upon the retirement
of the Prussians who were assisting the Schleswig-Holsteiners in removing
the Danish usurpation, the forces of the Duchies were driven beyond

the Dannewerk, where the Danes entrenched themselves, and resisted several strong attacks made by the Schleswig-Holstein forces to retrieve Schleswig. Upon this Austria sent an army into Holstein, demanded the Provisional Government to lay down their arms, and that she would see the rights of the Duchies maintained. Upon this, the Danish Government coming under certain pledges to Austria and Prussia that the constitutional rights of the Duchies should be respected, the Austrian army was withdrawn, and Austria and Prussia, trusting to these pledges, signed the protocol 1852. These pledges were, however, only made to be broken; so far, indeed, that last autumn the Danish Government had the audacity, as before stated, to declare Schleswig as integral portion of Denmark, and held Holstein only as an enslaved dependency, thus rendering Austria and her army of occupation mere instruments in accomplishing the usurpation of the Duchies. The death of the late king of Denmark and duke of the Duchies having changed the line of succession, Austria and Prussia, finding the pledges of the Danish Government completely broken by the continued Danish usurpation, upon the faith of which pledges they signed the protocol, have had no alternative but to withdraw from the protocol, and use force with those whom pledges could not bind, as the rightful means to check this impudent attempt to dismember Germany and enslave German people.

The tactics of the two great German states are now being developed. They have done the German work, and done it quickly, which saves miles of red tape, when cotton is so scarce, and thousands of lives. A few weeks' longer delay might have rendered the liberation of the Duchies a work of difficulty. Help to the Dane from Scandinavia and Britain was expected. Denmark by legislating the seizure of Schleswig as an integral portion of her dominions, completely broke from the protocol 1852, and gave an opportunity to the German Governments, who had rather unwisely signed the protocol, to free themselves from their engagements, and at the same time gave them as Germans full right, the right of nationality, whether with the sanction of the Diet of without it, to defend the integrity of ancient Germany by expelling the Danes from the Duchies. Now that the work has been so energetically accomplished, it will be right to offer terms to Denmark before pursuing the war. That Denmark renounce all claim to the Duchies which she had so unjustly forced them from their homes as conscripts – refund whatever contributions Denmark has levied upon the Duchies to pay the Danish debt;

also to pay the value of the German shipping (private property) she has captured on account of the Germans having spared private property they captured in Jutland – at least in this to make a balance. The integrity of Denmark was never interfered with, till she refused to restore the stolen German territory; and only when she attacked the private property of the Germans upon the seas, has Germany attacked the Danish property on land, in retributive justice. What confusion of moral judgement must reign in the head of Earl Russell, who thinks the seizure of private property at sea is more just than that of private property on land, when, if any difference exist, it is the reverse. The only reason I can see for his Lordship's opinion is that he himself may have his property on land. It was also amusing to hear Earl Ellenborough complain of the contributions the army of liberation had been levying upon the property of Jutland in time of war, and not say a word about the contributions levied by the Danes upon the Duchies in time of peace, one of which amounted to 18 million dollars, by which many of the land holders in the Duchies were ruined.

As the Duchies were regarded only as a field for plunder by the Danes, no wonder the Danes in Copenhagen are in consternation and wrath. The Duchies, naturally rich in agricultural wealth, afforded to the ambitious, grasping, idle Copenhagener a rich field for pillage, and they took very good care to work it.

At length force has been exhibited on the side of nationalities and constitutional rights, and has prevailed. Britain appears to have been deceived by the gradual usurpation by the Danes of the German Duchies, and influenced by the absurd idea that because Denmark is not of great extent she has a right to seize her neighbour's territory. This is indeed the chief reason I have seen given by the London journals for the seizure of the Duchies by Denmark. The protocol acted upon this principle, and the British, so generously inclined, wish to be generous at another's cost. Here the British will not take the trouble to make any enquiry into fact, but too willingly submit to be led by the Press, who in this case have resorted chiefly to the argument of sneer, abstaining from facts, or misrepresenting them. The rest of Europe cannot account for this Danish leaning, so opposite to British interests. It would seem indeed that the gentlemen of the British Press had taken up the Dano-German question as a competitive game, trying to surpass each other in contumely and abuse of Germany, and in praise of Denmark. This is not a very commendable game, and ought to be checked by everyone who has any regard for his country's reputation, or for common decency. Here, this unjust, calumniating conduct of the British Press is more hateful to honest peaceable men than even the pertinacity of the Danes themselves in holding their rapine. It brings the blush of anger and shame to the British brow where the facts are known. The Danish pertinacity is encouraged by British flattery and misrepresentation, and greater destruction of life property, and more suffering to the Dane, is the result.

Would that the same forces now employed in chastising the aggressive Danes, and even the obstinate misled Danes themselves, were, along with a French and British army, employed to right Poland and to drive ruthless Tartar hordes back to their dreary steppes. When nationality, when justice, when humanity has been outraged in the most horrible manner – to an extent that human nature can no longer bear the description – it becomes the bounden duty of civilized nations to interfere, right the injured, and punish the evil-doer in a manner as to be a memorable example to posterity.

It is strange that Britain, so proud of her own freedom, should threaten to enter into a great war in aid of usurpation against nationalities, and certain to be highly injurious to herself, to support a weak, ignorant, but presumptuous nation in an attempt to seize upon a portion of the territory of her neighbour, the most powerful people that exist – a people slow to anger, averse to quarrel, but who, as they are here through indignation of the present attempt as dismemberment of their fatherland, and un-called-for interference of other nations, have a determination, persever-ance, and mental and physical resources beyond any other continental people.

It may be asked, how comes it that the paltry state of Denmark adopted a line of conduct so absurd as to attempt to usurp the German Duchies? This impudent act of aggression has been gradually progressive, no doubt encouraged by the great forbearance of the Germans, but was only completed last autumn, when, upon the late king, also Duke of Schleswig-Holstein, dying without progeny, an edict was passed by the Parliament and Government of Denmark, uniting Schleswig, the northern half of the Duchies with Denmark, an act opposed to all constitutional right, nationalities and moral right, while Holstein was held by Denmark as a dependency – as a field for plunder by the hungry Copenhagener, as a sheep to be shorn, or as the Holsteiners say, a fresh-milk cow. This attempted dismemberment of Germany – this completed aggression, the seizure of ancient German ground, and its incorporation into Denmark, exceeded the bounds of forbearance. The German people could no longer brook the infatuated Danish usurpation. They demanded that the integrity of the empire and race should be upheld against all opposition, and this has been effectually carried out, and will be maintained against all opposition by a million men in arms of the foremost race existing

It is difficult to account for the defect of judgement exemplified in the conduct of the Danes upon other occasions as well as this. During the great French war, their leaning to France obliged Britain twice to clip the wings of Denmark, to prevent her flying off to the enemy, and now again Germany is forced, by the usurpation of the Duchies – a far more urgent occasion – to give the transgressors a check. To this mistake of attempting to make prey of a province of Germany, the ignorant and mischievous countenance of Britain has no doubt had its effect; but this is no reason why Britain should continue, by exhibiting feeling in their favour, to cause them to persist in evil. The special favour of the British towards this troublesome little kingdom, and their disfavour towards their old allies, in direct opposition to their own interest, to justice, morality, and constitutional right, arises from a combination of circumstances to which it is not here necessary to allude. Our chivalric Press exclaims: 'Can a chivalric Englishman stand idly by and see two great nations attack and trample upon a weak neighbour? This ignores the fact of criminal aggression by the weaker party. Some thirteen years ago, when the weaker Duchies, upon the desertion of the Prussians at the threat of Russia, were trampled upon by the comparatively stronger Denmark, we heard very little of this boasted chivalric feeling on the part of the British people to protect the weak. The only difference in the two cases is, that the Duchies were in the right and Denmark in the wrong. Shall we suppose British sympathies towards Denmark arises from a fellow-feeling – that she herself is a guilty aggressor? I leave Ireland to reply.

In Denmark, during the two last reigns, a great change has taken place in the government, in what is termed a popular direction. Previously, the king was a absolute monarch, and the measures of government were not quite so partial in favour of Denmark and to prejudice of the Duchies. But since the government came to take a representative character, and the monarch's power restricted, the Danish element and interest has prevailed, and Copenhagen had come to be what Paris is to France –

the absorber of all power and place, and the field of expenditure of nearly the whole income of the Peninsula as far as the gates of Hamburg. A strong navy has been constructed at Copenhagen, partly by pressed shipwrights from Holstein and timber from the Duchies. A sea and land force has been embodied quite incommensurate to the population and resources of the country, entailing debt and high taxation, for which the Duchies have been highly assessed, while the disbursement of the collected taxes has been almost wholly limited to Copenhagen and its vicinity, situated at the other extremity of Denmark from the Duchies. Hence the Duchies, under the new system of government centralization (here the reverse of central) were destined to have their life's blood sucked out by Copenhagen, the same as that of Ireland, and also to a considerable extent that of Scotland, by London centralization. This was the more felt by the Duchies, as the war preparation and *material*, which the taxation of the Duchies went to furnish, was to keep up their own subjugation. It is a general rule, that distant provinces, dependencies, under alien government, and more especially when of alien language, are regarded by the superior power merely as fields for plunder. It is also the case, that the more popular and republican the superior government, the more tyrannically oppressive is the treatment of the dependency. The Orations of Cicero illustrate how far this tyranny over a subjugated people can be carried. Having the sovereign and government present in a country, more especially an agricultural country, is of the very first importance to the general prosperity and to progress. Look at wretched Ireland, with the sovereign and principal landowners absentees. Hence the once populous Ireland is fast becoming a cattle and sheep run, and the Irish people banished from their own country. Without the intervention of Germany a like fate awaited the German Duchies. In fact, the young men about twenty were running away to escape the Danish conscription. Do the British people really think that the Germans would remain passive in seeing Germany dismembered – one of the oldest portions of fatherland seized by a piratical neighbour and the people trampled on in this manner? Such would have brought dishonour and contempt upon the German name.

The malign effect of alien government, and more especially by an alien race, has not been sufficiently pointed out. It has led generally to the sinking and destruction of the subject race, or their expulsion. This is exemplified in the case of Ireland, where the ancient Celtic and mixed population have, during the last twenty years, been destroyed or expelled, at least diminished to the amount of nearly three millions, first by the disastrous famine – which I, eight or ten years previously, had pointed out as imminent, from the extreme poverty and precarious potato diet – the natural result of the wealth, and produce of the country being carried away to England as rent to the absentee proprietors. A sweeping expulsion followed of the working agricultural population evicted from their small farms This clearance has been carried out by the great lords of the soil, mostly absentees, letting their land, formerly agricultural, as large grazing farms, cattle and sheep run; and, as the most efficient means of effecting a clearance of the rural population, sending round hired bands under their land-agent, protected by military, to destroy the villages, throwing down the houses, and leaving only heaps of ruins! This is alien government! This is only carrying out, though in a different manner the often-expressed wish of the spoliation class in Britain, 'That the only radical cure for Irish disturbance (disturbance produced by alien mal-government) was a dip in the ocean for twenty-four hours of the whole island'! No doubt the Danes and their British supporters would be satisfied could they decree Schleswig-Holstein to a similar fate. Yet, perhaps, the German population of the Duchies being, like the Scotch, one of the most industrious peoples that exist, the hungry Copenhagener would rather prefer to have them as two laborious bee-hives, making honey for Danish consumption.

Under present circumstances, the foreign minister of Britain having contemptuously refused to receive the address of the people of the Duchies (as if the people of one of the oldest states of Europe were of no more account than a flock of sheep of which the owner was doubtful, I think the people of the Duchies should address their kindred, the people of England and Scotland, and state the facts of the attempted usurpation by the Dane. It might even be useful to address all the states of Europe upon this subject. The other governments might not follow the example of the British foreign minister; the case of the Duchies may come to be their own In other parts of Europe, several peoples and portions of peoples are at present suffering under alien government, and it is high time, from the advance of the moral sense of the age, that justice and constitutional rights be strictly attended to, and any breach of national rights signally punished as an example to evil-doers on the large scale.

It might tend to raise the British a little more in the estimation of

Europe, that they exerted themselves to repair the evils which result from the infraction of the rights of nationality in their own dominions instead of defending an outrage upon nationalities in another. It would be amusing, were it not a too serious matter, hearing an English man declaim on the sacredness of nationalities as respects Italy and Poland, but taking the complete opposite side as regards the Duchies. How are we to account for this inconsistency? Is it from jealousy, or prejudice or ignorance, or merely in opposition to France, or is it as incense to the rising sun? I find it more difficult to solve this problem than the problem of species and vital development.

Is it because England is herself equally guilty with Denmark in trampling upon nationality that she so strongly supports Denmark in her predaceous aggression? The two cases of Scotland and Ireland exemplify, so far, the effect of alien government; the former robbed of the wealth which her extreme industry and economy creates to feed devouring London, the latter so deeply robbed and trampled upon as even to influence the character of the race, depriving it of all disposition to industry and economy. But we find the disposing causes to evil in alien government greater in the case of the Duchies subject to Denmark than in the case of Scotland and Ireland to England. It is only a small portion of the Celtic Scotch and Irish who do not speak the English language, while few of the people of the German Duchies speak Danish. It is necessary that the three British people should be under one monarch, but the presence of the monarch and ministry, to hold court, should be divided between the three kingdoms in the ratio of the population and amount of taxation paid by each, say eight months of the year in London, two in Edinburgh, and two in Dublin. This would afford an excellent change of air, physically wholesome and pleasant, and mentally give a strong impulse to the intellect, and also a knowledge of facts connected with human well-being and progressive improvement of race. In no other way could the monarch and ministry obtain a correct knowledge of the character, condition, and wants of the population of the three kingdoms.

Her Majesty, our queen, in her delicate moral sense, could not but acknowledge the justice of Schleswig-Holstein independence; and it is said that Her Majesty's sanction to the protocol of 1852 was obtained in rather a compulsory manner, much against Her Majesty's sense of right and better judgement. It is also said that upon a late occasion Her Majesty's sanction was requested by her ministry to some very improper interference with the German–Danish affair which might have led Britain into hostilities with Germany, and that her widowed Majesty requested to retire into a private room for a little time to ask of the spirit of her husband his assistance to direct her mind to what was right and just for her to do – that is to consider what her lamented husband, whose superior judgement she had been accustomed to lean upon and trust to, would have advised. Could anything be more affecting? Could anything more exemplify conjugal affection, sincerity, and desire to do right? After some time passed alone in reflection, it is said that Her Majesty stated she would rather resign the crown than give sanction to what was calculated to lead to an unjust war against the people of her mother and husband. What shall we think of thus harassing Her Majesty upon a question which should never have been proposed – proposition of interference which their own judgment and moral sense (if they had any) must have seen were opposed to justice, peace, order, and the prosperity of a kindred people. I hope we shall not have to listen much more to the boasted chivalric feelings of the British ministry or British Press in favour of the usurping Dane, or any other usurper attempting to trample down nationalities and constitutional rights.

With respect to the law of nations, no government or combination of governments have a right to interfere with nationality under any pretence whatever. The law of nations extends only to protect nationalities, not to crush them – to prevent one nation by an act of aggression absorbing another or portion of another and thus overturning the supposed balance of power.

The whole affair, apart from the meddling and muddling of diplomatic wiseacres, is as clear as day. I have pointed out the facts of the gradual encroachment made by the Dane upon the independence and nationality of the Duchies, the absurd attempt to metamorphose Germans into Danes – and consummated last autumn, as they thought, by their impudently decreeing Schleswig a portion of Denmark. Should a doubt be pretended of the German nationality of the Duchies, why not put the question to the people themselves?

Europe has listened *ad nauseam* to the cuckoo-cry of the British Press, 'Let us haste to save the integrity of poor brave Denmark'. Here is a most absurd misconception of misstatement. No one ever attempted to interfere with the integrity of poor brave Denmark, but Germany has interfered to rescue poor brave Schleswig-Holstein from the thrall of aggressive rapacious Denmark. Should Denmark fancy herself cut in twain by Germany taking back her own, I have only Hamlet's advice to give her, 'Live the purer with the other half'.

Patrick Matthew

London: 30 May 1864.

Letter III
Hurried Glance at the history of man in Europe

Have the British, the descendants of the Angel-Sachsen and North Frieze Germans, actually forgotten their own origin? Are they ignorant of the cause of the rise of Britain to her present superiority in the scale of nations – that it is the colonization of Britain by these very Duchies, of the purest of the ancient Teuton or German race, which they are now attempting to get enslaved – a race certainly the most remarkable the earth has produced, and the cause of the umbrellaed advance of civilization and the arts of life in the resent era? Has Britain forgotten that without the industry, the providence, the steady perseverance, the strong body and sagacious mind of the German element, she would have been little better than what Ireland is – tributary to some part of the continent, as she was before she received the German leaven of a race superior to the British Celt? Ireland, more distant from the Teuton supply, has only in the north-east corner received enough of that element to render that a district of progress; while the Celtic portion, subdued, but not colonised, by Teuton England, has been made a tributary land – a great portion of the agricultural wealth, agriculture being almost the only source of wealth in Celtic Ireland being regularly remitted to English landlords, whose progenitors had appropriated to themselves the land of Ireland; this regular drain where there is no genius for manufacturing industry necessarily leaves the country in indigence.

The history of the Teuton or German race is not sufficiently studied by the naturalist. This people in ancient times, as at present, occupying the region between the Rhine and Poland, including the Duchies, had made greater advancement in agriculture, freedom, social equality, organization, and high estimation of woman, than any other nation we have accounts of, and, being more robust in mind and body, and having greater powers of increase and of combination, they naturally overwhelmed the inferior races – Celtic, Cimbric, Belgic, and Slavic, around

them, subduing, partly colonizing, and giving branches of the German
language, and so far German civilization, to Sweden, Norway, Denmark,
Iceland, a portion of Belgic territory, the rich alluvium of the delta of
the Vistula, and ultimately Britain. Their northern strength brought them
into collision with rapacious military Rome, at the height of the Roman
power, which they withstood, while the Celtic and Belgic races of Spain,
Gaul, and Britain fell under the Roman yoke. Upon the decline of the
Roman power, and the split into an eastern and western empire, the
Germanized Teutons of the north threw out repeated swarms of armed
colonists, who overwhelmed Britain, Spain, France, Italy, and a portion
of Africa, giving a land aristocracy to these countries. Although in these
countries the population had greatly increased under the Roman government, the race had lost all manly independence, power of self-
government and self-defence, at least were incapable of resisting the
formidable Teuton. Hence the South of Europe became the prey of the
northern invaders. These new masters of southern Europe, not being in
numbers sufficient to become colonists over such extended possessions,
only afforded, as above stated, as aristocracy or ruling class, and seizing
upon all the land as landlords, gave rise to the feudal system. This system,
however, was or is only calculated to live its day. This Teuton aristocracy
in their turn yielded to the enervating demoralizing effect of the hot
south, for which they are unfitted by constitution of race, have generally
become useless as a ruling class, and in France, where a comparatively
energetic Celtic and Belgic indigenous population remained, this aristocracy has been ejected, and the feudal system swept away, which will
also take place in Spain and Italy as soon as the original Celtic and mixed
population become capable of the effort. To effect this gradually and
peaceably, the aristocracy of these countries, who must be aware they
are in a false position, ought immediately to do away with all the unjust
laws and customs made to support the feudal system – land entail,
primogeniture succession, etc., which, being directly opposed to the
natural law of competitive selection, is certain eventually to produce
degeneracy of race, and the sooner, as this aristocracy had been built up
by nature in adaptation to a cooler climate.

Although the powerful and expansive German had thus mastered
nearly the whole of Europe, owing to the colonists not having swept
away the indigenes from the conquered countries, as history states the
Jews and other barbarous peoples of the east have sometimes done,

Germany proper, that is, the ancient brood-ground, embraces much the same territory it did in ancient times (it being chiefly her British colony, which is extending so widely the Anglo-Saxon race over the earth), and is not now like some other nations, an encroaching power, seizing by hook or crook the possessions of their neighbour. On the contrary of late, her extreme forbearance has only served to encourage her northern neighbour to attempt the seizure of a portion of the German territory. The modern Germans, a peaceable, highly intellectual and industrious people, no doubt erred in not having checked the first encroachments made by the Danes upon the independence of the German Duchies, waiting, perhaps, in expectancy that the different law of succession would soon sever them. This the death of the late king of Denmark and duke of the Duchies has indeed effected. But, upon this event, the Danes not taking a hint from Germany to retire from the Duchies, Germany, irresistible when once roused and combined, has rightly exercised force to effect what constitutional right reason, and good advice was ineffectual in doing.

This is an act which Germany is compelled by the strongest bonds of honour and duty to her own countrymen to perform. To have permitted the enslavement of the Duchies by a neighbouring nation, who as a claimant had only the right of force and usurpation, would have branded the German people with lasting infamy. It is an old saying that 'He who will not protect his own is worse than an infidel'.

All this being patent, how comes it that a great portion of the people of Britain, and especially the British Press, have a hostile feeling to, look with a jaundiced eye upon, this patriotic act of Germany, even speak of employing hostile means of preventing Germany from protecting herself! – of protecting Denmark in her scandalous attempt at usurpation? Is this because Denmark and the Danes have been the faithful ally and friends of Britain? or is it because Germany and the Germans have been Britain's insidious enemies? Is this out of delicacy and regard for the feelings of our widowed Queen that these *loyal* haters of Germany look askance upon justice, right, nationalities, upon an act, considering the character of race, authoritatively demanded in human liberty and progress, quite as much as the manumission of the negro in the United States, Cuba, and Brazil?

War is war, however lenient the parties engaged may be towards the population where war rages, or however chivalric the contending parties may be towards each other. In an affair of life or death, victory of defeat, little ceremony is going, and the innocent or peaceable sometimes will suffer, however much the combatants may regret it. The British Press has been especially eloquent upon the asserted barbarity of the Prussians opening their fire upon the village of Sonderburg within the Danish fortified lines, the head-quarters of their forces, and where a considerable portion of the Danish soldiers resorted for sheltered night-quarters in warm beds, while the besieging army had little other cover than the dome of heaven. The villagers knew this, that they were in the Danish head-quarters – that if they did not remove out of harm's way to a more distant locality from the Prussia batteries – if they remained assisting the Danes, probably as their servants, cooking their food or cleaning their weapons, that they must take the consequences. The number of non-combatants injured were few, not the tenth part, I believe, of what the British Press reported. The Prussians threw a shot or two over the village as warning before shelling the village, and if the nonbelligerents did not remove, they had themselves to blame. Here the fault, if fault there was, did not so much lie in the Prussians as in the Danes making the village their head-quarters, as it were to shelter themselves under the Prussian clemency. I put the question to the gentlemen of the Press, who have been most eloquent upon this asserted barbarity, or, to use their own word, *brutality* of the Prussians, if they had been the commander of the Prussian besieging army, would they have acted otherwise in justice to the brave men under them engaged in a winter campaign, to whom speedy success was life – a lingering siege death to many, and perhaps defeat. To whom then would the term *brutal* be most fitting?

How can we account for this perversion of the British moral sense, to which the greater part of the British Press has so pandered? I cannot believe that it is entirely brought about by the misstatements and colouring of the Press. The germ must have previously existed, and the Press have only cultivated it. It is rather strange that the French people and Emperor seem to have a greater leaning to justice and nationalities than the British?

A conference is stated to be resolved upon to treat of the affair of Schleswig-Holstein. If well-informed, judicious, honest men, and of adequate powers, be employed, all will go right. Are those guilty of the same crime as that attempted by the Dane to be the judge? I hope the angel of justice will stand at the portal, and strike down every delegate of a government equally guilty as that of Denmark.

The conditions of the Protocol of 1852 require some notice, and show the utter incapacity or evil design of all connected. No statesman, if he had not an ulterior intention of embroilment, would have proposed such a *settlement* of the Duchies question, certain to act as a trap to catch the Danes in the self-same act of usurpation, plunder, and oppression, which Germany has at length been roused to put down. The condition of the Protocol place Schleswig-Holstein and Denmark exactly in the same false position they formerly fell into under the same sovereign – at least as false, certain to compromise the independence of the weaker, which, though an entirely different people, and its individuality secured by the most binding statutes, would sooner or later fall to be usurpated by the stronger. Otherwise Danes would not be Danes – would have lost their inbred character of race, which, when repressed, as sea-rovers, from plunder on the ocean, led them to try to carry it out by land. Under the protocol arrangement a German army would be required for protection, an army of observation constantly stationed on the northern frontier of Schleswig. Is the reason, judgement, sound sense of Europe, of the present intelligent age to be outraged by such an absurd protocol – *settlement* of the Duchies question? Let it be remembered here that the first false position of the Duchies (a weaker power brought under the same governing head with a stronger) was brought about constitutionally, but that, on the contrary, the new protocoled false position is in direct opposition to constitutional succession, as well as against all sense of utility, expediency, and justice.

Patrick Matthew

Gourdiehill: 30 April 1864.

P.S. – There is one circumstance of which I would remind statesmen connected with this Danish affair. It is a natural sequence in the condition of man, that the superior civilization under a state of peace gradually makes way against an inferior, when no strong boundary line divides them. Hence the line of demarcation between Schleswig and Denmark, as Germans and Danes, will gradually advance northwards, that is, if the Germans do not decline from their ancient energy. P.M.

Letter IV
Respect to Nationalities necessary to peace and progress in Europe

The following letter was written towards the end of 1862, but not published:

The present agitation of Europe is not caused by the quarrels of despots leading nations to destroy one another to gratify a mischievous ambition. It is now a wholesome agitation – an expansion of right and justice to free nations and peoples from foreign domination. On the Vistula and the Elbe, on the Po and the Danube, four different nations claim emancipation from foreign thrall, and form centres of disturbance, giving apprehension to existing governments and causing jealousies betwixt nations. This nothing can remedy till the cause of the evil is removed – peace and good neighbourhood cannot return to Europe till, in these four cases of usurpation, national independence be again achieved. A man is stigmatized by the term usurper when he displaces another person as governor of a nation, although with the consent of the majority of the people. How much more does a nation merit to be stigmatized as such when it usurps dominion over another.

The relative position and condition of Schleswig, one of the points of contention in the north of Europe, does not appear to be well understood in this country, or rather is misunderstood.

In Schleswig the German element prevails – the language and literature, the industry and mercantile connection, are German. This connection and national feeling, for a considerable time back, has been gaining ground, and mastering the Danish influence, in spite of all that Denmark can do, as a more advanced civilization naturally does in proximity to a less advanced. In the north of Schleswig, where the Danish language is still spoken by a portion of the population, it is limited to the lower and less educated grades, much in the manner that Gaelic or Celtic still is in Scotland and Ireland. In the middle ages Schleswig was governed by its own dukes, who joined Germany in war against Denmark. In the year 1375, the reining Duke Henry dying without issue, Schleswig fell by heritage to the Count of Holstein, and from that period dates the connection or union of Schleswig-Holstein. In the beginning of the fifteenth century, King Erich of Denmark attempted to dissever Schleswig from Holstein, then under their own duke of the Schauenburg family, but was defeated. From that time the independence and union of the Duchies was acknowledged by Denmark till the recent usurpation.

In 1448 the Count Christian of Oldenburg became King of Denmark by election of the Danish Council of State, and in 1460 became absolute monarch of Denmark, and about the same time was elected Duke of the Duchies, limited by a constitution which has been maintained till the recent Danish usurpation, while Denmark remained an absolute monarchy.

On being elected Duke of Schleswig-Holstein, Christian I solemnly pledged himself to maintain the following conditions, which all his followers, till the last three reigns, upon ascending the throne, also pledged to maintain:

1. The succession to the Duchies to be in the male line only (the succession in Denmark to heirs male and female was decreed in 1665).
2. Schleswig-Holstein shall for ever remain united (*ewig usammen bleiben*).
3. The inhabitants of Schleswig-Holstein, without their consent, shall have no new taxes laid upon them.
4. The internal administration of affairs in the Duchies, and everything regarding their own welfare, is to be conducted by themselves in conjunction with the Landtag.
5. All the authorities of Schleswig-Holstein must be natives of the country.
6. No foreign war can be commenced without the consent of the Schleswig-Holstein Council of State.
7. No Schleswig-Holsteiner is to be forced to serve the King of Denmark out of the Duchies.

That all these constitutional pledges have been violated by Denmark everyone knows. While not more than half of the revenue of the Duchies has been expended in the Duchies, the other half being a tribute to Denmark; besides, a considerable portion of the half expended in the Duchies, was in payment of Danish officials filling government offices in the Duchies. The regular taxes imposed upon the Duchies at the will of the Danish Government, and which only could be paid through the extreme industry of the German population, was not enough. In 1813 a contribution of more than eighteen million dollars was imposed on the Duchies to support the sinking of Denmark, and levied in such a manner upon the heritable property of the country as to produce incalculable evil, amounting almost to a general bankruptcy – and which the landed interest at this day has scarcely got above. This extraordinary impost upon the land of the Duchies took precedence of all heritable lands. And the monied interest of Hamburg etc., refused to allow their capital to be lent on Schleswig-Holstein property, upon such doubtful security – when a Danish king could come in and say, 'Though your bond was

the first registered, yet my impost shall take precedence of your bond.'
In justice his contribution must be paid back.

This enormous financial robbery was not enough, was only one item
of the whole amount of plunder. For a number of years back the pillage
of the Duchies by Denmark has been maturing to a complete system,
and has been brought to as high perfection as anything of human
construction can well reach. Every encroachment the needy place-hunters
of Copenhagen could contrive has been sedulously followed out. The
German population of the Duchies are comparatively a more industrious
people than the Dane; and the powerful Danish fleet of men-of-war, far
too great for any purpose of good and quite beyond Denmark's own
means, has, in fact, been constructed by the wealth and money produced
by German industry, and indeed maintained, and to a considerable extent
manned, from German resources. The Danes, originally sea-robbers, and
comparatively averse to honest industry, could never of themselves by
honest means have placed this fleet upon the ocean. In former times the
sea-kings of Denmark plundered in a bold above-board manner. But the
modern Dane has resorted to other means in carrying out his predatory
instincts. The Dane has succeeded, for a length of time, in turning the
industry of the patient German to account. But patience has its limits
even among Germans.

When Hanover and Britain came, much in the same manner as the
Duchies and Denmark, to be under the same monarch, no advantage,
no usurpation on the part of the stronger state, took place to render the
weaker subservient as a field for pillage, or to interfere with its nationality
as one of the German Bund. How, then, is Denmark to be permitted
this usurpation? Where would the honour and prestige of Germany be
were she to submit to such treatment of one of her own body? I have
already stated that in all respects Schleswig-Holstein has been treated as
a conquered country, and made a tributary of Denmark; the young men
of from twenty to twenty-one years of age taken away from their homes
to man the fortresses and fleet at Copenhagen, principally under Danish
officers, and to work in the dockyards, and so insufficiently paid that
their fathers (working-men) were under the necessity to remit money
to their sons to keep them from starving; no tradesman in the Duchies
was allowed to do a day's work in his calling to anyone except to a
master of trade and to become a master it was necessary to petition the
government officials at Copenhagen, and to pay a considerable sum for

the sanction, besides bribing the officials privately. The taxes, duties, the tolls, even in Holstein, were also obliged to be paid in Danish money – not the usual circulating money, the roads in Denmark were made with the money of the Duchies, and the roads in the Duchies neglected. Everything possible was also done in the dukedom of Schleswig, and even in Holstein, to put down the use of the German language and literature – in short, treating the people of the Duchies as conquered slaves.

Recently, upon the remonstrance of Germany, and, it is said, the advice of the leading potentates of Europe, the Danish Government made certain promises in regard to the taxation of the Duchies – that the supplies should be voted by the Representative Assembly of the Duchies. These promises, however, when they came to be explained by the Danish Government, when occasion came for their being acted upon, turned out to be sham. All that was carried out – all that was meant, said the Dane, was that the Representative Assembly should have the privilege of giving advice to the Danish Government in regard to this and other matters, but that their power of voting supplies could only extend to give their sanction to such taxes as the Danish Government might impose – a sanction power, without a veto power! – to be worked only as a convenient engine of taxation! Upon this subject I recently received a letter from a proprietor in the Duchies, of which the following is an extract: 'Our Representative Assembly will, I believe, without dissenting voice, reject every proposal which has been made by the Danish Government, and they cannot act otherwise without prejudice to the rights of Holstein as a German state. The Danish Government has acted a shuffling dishonest part in promising the great powers to lay the budget before the Holstein Assembly. Nothing of the kind has taken place. The royal commissioner has merely promised to supply material in case the Assembly wish to consider the part relating to Holstein of a budget already voted by the Danish State Council (a body in which Holstein is not represented), and which neither the Holstein Assembly nor the Danish Government have any power to change, and which will remain in force without change, though the Holstein Assembly should object to it or any part of it. The Assembly will refuse to take the budget under consideration of those terms.

'Under present circumstances, I think it is likely that Holstein will be occupied by German troops, but it does not necessarily follow that we

will have war with Denmark, and I do not think the time well chosen
for the Germans. The political affairs of southern and eastern Europe
will likely absorb all interest.'

It would be useless here to point out the bearings of the Schleswig-
Holstein difficulty upon the politics of Europe. Everybody knows that
in the case of a war in which Britain may be opposed to France, Denmark
would take part with the latter if she were not prevented by fear, while
Germany, if she thought her assistance would be needed, would assist
Britain. The Danes say, 'The present time is ours for securing the Duchies.
Warlike France will support us.' This support of anti-national rights on
the part of France is, however, somewhat doubtful. France may have
herself enough of work before her in putting her own house in order,
and in retiring with a good grace from her Italian difficulty, to intermeddle
in a question opposed not only to human liberty and progress, but also
to justice and constitutional right.

Patrick Matthew

Gourdiehill: 1862.

Letter V
Removal of the malign influences which repress human progress

Human error, taking the character of catching enthusiasm, has greatly
retarded human progress. In history we see it rush along like a torrent,
overwhelming reason, judgement, and the moral sense, 'the knowledge
of good and evil'. We have seen Christianity, or, in other words, the
principle of universal benevolence, justice, truth, take Manichean forms
– priest despotism, fanaticism, religious antagonism. We have seen it
even take a Judaic character of exclusiveness, and become a religion of
wrath, proceeding to horrible persecution of all who might dissent from
the reigning bigotry. Hence *autos-da-fé*, or, in other words, human
sacrifices (an ancient religious rite of man in a lower stage of mental
development), the burning of witches, the sacking of the fairest districts,
even of Germany, long-continued desolating wars betwixt Protestants
and Roman Catholics, each believing that in the destruction of the other
they were serving the Deity, never thinking of the low passions, pride,
and selfish interests by which they were guided. We see in the Western
World a most destructive war going on betwixt the pro-slavery, and,
to some extent, pretended anti-slavery portions of the American British,
apparently with no other result than extermination, especially of the

Irish, so ready to fight without thinking of cause – a war carried out on a scale to which the Schleswig-Holstein affair is as yet small. And we see the home British so fanatically beset by ignorance and wilful error, as to be in danger of engaging in destructive war against their brethren and natural allies of Germany, upon a question they have made no rational enquiry about. Having taken up the idea that it is chivalric in them to assist the weak against the strong, they hug the fancy in self-glorification so far as to propose that we should enter into the Quixotic scheme of defending the trampler upon nationalities and constitutional rights from the retributive justice which his aggressive acts have naturally brought upon him.

Are we to see a like spectacle of mutual destruction carried on in Europe as in America? The gentlemen of the Press, and even some of the members of both Houses of Parliament, speak of using compulsion towards the great German people, without ever a thought of what a war against united Germany would be. The gentlemen of the Press seem never to think of the animosity their insulting taunts, and despicable misstatements, are breeding in the German mind. Is this right conduct towards an old ally and good neighbour, because, after using every peaceful means to retrieve her own, the pertinacity of the aggressor obliges her to use force? Is this a justifiable reason for the late bearing of Britain, the ministers of the Crown using threats towards Germany? Are two of the most powerful nations existing, and like those of America of the same race, to enter into deadly conflict on account of a most unjustifiable interference by Britain to vindicate Denmark in her attempted usurpation of the Duchies, a question with which Britain has no connection.

The present fantasy regarding Schleswig-Holstein, the lapse in the British mind from the wonted calm judgement into unreason and error, shows how prone the human organism is to misconception, when it willingly surrenders its reason and judgement to its feelings worked upon by an unprincipled Press, twisting wrong into right and right into wrong. The reigning British fanaticism in favour of the aggressive Dane can only be accounted for by the new-discovered influence Biology, where the more numerous the part to be acted upon, the stronger becomes the mutual fantasy, and at the same time more extended the fascinator's power. The phenomena of Biology are only coming into view. This influence or power seems a natural provision to effect social and political

combination, and necessary to the existence of civilized man. It extends
at least to some of the lower animals, and presents new views of the
principle of life. Being a law of our existence, it, like others, is liable to
be perverted to evil, which this fantasy regarding the Dano–German
question affords so remarkable an instance.

History and existing facts lead to the conclusion that small independent
states are preferable to large ones – are more combined in feeling, admit
of being better governed, give the individual greater liberty of action,
and raise him to a higher order of being. Man never rose higher than
in the small states of Greece, and we may add Italy, previous to and after
the great Roman monopoly. Holland, Belgium, Switzerland, Portugal,
have also risen high in proportion to their population and territory. And
both in Denmark and Schleswig-Holstein, I have no doubt the condition
of man – the independence and freedom of the individual, the morality
and the wealth of the country – will rise higher entirely divided than in
any way united. With regard to the great German Empire, centralization
ought to be carefully avoided. Let there be one language one literature,
one spirit to resist foreign aggression, one feeling of nationality and
brotherhood, one freedom of commerce, except perhaps in articles
deleterious to humanity. But let each state keep its own house in order
in the manner it may find most effectual – all German states striving,
competing, to have the richest garden and the cleanest house – freest
from the weeds of pauperism and filth of crime – and above all, the
finest specimens of man as well in mind as in the physique. The British
Government has for a number of years back acted with great judgement
in increasing the power of the local representative governments of our
colonies, thus in a great measure doing away with that baneful centralization of all power in the parent government, which is only calculated
to injure both parent and offspring, and eventually bring them to collide.

The resurrection of Poland, the triumph of nationality in that country
as well as in Italy, would have settled the Schleswig-Holstein question.
The power of public opinion which had aided nationality in Poland
would not have acted against it in the Duchies. A line would have been
drawn across the peninsula a little to the north of Flensburg, where the
races and languages change – the Danes to be Denmark, and the Germans
Germany, the value of Poland as a field for human extension – for dense
population under good *home* government, and protection to property, is
not sufficiently known. One acre of what I have seen in Poland is worth

two of the most of Prussia. Poland, severed from Russia, would prevent the aggressive power of the latter to the westward (as it at one time did Turkish aggression), and bar the Russian in his Tartar steppes. If through Britain this had been achieved, she would have in future commanded the confidence and esteem of all Europe. At present she is working to lose it. I do all I can to set her right; and have given these letters nearly in the form they at different times were written as the ideas rose in my mind perhaps more natural and more effectual than combined in one regular treatise. I entreat the gentlemen of the Press to aid me in this. Nothing shows the innate preponderance of Right over Wrong in the human mind, that man is not 'deceitful above all things and desperately wicked', than receding from wrong as soon as the mind feels it is wrong.

Nationality sometimes takes an intricate character. In the case of the Duchies no intricacy exists. The right is clear as any social and constitutional right can be. In the case of the portion of Poland under the Prussian and Austrian rule, if the majority of the population wish to remain under these comparatively advanced governments, to which they for any years have been accustomed, where property is protected (the great desideratum), and good laws made be observed, they have a right to remain as they are, although the portion of Poland now under Russia, or rather under anarchy, should regain its independent nationality. The case of Savoy, handed over to France by diplomatic intrigue, is of a different character, more especially as the assent of the people was given evidently under coercion, directly or indirectly. In the case of the United States of North America, the right of the southern portion to secede was clear, and the northern portion had no right to oppose, but under the plea that they could not tolerate a slave-holding power on their frontier, as piratical and dangerous, the basis of the social and political existence of the southern being slavery. In the case of British India, the British domination can only be defended upon the plea that the great body of the population had been so enslaved by religious, social, and political despotism, that it was a moral duty to liberate them, and bring them under the improving influence of British science and the modern arts of life. In the case of British colonization of North America, Australia, New Zealand, etc., where a few tribes of roving savages stood in the way of a dense population of civilized man, where the occupants, if occupants they could be called, had made no progress, and were incapable of making progress in cultivating the earth, and rendering it productive so as to support a dense population, civilized man, increasing rapidly, has the right to enter the wilderness where man has not placed his mark, cultivate it for his subsistence, and resist any wild hunters or pretended owner where the face of nature shows no trace of culture, nor mark of ownership.

P. Matthew.

Matthew's Views on the Proposed Tay Railway Bridge

Commentary. Letters to the Press

Towards the end of 1869 the butterfly mind of Patrick Matthew became concerned with public plans for a railway bridge across the Tay. The site intended was at a very wide point of the estuary where the bridge would consist of 80 spans across the two-mile stretch of river. The reason for the site in this particular area was the ambitious plan of the North British Railway to dominate its rival the Caledonian Railway for control of Eastern Scotland. Patrick Matthew first wrote to Prime Minister Gladstone and the letter was acknowledged by 10 Downing Street on 7 October 1869. This was followed by a short letter to the *Dundee Advertiser* on 13 December 1869.

Matthew's second letter appeared in the *Dundee Advertiser* on 4 January 1870. The objections were many: the site would be safer and less costly if the bridge were erected upstream near Newburgh. Indeed, the present road bridge has been erected exactly at the site Matthew proposed for the railway bridge. He was not opposed to the erection of a bridge as such. The next point was the imperfect state of the casting of iron. The bridge was to be built in cast iron and Matthew pointed out at the time what the imperfections implied: 'Cracks, flaws, and inequalities of crystallization and extension of crystallization in cast iron, and what is termed brunt, burned, in malleable iron, are often imperceptible by the eye, and cannot be tested. In an extent of bridge such as this, about three miles, where hundreds of beams are employed, and where defect in one may ruin the whole, destructive accident is highly probable.'

It is unfortunate that Matthew's prediction of the fate of the first Tay Bridge has not been and was not clearly appreciated. Instead of understanding Matthew's scientific objections, the local people looked on him as a seer — 'the seer of Gourdiehill'. The truth is that the first bridge collapsed because there were many imperfections in the iron castings which were recognized by the workmen on the site and the civil engineer in charge – Thomas Bouch. Driven on by wild ambition Thomas Bouch ordered the men to fill the holes in the girders with Beaumont's egg-mixture of iron filings, egg yolk and lamp black which, when set, was extremely hard but not sufficiently strong to withstand the strain of a bridge swinging in a violent storm and a heavy train passing over. For some reason Matthew's analysis never appeared at the public inquiry although the flaws in the casting were the main indictment of Thomas Bouch.

Matthew's next point referred to the underwater geology of the area with the warning that great inequalities in the estuary bed would be found. The first survey made no mention of such inequalities but when the foundations came to be made on the north shore the enormous technical problems were only then appreciated. Although Patrick Matthew appealed to many people, including Sir John Gladstone, he was told that the plans were too advanced to be altered. However, a notice appeared in the *Dundee Advertiser* on 26 July 1870 to the effect that two and half times the numbers of the original spans and piers on the north side had been approved. This was what Matthew had argued would be required on the north shore because of the inequalities of the bedrock. How Matthew had acquired this intelligence when official surveyors were quite ignorant of it remains a mystery. At Newburgh, Matthew argued, the red sandstone at no great depth afforded a superior foundation.

Then the cost of repairs to such a long bridge would remain a burden for many years to come. All in all, Matthew argued, engineers were not to be trusted with affairs outside their ken. He pointed to the blunder of Brunel's Great Eastern and of Stevenson over the Suez Canal.

The next letter appeared on 21 January 1870. Matthew now changed his tactics from engineering problems to the cost of such a bridge at a time when there were no plans to alleviate the appalling housing conditions of the workers of Dundee. The death rate of children under five years was about 40 per cent and Patrick Matthew for the first time in his life, apparently, found this appalling. He now set out a quite original blueprint for urban planning which long predates the humanism of the town planning of Patrick Geddes. Matthew's argument now was: build the bridge at Newburgh, which will cost less, and spend the rest of the money improving the housing conditions of Dundee. Towards the close of the eighteenth century Dundee was a fairly compact town recovering from the disaster of its siege and capture by Cromwell's army under General Monk in 1651. Then rapid industrialization had produced in the nineteenth century densely populated housing mixed up with intensive industrial sites. During this period town planning was ignored and the mediaeval town of Dundee was transformed into an industrial hell within thirty years. Town Councils were not noted for their foresight or humanity. Patrick Matthew had lived in the area all his life yet he never seems to have been previously conscience-stricken by the unwholesome slums of Dundee.

The final letter appeared in the *Dundee Advertiser* of 28 January 1870. In it Matthew repeats his argument for a bridge at Newburgh but adds a warning about Dundee lying within an earthquake zone with its centre at Comrie. Shocks had frequently been experienced in the Dundee area and Matthew warned that the 'sleeping giant' might have disastrous effects on the stability of the bridge. There the matter was left and there is no further evidence of Matthew's involvement in the bridge affair.

The bridge took six years to build. After completion there were ten months of testing for many factors – but not wind pressure. After three days of examination the Government inspector passed the bridge as safe and fit for use. On the evening of 28 December 1879, five years after Patrick Matthew had passed on, the bridge collapsed while a train was passing over, during a violent storm. And then the local people remembered the warning of the 'seer of Gourdiehill' which had all come to pass, and he was held in deep reverence. But the chill wind that came and took away the soul of Patrick Matthew ended the life of one of the most extraordinary men of nineteenth-century Scotland.

Dundee Advertiser, 13 December 1869

Sir,

Those who have been accustomed to read some of my thoughts which I have now and then laid before the public, will smile a the very correct description you give of me – a venerable, crotchety old man, with a head stuffed with old-world notions, quite unsuited to the present age of progress. But let that pass as a mere figure of speech given *pour rire*. With regard to this Dundee Bridge, it would be well for the engineers who have designed it, before they commence its construction, to calculate what its removal would cost – especially that portion of which, with a bend, approaches the north shore, so well calculated to divert the tidal flow to the middle or south deep, and sand up Dundee harbour. You state that this new line is three miles shorter than a line near Newburgh, and which you term a circumbendibus. You seem to forget that the Dundee Bridge line is more of a circumbendibus from Leuchars to Dundee than any part of a line diverging from the Newburgh line a little south of Clatchart Craig, and proceeding in a straight line across the river to the Caledonian line, three-quarters of a mile east from Errol station. I challenge the measurement of the two lines across from Falkland Road, or even from Ladybank, to Dundee.

I am etc.
Patrick Matthew
Gourdiehill
10 December 1869.

Dundee Advertiser, 4 January 1870

Sir,

Have the partisans of the proposed Dundee Bridge employed much thought upon the subject? They seem to have been so dazzled with the magnitude of the undertaking as to be blind to the difficulties next to insuperable. They certainly have not weighed the chances against its success with those for it – at least to me adverse chances far predominate. Its supporters seem not to be aware that in the case of such a bridge of more than a hundred spans the chance of accident is increased more than a hundred times. They now speak of fewer spans; this does not add to the security.

Here the chance of accident is also greatly increased by the height of the piers, and especially so when the bridge is crooked, and exposed to the impetus of a heavy, rapidly-rushing train, which acts with centrifugal force to throw the bridge outward from the centre of the curve. Besides, when the bridge is of long spans, and of iron, the long girders are subject to considerable expansion and contraction with every rise and fall of the thermometer – thus always in motion, creeping backward and forward upon the pier tops. The bridge is thus to some extent defective of adhesion, and the stability of each span mainly dependent upon its own weight pressure; or, if the girders are coupled together, the whole crooked bridge would be liable to an eel-like motion. The vibration given by the rapid motion of the heavy train (several hundred tons), with the creeping motion of the long girders, at such a height, and more especially if the foundation was not very secure, would in the course of a little time loosen the adhesion of the stones composing the piers, rendering the piers unsafe – that is, if they are not sooner thrown from the perpendicular and upset by the long lever power which their great length affords to a centrifugal force exerted at the top, to twist or sway them aside. Where there is a curve this force will be strongly exerted by a heavy rapid train. Were it not rapid, it would be behind the boat in speed, and useless. The boat passage must therefore be kept distinct from the North British Railway Company to prevent monopoly – that is, in the case of an improbable success in being erected and approved by inspectors.

There is another danger to which this enormous long and high bridge is exposed. Being chiefly an iron structure, there is a difficulty – an impossibility – of knowing the strength or an iron beam or tie as you can that of a beam of timber. Iron is also of different strength at different temperatures. Cracks, and inequalities of crystallization and extension of crystallization in cast iron, and what is termed brunt, burned, in malleable iron, are often imperceptible by the eye, and cannot be tested. In an extent of bridge such as this, about three miles, where hundreds of beams are employed, and where a defect in one may ruin the whole, destructive accident is highly probable. Besides, lightning in a thunder storm, attracted by the great height and length of an iron bridge, may do serious damage may even injure a particular beam upon which the whole depends, although the injury be imperceptible.

The locality of Dundee presents much volcanic and earthquake disturbance. Bluets of lava here, forming projecting basalt rocks; deep depressions there, filled with sedimentary and volcanic mud, and various kinds of drift-instance the Meadows and the adjacent basalt rocks. We may expect similar inequalities in what is under water. The foundations of the piers will, we may expect, be very unequal, very unsafe, or very costly; some of them standing firm as the rock itself, others as false as the foundation of the Royal Exchange. At Newburgh, the red sandstone at no great depth, affords a superior foundation.

Should the Bridge Company have to keep the bridge in repairs, the great amount of repairs which such a length and height of Bridge would in all probability require, would go far to consume its revenue, while the charge of the Railway Company for stoppages which the repairs at times would cause, would be made to balance as far as possible the revenue they agreed to pay the Bridge Company. In the case of accident with a heavy passenger train (most likely with a heavy), the whole passengers would be killed or drowned. A few years ago a passenger train in France fell through a bridge into the water below, where only one man escaped, who dived through a carriage window. In the case of the Dundee Bridge, where from such a length and height liability to accident is so great, the highly possible accident of a drowned train would damn the Bridge for ever, and subject the Bridge Company to enormous damages, besides the lost principal. Nothing could exceed the horror of an islet in the Firth formed of iron, stones, and wood fragments, and of mangled human bodies, amongst which eels peered out, collected from all parts of the Firth by the carrion smell of which they are so very sensible. The eels (water-serpents), according to our Christian creed, might every one of them be demon possessed, come to gloat over in delight the horrible wreck and banquet. What more likely than an accident? Would the share holders persist in repairing the Bridge preparatory to another demoniac feast? Or would the Government, in tender regard for the life of Her Majesty's subjects, not give order for the Company to remove the whole of the unhallowed fabric? At what cost would this be effected? Or would the North British not keep them to their bond?

The blunder of Brunel with the Great Eastern in constructing it so large, shows how far engineers may be defective in judgement on subjects a little remote from their own line, and even in his own line instance his difficulty in its launch, said to have cost £8,000, he having persisted in laying down the keel in a high position requiring launching when my friend, John Scott Russel, strongly counselled him to build the vessel low down, where, with a high tide, it could be floated off. This double blunder of Brunel, as well as the blunder, if not something worse, of Stevenson regarding the Suez Canal, shows how little engineers of the highest standing are to be trusted. Still, the mesmeric or glamour* effect

---

* A word of the same meaning as the old Scots word glamour, so far as I know, is not to be found in any other language. The new term mesmerism, mesmeric, approaches it. This is one of the many proofs of the superiority of the Scottish mind.

of a confident engineer and eloquent orator at a public meeting is often irresistible, although what they project be highly absurd.

The Great Eastern was just such another great blunder as the erection of this great Bridge would be. They are both steps wide of precedent and beyond experience. It is only by a use, quite unthought of at its erection, that the great ship has not been a great failure from the first. In the case of the Bridge, there is no new purpose that can occur to render it profitable.

There is still another consideration of great importance to the shareholders. Seeing the very frightful and dangerous appearances of the Bridge, so slim and raised up in mid air, would people not prefer another route to that of the North British? Would the North British then find it profitable to use it? Would not the inhabitants of Newport prefer the safer water conveyance? In the case of accident, and one girder slipping off by the centrifugal impetus of a heavy train, would not the jerk and connected flooring bring the whole down like a pack of cards or dominoes placed on end in line? Also, in the case of war could not a mischievous enemy at the mouth of the Firth, during the night and a making tide, drop a few explosive carcases, joined together by ropes, to float up, and, becoming entangled with the Bridge piers, blow it up?

Taking all these considerations into view, the erection of the proposed Bridge of Dundee, and not higher up the river – the natural place which common sense points out – would be a rather precarious undertaking, while the maintenance of it afterwards would be attended with so much risk and danger that I should think it prudent of the Bridge Company, should they persist in adopting this very ill-advised line, to take the designation of 'limited'.

With regard to a bridge at Newburgh, it would be of great advantage to have it a low bridge. Perhaps the Perth people might be made to consent, provided they were paid yearly one amount of their present shore dues, which would not be much, as few masted vessels now go up. Steamers without masts are by far the most economic vessels for going up the narrow and crooked river to Perth, and a masted vessel is often required to be towed up by a steamer. Or even a drawbridge could be opened for an hour at high water for a time till the practice of using masted vessels up to Perth fell off, and only steamboats used. It is only about high water that a small masted vessel can proceed up or down the narrow river at Newbridge. Here a small local, even doubtful, advantage should give place to a great general good.

Let me not be misunderstood. My great desire is to place Dundee upon the most advantageous line of rail for the north and south and east and west communication in Scotland at the least cost or danger.

I am etc.

Patrick Matthew

Gourdiehill Errol

28 December 1869

(Mr Matthew's objections to the Bridge in an engineering point of view are such as the engineers who are ready to undertake the contract for its erection have no doubt fully considered. Mr Matthew has marshalled together all the possibilities of accident in such a way as to seem very frightful, but if we put together all the similar possibilities of accident to a steamboat crossing the river would any one ever venture to the other side? Would it not be easy, also, to give such a catalogue of possibilities of danger in walking on the street as would frighten any nervous person from going out of doors? As to the liability of the shareholders Mr Matthew seems to overlook that the Bridge is to be maintained and worked after erection by the North British Railway Company – Ed *DA*.)

Dundee Advertiser, 21 January 1870

Sir,

Are the energetic manufacturers of Dundee to allow the impure crowded heart to remain a lazaretto – an hospital, not where disease is cured, but where it is cultivated? It would almost seem that in the building arrangements a home for disease and misery had been intended; at least, had any architect planned it, he must have had Pandora's box in his fancy, and taken it as a model of a city. I have seen many cities, some of them had enough as to sanitary provisions, but none more fitted for a population check or to produce degeneracy of race than the crowded buildings, the narrow unwholesome lanes and closes of Dundee. The high mortality rate per 1,000 confirms my views. The sad imprisonment, the attempt to rear children in these loathsome dens, is not regarded in the child murder light that it ought to be. Unfortunately there are certain infectious diseases to which children are subject, and to combat which requires considerable vigour in the child. How is it possible for the poor delicate sufferer, imprisoned from its birth in these loathsome fetid dens, who has never breathed a mouthful of fresh air, and seldom enjoyed an invigorating sun ray, to struggle through these trying diseases? The direct rays of the sun afford a stimulus necessary to the high development of the human vital powers, physical and mental. Artificial heat, or common fire is not enough. Artificial heat rays, unless raised to white heat, do not pass through glass or water, and even, as Tyndal says, not through transparent water gas, although through dry atmospheric air. The sun's rays have especial vital powers. It is said that the tadpole is not developed to a frog when retained in darkness, but remains a tadpole fish, probably to extend in growth, and generate in this lower undeveloped stage.

The absence of light no doubt prevents development, and excessive haze and cloud in the primary condition of our planet, owing to greater centres or ground heat, may have been the cause of the power development of pristine life. In the dark casements of fortresses, where soldiers' wives sometimes reside, monstrous births are said to be not infrequent. Our window curtains and blinds ought to be removed, and the legislators of a window tax ought to have had their eyes put out. In our crowded cities, few children, however, do escape, or pass easily through infantine diseases, it would seem from the very unwholesomeness of the slums. Here it would appear that, from the vitiated state of the atmosphere and condition of the child's fluids, the animalcules of the infection did not find a propitious field for extension, the amount generated of carbonic acid and other impurities of crowded human life, and especially the effluvia emitted by ill-managed drains, being sufficient to poison the floating-about germs of the diseases, though the children may survive under the fetor, but with constitutions irreparably injured. The human organism is in a similar manner found to survive under an amount of mediated sulphur, mercury, chlorine, gas, etc. which kills the animalcules or the germs of animalcules of various kinds of infection (not of cholera). This may account for various instances where certain kinds of infectious disease seemed to prefer health localities. The murder of thousands of children, however, every year in this country, and the degeneracy of race, caused by crowded cities, such as the heart of Dundee, demand immediate reform – cannot longer be tolerated.

I never pass through the wretched, filthy passages of the heart of Dundee, and see the poor, pallid, feeble children – dwining atomies – creeping about in whose unwholesome dens – to them, horrible prisons but that I feel a sentiment of self-blame, of self-reproach. This feeling of self-reproach that the sight of evil, especially remediable evil, generates seems common to all whose feelings are not blunted by custom, by everyday observance, I ask myself, do I do my duty in not striving more to reform this horrible evil? The purest, natural sentiment expressed by the promulgator of Christianity was 'Let little children come to me', this was clearly in the sympathetic sense.

At the *soi-disant* science meeting, held at Dundee more than two years ago, I proposed that the Society should devote a day with me to an excursion to the central parts of Dundee to obtain some knowledge of the condition of humanity in the city itself in which their conference was held – a city excursion such as this being, as I thought, calculated to give more important scientific knowledge than their country excursions to the seats of neighbouring noblemen. The scientific meeting did not respond to my invitation. I ought to have known that the science of man was a tabooed subject with aristocratic scientific meetings.

I look upon the crowded, impure heart of Dundee as a horrible altar where every year hundreds of little children, like hecatombs of cattle, are sacrificed. Surely unwholesome dwellings, murdering a hundred times more victims than unwholesome food does, should also be legislated against. If laws already enacted do not empower city Magistrates to do their duty as to this, they ought to agitate for extended powers. It is lamentable that with the finest natural position for a city – a site upon the sunny slope of graceful hills, looking down on the most beautiful arm of the sea and richest land prospects that the whole east side of Britain affords, of yore obtaining the name of Bonnie Dundee – it is, indeed, lamentable that a great part of the city, with wide space eastward and westward to extend, if required, for miles, from Broughty to Inver-gowrie, should be so wretchedly huddled together as in no way to benefit its admirable position, but, on the reverse, to be noted for crowded unwholesomeness – all natural advantages, superior ventilation, sunny position, rich prospect of land and, water, all walled up. Priests, hired special pleaders, teachers of Judo-Christianity easily, conveniently, get over this wretched condition of central Dundee, and many other evils. They have managed to throw the guilt of this upon original sin, which is only to throw it on the Deity. This is rather unfair, as we ourselves are the guilty parties and have the power of reform if we had the will. Thanks to the Scottish mind, a new power or force has been discovered to supersede the heavy labour necessary to produce the comforts of life, so as to inaugurate a new condition of humanity, the benefit of which ere long must be extended to the working man, by giving him fewer hours for labour and more time for intellectual advancement. Now, alas, Parliament is not merely a convenient engine for throwing the brunt of taxation upon the industrious working man, of keeping up class legislation, land monopoly, and indirect slavery after the direct has exploded. We have seen the sad destruction of human life and property, and entailed debt on the North American States which now presses so heavily on American Industry and human progress, a natural consequence of the legal removal of direct slavery too long delayed, producing a disastrous explosion. This is a warning to us to reform indirect slavery in time, that we may escape a similar explosion even more disastrous, owing to a great proportion of our population being engaged in manufacture, to whom peace, order, credit, protection of property is a first necessity. Is it to be expected that human sufferance can hold out much longer under such wretched habitations as those of our city working men? In the above account I have not alluded to the effect that such vile dwellings have in leading the family head to habits of public-house dissipation, poverty, and in morality, or to all a mother's care being expended in vain, her hope and anxieties ending in affliction.

In regard to the town of Dundee, how is its improvement to be effected? Had I the laying out of this city primarily as a manufacturing seat in this splendid site, as a model for cities having a sloping rise of position to a south or south-west exposure, I would have arranged the working men's houses in streets of single row, and only two storeys high, with roofs as flat as possible, with the street road behind, and a garden of the breadth of the house in front, the streets rising in terraces from the water side or the foot of the rise, so that every house would command a view southward over all the fine prospect which the frontage afforded, each head of a family having, as in most parts of England, a separate house – a fashion which Scotland ought to adopt; the manufacturing buildings to be where there were flat spaces and water supply. The fine gradual rise of the ground from Broughty to Invergowrie would afford space enough for the city arrangements. As things are, we have no remedy but to pull down the obnoxious slums, and to form new, open, well-ventilated streets. Money, at 3½ per cent, should be raised by Government security for this purpose.

But I must stop here. The reader will easily adapt what I have said to the present scheme of throwing away an enormous amount of capital upon a wild fancy of bridging the Tay Firth, in order to place Dundee on the great south and north and east and west lines of Scotland, when the same can be done farther up the river in every respect more advantageously, and at less than one-third the cost – the economizing of capital being so very necessary to reform the horrible slums in the heart of Dundee city. The communication by water of the east portion of Fife and Newport is already, or at least can easily be made, more convenient and cheaper than the bridge could be, even were it to succeed. I am astonished at the inertness of the Harbour Board in regard to the almost irreparable injury to the Harbour that the bridge is calculated to effect by causing a sand deposit in front. This I have already pointed out in a former letter. I have, therefore, to solicit a little further consideration on the subject by the Wormit bridge proposers, already it would seem taking form as a company, and I would strongly advise them to come a little further west where a practicable site for the bridge awaits them. Were a line brought direct from Falkland Road Station, not round by Ladybank, this line would, I believe, be shorter by Newburgh to Dundee than round by Wormit, while from Ladybank it would, it seems, be only half a mile longer – only one minute delay for security and cheapness. I have only expressed one-half of what I intended to state and may in a future letter recur to the subject.

I am etc.
Patrick Matthew
Gourdiehill Errol
10 January 1870

Dundee Advertiser, 28 January 1870

Sir,

It would seem that the leading men of Dundee looked upon the Tay Bridge as a trophy of constructive power beating creation – as an imposing, magnificent object in the vista, reflecting grandeur upon the city, and evincing the spirit of the citizens of Dundee. There is, however, a reverse picture, a failure in the construction, even at double the estimated cost, or a breakdown after being constructed, either of which is highly probable, and neither of which would throw much fame upon Dundee engineering. Here it is not to enthusiastic engineers that the citizens of Dundee must trust, but to their own good sense and judgement. Even were they to succeed, not in obtaining a return of interest for the capital invested (sunk is a better word) – that is out of the question – but in erecting the bridge, I could not admire it. I would only put the rainbow bridge, with its disposition to destruction, into one scale, and the sanitary improvement of the impure heart of the city, along with the superior bridge at Newburgh, in the other scale; which would kick the beam?

Need I mention that there is a sleeping giant buried under the Comrie district, whose struggles are felt every season, and which sometimes extend all around over a radius including Dundee, and of which I have felt several in the Carse of Gowrie? Comrie is apparently an especial centre of earthquake action. More than fifty of these shocks have been felt in the neighbourhood, some of them such as to crack walls. It is not at all improbable that these motions may come to a greater head, and 'wee bit shakle', as the Dundonian term is, extend to Dundee, scarcely sufficient to throw down one or two of the tallest and slimmest chimneys, but quite sufficient to capsize the Wormit Bridge, which, being so high and top heavy – so crank, like a narrow boat with tall people standing in it – would be easily upset. The dry earthquake wave in the lower region of the Mississippi has been so great that the tops of tall trees are said to have thrashed the ground, and to have resumed their former position when the wave has passed. The Wormit Bridge which, from its great length across the probable line of the earthquake wave, although the wave was slight, would thrash the water, but would not really rise again, even by the help of man.

The cost of Dundee bridge, such a bridge as might stand till it was surveyed according to contract specifications, and paid for – but such as would likely ere long prove a man-trap (a suitable name) – is estimated between two and three hundred thousand pounds. But in all probability the cost would be much more than double to erect a bridge that any sensible man would trust his life upon. The cost of the bridge, etc. at Newburgh would not exceed fifty thousand, immediately above the harbour, and which would command confidence, while in utility, and even as regards Dundee, it would surpass the other. To me it seems especially in the interest of the North British to adopt the Newburgh line. A Wormit line, even at the present estimated cost, along with extensive repairs, would throw an amount of bridge rent and responsibility upon their line, which would render their shares unsaleable, or at less than nothing, at a minus cost per share. The Newburgh line is the only practical means of raising their shares. I cannot but regard the Wormit bridge scheme being grasped by the North British, as a drowning man catching at straws. The North British, as well as some of the Dundee people, seem too much in the hands of scheming engineers, whose love of fame has interfered with their better judgement and prudence. Should the Wormit bridge scheme be carried out, or even be commenced, litigation is almost certain to ensue between the Bridge Company, the Railway Company, and the undertakers, which no one can see the end of or the consequences but where the Company parties in such cases are generally outwitted by the undertakers. In such schemes, hazardous, liable to unforeseen accident, incalculable in cost, even impracticable, or too low taken, they end in litigation and loss. I see in this ternary proposed agreement a future disagreement and entanglement productive of a loss to all concerned. My desire is the well-being of the North British, as well as the improved railway accommodation of Dundee. I cannot see why the Newburgh rail should not join the Caledonian east of Errol station. Here I would say, 'Gree, bairns, gree.' Such junctions should be submitted by Act of Parliament to arbitration. Railways have been made under Parliamentary sanction, and they remain under Parliamentary control. Were the North British getting into funds, an especial railway could be carried on from the Newburgh crossing through the Carse right to Dundee Previous to the. commencement of the railway from Edinburgh to Dundee, I pointed out to old Sir John Gladstone that a crossing at Newburgh was necessary – that one crossing of the line by water was bad enough, but that two crossings by water should be avoided. He replied that their schemes were already too far advanced to change. I returned an answer simply that if this was the case the sooner their plans were changed the better for all concerned. Facts have borne me out; and the sooner the present scheme of a Wormit bridge be changed, the better for all concerned.

Upon further thought, I have come to the opinion that the Newburgh bridge should be immediately above the shore at Newburgh. Here the higher land approaches close to the river, and where a bridge of 300 yards would be sufficient. The line would then cross the island, and be carried on to the north side on piles, or by a mound. On the north side of the island no vessel ventures. This would lengthen the line by about a mile, but it would save upwards of fifty thousand pounds. This line and bridge, as far as the north shore, could be accomplished for about fifty thousand, while the Wormit bridge is doubly and quadruply and centuply hazardous!

Were the Newburgh line adopted, and nine tenths of the probable cost of the Wormit bridge wisely and economically invested upon the sanitary improvement of Dundee, what an immense saving would ensue, in children now sacrificed, shall we say to Mammon or Baal? constitutions broken, degeneracy of the tree of life in our working population – pain, misery, and sin. Should the depopulation of our country villages and cottages go on, where? From whence will a new supply of stamina of race be derived to supply the waste of cities? These evils are all remediable, but which people calling themselves Christians do not remedy? while, were this great amount of capital sunk in a monster bridge, it would ere long, in all probability, be entirely lost, accompanied by a great sacrifice of human life, the remains forming a Golgotha islet in the Firth-the natural punishment of human folly. Here the blunder is worse than a crime. Which of the two would be preferred by the people of Dundee, if put to the vote? To have the abominable nests of disease and child murder in the heart of Dundee cleared out, and also a bridge, in every way superior for Dundee railway accommodation, further up the river; or, in place, have a slim dangerous bridge at Wormit Bay?

I am, etc.

Patrick Matthew
Gourdiehill
19 January 1870

P.S. The Emperor of France, after doing all he was able to centralize France into himself, has turned over a new leaf, and is now attempting to decentralize in both cases. We have some need to follow his example at least in decentralizing in Scotland from London, and have more power to conduct our own affairs ourselves. At least, Parliamentary sanction to improvements ought to be simplified and lowered in cost. Parliament, in self-defence, over-loaded with the weight of power, seems to permit excessive charges upon obtaining Bills to prevent being pestered with distant local trifles. But why can local trifles not be settled at home by those best acquainted with the circumstances?

PM

Dundee Advertiser, 11 February 1870

Sir,

It always ought to be kept in mind that a Bridge at Dundee would greatly interfere with the naval use of the Firth of Tay upwards, especially on the Fife side, cities and harbours may yet be erected. I do not, therefore, think that Parliament should sanction such a bridge, more especially when a superior position, in every respect more favourable, exists immediately above the shore at Newburgh, the natural position where the firth ends and the river begins. In the actual case of a Bridge at Dundee of about three miles in length, in place of one at Newburgh of 300 yards, it is highly probable that the repairs of such a length of bridge under such precarious circumstances, which I have in former letters pointed out, may exceed the income derived from it, even should it be possible to keep it in repair. It might therefore be necessary that in the case of a Bill being obtained for such a Bridge, that should Government at any future time see the utility of taking the railways of Scotland in its own hands, when, no doubt, it would proceed to erect a bridge at Newburgh, that it be stated in the Bill that no contract entered into between the North British and the Dundee Bridge Company should be binding on the part of Government, so that the costly Bridge might be left alone in its glory. It would not be right that the country should be assessed to keep up a mischievous, useless, and expensive bridge that ought never to have been erected. It ought also to be stated in the Bill that any accumulation of sand or mud injurious to Dundee Harbour caused by the Bridge should be removed by the Bridge Company.

With regard to the tunnel from the west end of the town to the east end, it might be well to delay it till the Bridge at Newburgh was erected, more especially as there is so much to do in improving the sanitary conditions of the heart of the city, at present remaining a disgrace to humanity – a horrible crime of past neglect. Many years ago I published in a Dundee paper a proposal to convey all the sewage of the town to Barry sands, east of Broughty. The new streets necessary to give full ventilation to the heart of the city would require a new drainage, so placed as be best suited to fall into two cisterns low down at the east end of the city, placed close together, so that when one was being cleaned out, the engine might raise the water in the other to the height required.

It ought not to be forgotten that in most public Company undertakings there are two objects in view, to obtain some apparently desirable purpose, which, like our proposed Wormit Bridge, is being hung up in the public eye by paintings or writings *en couleur de rose*, and thus aided by mesmeric influence; while there is an underneath object of procuring employment to the self-interested proposers and lawyer business. The number and amount of losses caused by these Companies have of late years been enormous. The old Fife Bank many years back is one of these nearest to ourselves, where it is said every share of £100 cost more than £500, and emptied the pockets of most clergymen in Fife, and of not a few of those of the farmers. To me the proposed Wormit Bridge appears one of the most hazardous of these schemes that have been brought before the public. Perhaps I ought to apologize to the men of Dundee for appearing to mistrust their judgement so far as to think it was necessary to waste ink upon a subject they are quite as well able to judge as I am. I certainly would not have done so, at least to such an extent, had I not had two other subjects to introduce, one of which I have truly at heart – the sanitary improvement of the town of Dundee. In this I hope my ink will not be spilt in vain.

I cannot exonerate the Magistrates of a city who are content to remain inactive when within their jurisdiction such a horrible destruction of infant life and lasting injury to the human organism is allowed to go on, the cause of which is patent to all, and removable. The fabled slaughter of the innocents has been again and again related to us, and painted by the first masters. The wholesale murder of the children of Palestine, as well as their parents, by fanatic Arab robbers has been told us without much comment. In China and in some of the Pacific islands child murder has been described as existing in all its horrors. But no account of child destruction that we have heard related, fact or fabled, can match in cruel lingering sufferings the attempt to rear children in the fetid slums of Dundee. If the Magistrates have now power to clear out these abominations – not to permit any house proprietor to let a dwelling where a healthy family cannot be reared, or grown-up life can remain in health – they ought to procure power, or resign their charge. I would ask the Magistrates and leading men in Dundee – Is half-a-million sterling to be sunk upon a Bridge at Dundee when one-tenth of the sum would suffice to erect a Bridge where it ought to be, and where it would not injure Dundee Harbour, nor interfere with the navigation of the upper firth? When so much requires to be done with capital within the city, it is injudicious, it is wrong – is it not so far criminal? – to divert so large an amount of capital away from where in utility, in humanity, it is so much needed – and for what? To carry out that which every thinking man must regard as a wild and dangerous scheme – a Rainbow Bridge, unprecedented in height, in so stormy a position, and about three miles in length, over an arm of the sea.

The Dundee Magistrates have a noble work before them – a glorious though difficult work, and which I hope they will be enabled to work out so as to obtain the blessing of every working man in the city. It is not superb buildings that are required. There is nothing more hateful than useless grand temple edifices, mingled with wretched hovels for the great body of the people, or, what is worse, with crowded dens of misery and disease. It is these latter that the intelligent Magistrates of Dundee have before them to remove. What is wanting in Dundee is not middle-class houses, but good airy, open streets of houses for working men, not more than three storeys high, with dry, open back spaces for children playing in and clothes drying, with broad street pavement in front. Here it will not be possible to get houses for each family, and the double house, with numerous rooms, well lighted from both sides, with two or perhaps four families in each flat, with inside divisions with walls of bricks, must be adopted from economy as most suited but always to have spacious stone stairs, so broad in the step that children could not tumble down. Plans of such houses, with prizes for the best, might be requested. I notice in your paper of the 20th a statement that what I urged against the Wormit Bridge told equally against Newburgh Bridge. How can that be? A bridge of 300 yards can be easily repaired, and in a few days, while a bridge of three miles might require years for repair, being at least in the double ratio of the length, would be upwards of thirty times more likely. My opinion is that the proposed bridge at Wormit Bay would never pay the expenses of repairs, should it stand to require repairs. I trust I may not again think it necessary to spill more ink upon such a nonentity as the Wormit Bridge.

I am etc.

Patrick Matthew

Gourdiehill Errol

13 January 1870

Reviews of *Naval Timber*
and Arboriculture

*1. The most important review was by J. C. Loudon in the
Gardeners' Magazine 1832, 7, 702–703*

Matthew, Patrick: *On Naval Timber and Arboriculture; with Critical Notes
on Authors who have recently treated the Subject of Planting* 8vo, 400 pages.
London, 1831. 12s.
In our Number of February, 1831 (Vol. VII. p. 78), we have given
the title of this work, with a promise of a farther notice. This is, however,
now so retrospective a business, that we shall perform it as briefly as
possible. The author introductorily maintains that the best interests of
Britain consist in the extension of her dominion on the ocean; and that,
as a means to this end, naval architecture is a subject of primary
importance; and, by consequence, the culture and production of naval
timber is also very important. He explains, by description and by figures,
the forms and qualities of the planks and timbers most in request in the
construction of ships; and then describes those means of cultivating trees,
which he considers most effectively conducive to the production of
these required planks and timbers.
   'The British forest trees suited for naval purposes', enumerated by the
author, are, oak, Spanish chestnut, beech, Scotch elm, English elm,
red-wood willow (*Salix frágilis*), red-wood pine, and white larch. On
each of these he presents a series of remarks regarding the relative merits
of their timber; and even notices, under each the varieties of each, and
the relative merits of these varieties. Indeed, our author insists particularly
on the necessity of paying the greatest attention to the selection, both
for planting and for ultimate appropriation, of particular varieties, he
contending that vegetable bodies are so susceptible of the influence of
circumstances, as soil, climate, treatment of the seed, culture of the

seedling, &c., &c., as to be modified and modifiable into very numerous varieties, and that it is an essential object to select the variety most adapted to the circumstances of the plot of ground to be planted. This may be very true; but it is also true that extreme will be the difficulty of diffusing, among those most engaged in the operative processes of forestry, sensitive attention to these points.

'Miscellaneous Matter connected with Naval Timber.'

Under this head the author has remarks on nurseries, planting, pruning timber, and the relations of our marine.

The last chapter is a political one; and, indeed, throughout the book proofs abound that our author is not one of those who devote themselves to a subject without caring for its ultimate issues and relations; consequently his habit of mind propels him to those political considerations which the subject, 'our marine', naturally induces: benefiting man universally is the spirit of the author's political faith.

Two hundred and twenty-two pages are occupied by 'Notices of authors relative to timber', in which strictures are presented on the following works: Monteath's Forester's Guide; Nicol's Planter's Calendar; Billington On Planting; Forsyth On Fruit and Forest Trees; Mr Withers's writings; Steuart's Planter's Guide; Sir Walter Scott's critique, and Cruickshank's Practical Planter. The author's opinions and the opinions and practices of these writers must await the patient investigator of arboriculture, and those who delight in the comparison of divers and diverse opinions. This part of the book is one which has been, or will be read with considerable interest by the authors of the above works and their partisans. An appendix of 29 pages concludes the book, and receives some parenthetical evolutions of certain extraneous points which the author struck upon in prosecuting the thesis of this book. This may be truly termed, in a double sense, an extraordinary part of the book. One of the subjects discussed in this appendix is the puzzling one, of the origin of species and varieties; and if the author has hereon originated no original views (and of this we are far from certain), he has certainly exhibited his own in an original manner. His whole book is written in a vigorous, cheerful pleasing tone; and although his combinations of ideas are sometimes startlingly odd, and his expression of them neither simple nor lucid, for want of practice in writing, he has produced a book which we should be sorry should be absent from our library. We had thought of presenting an abstract of the author's prescriptions for pruning trees intended for the production of plank; but, on second thought, we shall omit them, and refer the reader for them to the book by the author himself.

2. The review in the United Services Journal 1833, 33, 457–466

This is a long review which expands beyond the actual book under review. The reviewer dismissed the political aspects of the *Appendix*.

In thus testifying our hearty approbation of the author, it is strictly in his capacity of a forest-ranger, where he is original, bold and evidently experienced in all the arcana of the parentage, birth and education of trees. But we disclaim participation in his rumination on the law of nature, or on the outrages committed upon reason and justice by our burthens of hereditary nobility, entailed property, and insane enactments.

3. The review in the Metropolitan, 1831, 2, 44.

On Naval Timber and Arboriculture: with Critical Notes on Authors who have recently treated the Subject of Planting by Patrick Matthew, 8vo. Longman & Co.

This is a sensible and clever practical work. The writer seems to understand his subject, and has called the attention of the public to our woods and forests, and to the great staple from which our navy is to be supplied with the means of existence. After treating of plank and timbers, Mr M notices British forest-trees suited for naval purposes, and then follows miscellaneous matter relating to naval timber. We find in Part IV a judicious notice, or rather notices, of the authors who treat of arboriculture, who have lately appeared before the public; on those there are very just comments. We had no notion that a heavy duty was laid on all timber for ship-building that comes from abroad. The removal of this duty and that on hemp, would give our ship-owners superiority over all foreign vessels in the carrying trade. The Americans alone could compete with us. Yet, living as we do by the ocean, and on the ocean, so impolitic is our taxation, that the materials for building our vessels are so taxed in timber and hemp alone as to make them cost 10/. per register ton instead of six, for which they might be had. Let Lord Althorp think of this. Every timber-grower will read Mr Matthew's work to advantage. It is earnestly and rationally written.

4. *Quarterly Review 1833, 49, 125–135.*

This is a very long review which goes beyond the book to discuss arboreal problems.

Art. VI – 1. *On Naval Timber and Arboriculture; with Critical Notes* by Patrick Matthew. 8 vo. London, 1830.

Mr Matthew is, we do not doubt, a skilful planter; and, though his 'Critical Notes' are pert nonsense, his book, on the whole, is not a bad one; but it will be evident, before we conclude this paper, that he has never had even a glimpse of the rationale of what is called dry rot in timber. In the mean time let it be observed, that, in point of fact, all rot, whether animal or vegetable substances, in whatever dust or snuff it may end, does and must begin with moisture.

Bibliography

Appel, T. A. (1987) *The Cuvier–Geoffroy Debate. French Biology in the Decades before Darwin.* Oxford University Press.

Ashworth, J. H. (1935) Charles Darwin as a student at Edinburgh. *Proc. Roy. Soc. Edin.,* 55, 97–113.

Atkins, H. (1974) *Down – The Home of the Darwins.* Published under the auspices of the Royal College of Surgeons of England, Lincoln's Inn Fields, London.

Beddall, B. G. (1972) Wallace, Darwin and Edward Blyth: Further Notes on the Development of Evolution Theory. *J. Hist. Biol.,* 5, 153–158.

Blake, R. (1966) *Disraeli.* Eyre and Spottiswoode, London.

Blyth, E. (1835–37) An atttempt to classify the 'Varieties' of animals, with observations on the marked seasonal and other changes which naturally take place in various British species, and which do not constitute varieties. *Mag. Nat. Hist.,* 3, 40–53. Art IV, 9, 393–409. Art I, 9, 505–514. Art I.

Bowler, P. J. H. (1976) Alfred Russel Wallace's Concepts of Variation. *J. Hist. Med.,* 29, 196–212.

Brackman, A. C. (1980) *A Delicate Arrangement: The Strange Case of Charles Darwin and Alfred Russel Wallace.* Times Books, New York.

Bronn, H. G. (1861) Essai d'une réponse à la question de prix proposée en 1850 par L'Académie de Sciences. *Supplement aux Comptes rendues des Sciences de L'Académie des Sciences,* 2, 377–918.

Buckle, H. T. (1857–61) *History of Civilisation in England.* Routledge, J. M. Robertson (Ed) (1904), London.

Buffon, G. L. L. (1807) *Natural History.* Tr. Barr, London.

Butler, S. (1879) *Evolution; old and new.* Shrewsbury ed, 1924.

Calman, W. T. (1912) Patrick Matthew of Gourdiehill, Naturalist. *Handbook Brit. Ass. Adv. Sci.,* 451–457.

Cannon, H. G. (1955–56) What Lamarck really said. *Proc. Linnaean Soc.,* 168, 70–85.

Chambers, R. (1844) *The Vestiges of the Natural History of Creation.* London.

Clube, V. and Napier, B. (1982) *The Cosmic Serpent.* Faber & Faber, London.

Coleman, W. (1964) *Georges Cuvier.* Harvard University Press.

Corsi, P. (1978) The importance of French transformist ideas for the second volume of Lyell's Principles of Geology. *Brit. J. Hist. Sci.,* 11, 221–244.

Corsi, P. (1988) *The Age of Lamarck. Evolutionary Theories in France 1790–1830.* University of California Press.

Cuvier, G. (1829) On the State of Natural History. *Edin. New.Phil. J.* 6, 1–14.

Darlington, C. D. (1959) *Darwin's place in history.* Blackwell, Oxford.

Darwin, C. (1845) *Journal of Researches.* Ward, Lock & Co. Ltd., London.

Darwin, C. (1868) *Variation of Animals and Plants under Domestication.* John Murray, London.

Darwin, C. (1871) *The Descent of Man.* John Murray, London

Darwin, C. (1874) *The Descent of Man.* John Murray, London.

Darwin, C. (1872) *On the Origin of the Species by Means of Natural Selection (6th edition with addition of Historical Sketch).* John Murray, London.

Darwin, Erasmus (1801) *Zoonomia* Part 1, Chapter 39, section 4.8. Third edition, London.

Darwin, F. (1902) *Life of Charles Darwin.* Ed. Francis Darwin, John Murray, London.

Darwin, F. and Seward, A. C. (1903) *More letters of Charles Darwin,* 2 vols. John Murray, London.

Dawkins, R. (1988) *The Blind Watchmaker.* Penguin Books, London.

De Beer, G. (1961–62) The Origins of Darwin's ideas on evolution and natural selection. *Proc. Roy. Soc.,* 155B, 321–338.

Dennett, D. C. (1995) *Darwin's Dangerous Idea.* Allen Lane, The Penguin Press.

Desmond, A. (1984) Robert E. Grant. The Social Predicament of a Pre-Darwinian Transmutationist. *J. Hist. Biol.,* 17, no.2, 189–223.

Desmond, A. (1987) Artisan Resistance and Evolution in Britain 1819–1848. *Osiris,* 2nd series, 3, 77–110.

Desmond, A. (1989) Lamarckism and democracy: Corporations, corruption and comparative anatomy in the 1830s. *History, Humanity and Evolution.* Ed. J. Moore, Cambridge University Press. 3, 99–130.

Desmond, A. (1989) *The Politics of Evolution: Morphology, Medicine and Reform in Radical London.* Chicago Univ. Press.

Desmond, A. and Moore, J. (1991) *Darwin.* Michael Joseph, London.

DeVries, H. (1905) *Species and Varieties; their origin by mutation.* Chicago.

Draper, D. W. (1871) Dr Draper's Lecture on Evolution. *Popular Science Monthly,* 12, 175–192.

Eiseley, L. (1958) *Darwin's Century.* Anchor Books, Doubleday and Company, Inc. Garden city, New York.

Eiseley, L. (1959) Charles Darwin, Edward Blyth and the theory of Natural Selection. *Proc. Amer. Phil. Soc.,* 103, 94–158.

Engels, F. (1940) *Dialectics of Nature.* Lawrence & Edit. J. B. S. Haldane. Lawrence & Wishart, Ltd., London.

Fleming, J. (1826) The Geological Deluge, as interpreted by Baron Cuvier and

Professor Buckland, inconsistent with the testimony of Moses and the Phenomena of Nature. *Edin. Phil. J.*, 14, 206–239.

Freeman, R. B. and Gautrey, P. J. (1969) Darwin's questions about the breeding of animals, with a note on queries about expression. *J. Soc. Biblphy Nat. Hist.*, 5, 220–225.

Gammage, R. G. (1894) *History of the Chartist Movement 1837–54*. Merlin Press, London.

Gazdar, L. (1995) When does a Lurcher become a Greyhound? *The Countryman's Weekly*, 14, 21 April.

Gillispie, C. C. G. (1951) *Genesis and Geology*. Harvard University Press.

Gloag, J. (1970) *Mr Loudon's England*. Oriel Press Ltd.

Gorman, M. L. and Stone, R. D. (1990) *The Natural History of Moles*. Christopher Helm, London.

Gould, S. J. (1983) On original ideas. *Natural History*, 1, 26–33.

Gould, S. J. (1987) The fraud that never was. *New Scientist*, 113, 32–36

Grant, R. (1826) Observations on the nature and importance of Geology. *Edin. New Phil. J.*, I, 293–302.

Grote, A. (1875) Memoir of Edward Blyth. *J. Asiatic Soc. Bengal*, (August).

Gruber, H. E. (1974) *Darwin on man*. Wildwood House, London.

Gruber, H. E. and Barrett, P. H. (1974) *Darwin on Man. A psychological study of Scientific Creativity. Together with Darwin's early and unpublished Note-books*. Dutton, New York.

Haldane, J. B. S. (1938) *The Marxist Philosophy and the Sciences*. Allen & Unwin, London.

Hunter, J. (1859) *Observations and Reflections on Geology*. Taylor and Francis, London.

Huxley, J. (1942) *Evolution: The Modern Synthesis*. Allen & Unwin Ltd., London.

Huxley, T. H. (1854) Vestiges of the Natural History of Creation. *Brit. & Foreign Medico-chirurgical Review*, 13, 425.

Huxley, T. H. (1888) *On the reception of the Origin of Species in Life and Letters of Charles Darwin*. F Darwin (Ed) 2, ch 5, Murray, London.

Keith, A. (1929) *The Antiquity of Man*. Williams and Wingate Ltd., London.

Keith, A. (1955) *Darwin Revalued*. Watts & Co, London.

Kohn, D. (1982) *The Darwinian Heritage. B. Cohen – Three notes on the reception of Darwin's ideas on Natural Selection*. Princeton Univ. Press.

Lamarck, J. B. (1809) *Zoological Philosophy*, English translation by H. E. Elliot, 1914, Macmillan, London.

Lawrence, W. (1818) *Lectures on Physiology, Zoology and the natural history of man*. London.

Limoges, C. (1970) *Etude sur la première constitution d'un concept (1837–1859)*. Presses universitaires de France, Paris.

L. L. D. (1888) *Life and Letters of Charles Darwin*. Edit. Francis Darwin, 3 Vols, John Murray, London.

Lyell, C. (1832) *The Principles of Geology*. John Murray, London.

Lyell, C. (1863) *The Geological Evidences of the Antiquity of Man*. Murray, London.

MacLeary, W. S. (1830) On the dying struggle of the dichrotomous. *Phil. Mag.*, 47, 137.

Marx, K. (1930) *Briefwechsel*, Part 3, Vol 3, of Marx–Engels, *Gesamtausgabe*, Berlin.

Matthew, P. (1831) *Naval Timber and Arboriculture*. Adam and Charles Black Edinburgh. Longman, Rees, Orme, Brown and Green, London.

May, W. (1911) Darwin und Patrick Matthew. *Zoologische annalen*, 4, 280–295.

Mayr, E. (1969) *Populations, Species and Evolution*. Belknap Press of Harvard University Press, Cambridge, Mass.

Mayr, E. (1982) *Growth of Biological Thought*. Harvard Univ. Press.

Melville, L. (1935) *Errol, its legends, lands and people*. T. Hunter and Son, Perth.

Milner, R. (1990) *Encyclopaedia of Evolution*. Facts on File, New York and Oxford.

Moore, J. R. (1978) *The Post Darwinian Controversies*. Cambridge Univ. Press, London.

Morrel, J. B. (1972) Science and Scottish university reform, Edinburgh in 1826. *Brit. J. Hist. Sci.*, 6, 39–56.

Naudin, C. (1852) *Rev. Hort. Ser.*, 4, 1, 102.

Ospovat, A. M. (1976) The distortion of Werner in Lyell's Principles of Geology. *Brit. J. Hist. Sci.*, 9, 190–198.

Pearson, K. (1923) Charles Darwin 1809–1882. Cambridge University Press, London.

Postgate, J. (1995) Who's holding the moral high ground? *New Scientist*, 146, 45–46.

Pritchard, J. C. (1813) *Researches into the physical history of man*. London.

Ridley, M. (1982) Coadaptation and the inadequacy of natural selection. *Brit. J. Hist. Sci.*, 15, 45–70.

Romanes, E. (1896) *The Life and Letters of George John Romanes*. Longmans, Green, London.

Russell, D. A. (1982) The Mass Extinction of the Late Mezozoic. *Scientific American*, 246, 48–53.

Schmidt, O. (1881) The doctrine of Descent and Darwinism. *Int. Scientific Series*, Vol. XII, Kegan Paul & Co., London.

Schwartz J. S. (1974) Charles Darwin's debt to Malthus and Edward Blyth. *J. Hist. Biol.*, 7, 301–318.

Sebright, Sir John Saunders (1809) *The art of improving the breeds of domestic animals*, A letter addressed to Sir John Banks, London.

Secord, J. A. (1991) Edinburgh Lamarckians: Robert Jameson and Robert Grant. *J. Hist. Biol.*, 24, 1–18.

Sedgwick, A. (1890) *The Life and Letters of Reverend Adam Sedgwick*. Cambridge 1890, Edit. J. W. Clarke and T. Nick Hughes.

Smith, H. H. (1974) Time in Organic Evolution. *Advances in Biological and Medical physics*, 15, 79–110.

Spencer, H. (1852) *The development hypothesis*. Leader, 20 March

Stauffer, R. C. (1972) *Charles Darwin's Natural Selection*. Cambridge Univ. Press.

Stone, I. (1980) *The Origin*. Corgi Books.

Thorne, A. and Raymond, R. (1989) *Man on the Rim*. Angus and Robertson Publishers, Australia.

Trow-Smith R. (1959) *A history of British Livestock Husbandry 1700–1900*. Routledge and Kegan Paul, London.

Wallace, A. R. (1855) On the law which has regulated the introduction of new species. *The Annals And Magazine Of Nat. Hist.*, ser.2, 16, 184–196.

Wallace, A. R. (1858) On the tendency of varieties to depart indefinitely from the original type. *J. Proc. Linn. Soc. Zoology*, 3, 53–62.

Wallace, A. R. (1901) *Darwinism*. MacMillan, London.

Wallace, A. R. (1916) *Alfred Russel Wallace, Letters And Reminiscences*. Harper, N.Y.

Wells, K. D. (1973) The historical context of Natural Selection. The case of Patrick Matthew. *J. Hist. Biol.*, 6, 22–258.

Wells, W. C. (1818) *Two Essays*. London.

Weindling, P. (1980) Science and Sedition: How effective were the Acts Licensing lectures and meetings 1795–1819. *Brit. J. Hist. Sci.*, 13, 139–153.

Whewell, W. (1847) *History Of The Inductive Sciences*. 3 Vols, London.

Wilson, A. (1970) *The Chartist Movement In Scotland*. Augustus M. Kelly, New York.

Young, D. (1992) *The Discovery Of Evolution*. Natural History Museum Publications, Camb. Univ. Press.

Zirkle, C. (1941) Natural Selection before the Origin of Species. *Proc. Amer. Phil. Soc.*, 84, 71–123.

Index